EVEN THOUGH I HAVE CANCER...

An Energetic Approach to Healing With Tapping and Emotional
Freedom Techniques (EFT)

Emma Roberts, EFT Master

Published by

The iEFT Centre
4 Nicosia Road
London SW18 3RN

For my gorgeous girls
Emily, Chloe and Polly
in the hope that you never need to use this book

and in memory of
Dr Anna Donald
1966 - 2009

Table of Contents

Disclaimer:

While impressive results have been reported with EFT and other Energy Psychologies, the field is still considered experimental. Given that, nothing in this book should be construed as a promise of benefits or guarantee of any results.

This book represents the views and the opinions of the author, who is not here engaged in rendering medical, psychological, legal, or other professional advice. The reader therefore takes complete responsibility for his or her health and well-being.

The ideas and information in this book are not intended as a substitute for medical or psychological care. If you are under medical or psychological supervision, please consult your health care professional before using the procedures described in these notes. The author and editor disclaim any liability or loss incurred directly or indirectly as a result of the use or application of any of the contents of this book.

The case studies in this book are based on clients I have met over the years. Their names have been changed, along with any identifying features/case details in order to protect their privacy.

Foreword

When Emma and I founded The EFT Centre in 2004 I don't think either of us had any idea of the amazing journey we were about to go on together. Emma would probably be the first to say that if she had she would have got off straight away! We were already firm friends and used to working together teaching Hypnotherapy and NLP, as well as EFT. We had both become passionate about the possibilities for our latest work with Energy Psychology and thought it would be fun to share it more widely. In fact, we were probably more motivated by the desire to have fun and hang out together than by anything else. And so it remains to this day!

Emma and I have worked together for several years running group workshops at the Breast Cancer Haven in London. I have witnessed first hand her skill and sensitivity, I have seen her grow through experiences and challenges, and still I continue to be amazed by her. This book is an opportunity to be with Emma in the deepest sense. It is borne out of the essence of who she is. It will help you because it is really speaking to you - with Love and understanding and gratitude for your presence. I am so proud to be her friend and fellow-traveller.

Sue Beer, February 2010

At Breast Cancer Haven we have now been working with people with cancer for over 10 years and have offered over 100,000 individual appointments to over 6,000 visitors. Our knowledge and understanding of the mechanisms of cancer are extensive. We offer an in-depth, life-changing transformational programme that addresses all aspects of a person – the physical body, the mind, emotions and spirit and offer information, counselling, support and one of the widest ranges of complementary therapies available in the country, all targeted at reducing the side effects of conventional treatment and helping the individual through their experience of cancer.

What we are principally looking for are tools to help people participate in their own healing and play a part in their own recovery – to enable them to observe where their lives have gone off balance and help them to rectify what they feel they need to change and in so doing, take charge of their own health. In the busy lives that we all live now, it often takes something as dramatic and terrifying as a diagnosis of cancer to permit us to stop, get off the treadmill and re-assess the aspects of our lives that are not working for us and may well have contributed to the breakdown of our health in the first place.

Illness often seems to develop as a result of years of stress, usually over a long period of time, and sometimes, but not always triggered by a difficult emotional trauma. To get better, it is essential to remove the accumulated stress – that people sometimes describe as 'eating away at me, all day every day..'

You cannot change the events of the past, or other people and their behaviour, but you can disconnect the effect that that event or person has on you on a daily basis – freeing up the body's energy resources to let the overwhelmed immune system get on with its job of repairing and renewing.

Of all the therapies that we offer, Emotional Freedom Techniques is, in my opinion, one of the most powerful and immediate tools for change. In a matter of minutes, extreme physical pain or emotional trauma can be reduced to manageable levels, and even disappear entirely. It is a technique that takes a short time to learn and can be applied to every seemingly insurmountable area of pain with extraordinary results. Most importantly, it is one of the few therapies that enable people to continue with their healing at home, day by day.

I first met Emma Roberts over 30 years ago, and have watched her become one of the most experienced and compassionate therapists of my acquaintance. She has a breadth of knowledge and natural intuition, and a sense of how to release the most difficult of emotions and thoughts, gently and sensitively. This book includes all the expertise of her years of experience and discusses ground breaking techniques that move the potential for the treatment and recovery from cancer light years ahead.

The book is a hands-on, first of its kind 'companion', that looks at every area that must be addressed for full healing to occur. It offers an overview of where you may have gone out of balance and an extraordinarily comprehensive step-by step guide to what to look for and how to deal with it when you find it.

It covers a wide range of topics. It addresses the workings of the immune system, diet, pain and the importance of removing the trauma of the shock of the diagnosis. It is invaluable in discussing how best to minimise and deal with the side effects of chemotherapy, radiotherapy and surgery, including the physical and emotional side effects of the treatment and the drugs – the tiredness, hot flushes, aching bones, rashes; the depression, fears, anger and guilt.

For the partner of the person undergoing treatment for cancer of any kind, there is often a feeling of powerlessness – of not being able to help participate in the other person's illness in any constructive way. Patients talk repeatedly of how alone they feel on their 'cancer journey'. In working through the various chapters –which can be read in any order, or dipped into whenever that chapter heading feels appropriate – this book offers a practical and emotionally bonding way of enabling the patient to feel supported and family and friends to feel that they are helping constructively. For children, it can almost be a game – tapping on Mummy or Daddy 'to make the pain go away'... It stops them from being shut out and enables them to be included.

There are three books that I would turn to if I found myself diagnosed with cancer – and this is one of them. No-one with cancer should be without it.

Sara Davenport, February 2010
Founder, Breast Cancer Haven

Acknowledgements

So many amazing people have played an important role in the coming together of this book that it feels a bit like writing a list of Oscar nominations. I feel incredibly blessed to have had such enormous support and encouragement on this project, and such love. To see it evolve from an idea and a challenge into a reality has been extraordinary, and if, as I hope, it helps even one person with cancer then my dream in writing it will have come true.

My personal gratitude list:

To my family - Jules, Emily, Chloe and Polly, and of course Milly, thank you for putting up with my endless hours locked in my study and for still smiling when I emerged; for allowing me the space to develop myself and my work, and for your continuing love and support and endless cups of tea!

To my friends - thank you for miraculously still being there despite being ignored for so long. I do value you enormously.

To my clients - thank you for being my inspirational teachers, without you there would be no book. Your strength and courage never cease to humble me.

Sue Beer - thank you for being there as we work together to explore the world of cancer; for supporting me throughout this project; for being the best business partner imaginable; for listening, teaching me, believing in me, but above all for laughing with me. You, more than anyone, have been on this book's journey with me and I could not have asked for anyone better by my side. I feel very blessed that we met.

Christine Wheeler - thank you for agreeing, somewhat foolishly perhaps, to take this project on; for all your wisdom in editing, your insights and your ideas, plus your immense love and wonderful sense of humour. It can't be easy working with a first timer!

Carol Look - thank you for your unerring faith, support and love; for teaching me so much about this work and for being there whenever my belief failed me. Also thank you for coming up with the inspirational title for this book and having the generosity to offer it to me, thank you!

John Lenkiewicz - thank you for your consistent unfailing loving support; for picking up more pieces than I care to remember; for being there in my darkest most challenging moments, as well as my lightest; for having total absolute belief and trust in me; for your wisdom and strength, and for teaching me so much. Thank you from the bottom of my heart. I hope this makes you proud.

Ann Adams - thank you for your constant love and support, for being your clear thinking, no nonsense self and for being there for me as I step up to plates which seem well out of reach (often of your creation)!

Sara Davenport - thank you for a lifelong friendship; for believing in me and my work and introducing it into the Breast Cancer Havens; and for your wonderful infectious enthusiasm for life.

Emma Cannon - thank you for your incredible love and openness; for your willingness to explore new avenues; for your beautiful energy and for being you.

John Tindall - thank you for trusting me with your most vulnerable clients, and for your wonderful support and belief in me.

Phil Parker - thank you for starting me on my therapeutic journey all those years ago; for giving me opportunities to build my confidence and for constantly being there for me over the years. I value our friendship very much.

Ann Ross - thank you for sowing the seeds of the idea for this book and gently encouraging me to put it out there; and for your quiet loving support.

Tania Prince - thank you for all your support over the last year as I put this book together. Your sense of humour and your solid friendship have been invaluable.

Steve Wells - thank you for creating your amazing Values workshop where this idea became a reality; for your friendship, love and support and for your wonderful loving sense of humour. You have taught me so much.

David Lake - thank you for your gentle support and infinite wisdom. Again, I have learned so much from you.

Elna Forsyth - thank you for being my partner in that original Values exercise and helping me see a clear outcome.

Pat Carrington - thank you for creating the wonderful Choices protocol which opens so many healing doors.

Fanny Ward - thank you for your infinite patience in trying to decipher my notes and making some sense of them for me!

The other UK EFT Masters - thank you to Tam and Mair Llewellyn, Judy Byrne, Jaqui Crooks, Gwynneth Moss, Karl Dawson, Paul and Val Lynch for your constant love and your belief in the importance of this book. I am so grateful our paths crossed all those years ago! The bond between us will be there forever.

George Jelinek - thank you for walking through The EFT Centre door that day; for your deep capacity for love; for your infinite wisdom and for your beautiful twinkle. I miss you.

Finally, this book comes with enormous gratitude to Gary Craig, the founder of Emotional Freedom Techniques (EFT), without whom this work would not have been possible. Thank you Gary!

About the Author

Emma Roberts is an EFT Master (one of only 29 worldwide) and the co-founder of The iEFT Centre in London, UK. She is one of the originators and pioneers of Integrated Energy Techniques (IET), bringing together energy psychology and the very best ways of working with Ericksonian Hypnosis, NLP, Coaching, Cognitive Psychotherapy and Psycho-spiritual approaches.

Her work with Breast Cancer Haven, alongside her private practice, has inspired Emma to find a way of offering her skills and the tapping to a wider population, particularly those suffering from cancer and other serious disease, allowing them the possibility of taking an active role in their own healing process. Emma is passionate about her work, and excited by the infinite possibilities offered by EFT. She feels strongly that we are on a voyage of discovery with the energy psychologies, a journey that will challenge the way we perceive medicine and healing. Her greatest wish is to see EFT integrated within mainstream medicine as an adjunct and enhancement to existing methodologies.

About the Artist

As well as being artist and illustrator I am also a Level 3 EFT practitioner. Having trained with Sue and Emma, I was delighted to have been asked to illustrate the covers for their books.

The elements which most resonated with me while reading Emma's book were a sense of movement, peace, hope and energy. I also associated with the layers of thought and depth of emotion that cancer brings to those touched by it. My art work is often ambiguous in nature and you will read into it a different meaning to everyone else who sees it. I do hope however I have captured a sense of what cancer means.

Recently I also travelled my own journey with cancer, my mum was diagnosed with a brain tumour and we worked together throughout her whole treatment, Using EFT she lost all her resentment and anger towards her condition and saw it as an opportunity to really enjoy life. I am incredibly grateful for EFT and how it transformed my own experience of dealing with cancer.

Alex Buxton February 2010

EVEN THOUGH I HAVE CANCER........

An Energetic Approach to Healing With Tapping and Emotional Freedom Techniques (EFT)

Everything that happens in your life, and everything that happens in your body, begins with something happening in your consciousness. ...the causes of symptoms are within. While it's true that germs cause disease and accidents cause injuries, it is also true that this happens in accord with what is happening in the consciousness of the person involved. Germs are everywhere. Why are some people affected and not others? Something different is happening in their consciousness. ... If our consciousness is directing how we develop symptoms, it can also direct how we release these same symptoms. If our consciousness can make our body ill, our consciousness can make our body well. ...You have the ability to love wherever there was a perception of a lack of love, or a call for love. Love heals. You have in your consciousness the potential and ability to heal anything, on any level, in yourself as well as in any other Being, since it's all just love and energy. What remains is for you to realize this fully and actualize that potential. ... Anything can be healed.

Martin Brofman, Ph.D.

CHAPTER 1

INTRODUCTION

'Hope begins in the dark, the stubborn hope that if you just show up and try to do the right thing, the dawn will come. You wait and watch and work: you don't give up'
Anne Lamott

Welcome to what I hope will be a turning point in your journey with cancer, whatever stage, whatever your prognosis, whatever your history, whether you have the disease or are working in this arena as a therapist. This book looks at the use of EFT, more commonly known as tapping, in the support and healing process of cancer.

What is EFT/the Tapping?
EFT (Emotional Freedom Techniques), or tapping, is a tool, not a therapy, and as such is available to everyone regardless of qualification, age or background. It simply involves systematically tapping around various acupressure points on the face and torso, whilst tuning in to a specific problem, negative emotion or negative memory. This seems to release the intensity, or charge, on the problem and rebalances, or calms, us both physically and emotionally. I will discuss this in much more depth in subsequent chapters. The tapping knows no discrimination. All it asks for is an open mind and a sense of humour as you will be tapping on various points of your body whilst talking aloud to yourself!

This book is for everyone, for cancer patients and therapists, doctors and other health care professionals alike to gain new insights and ideas for working with this complex field of serious disease. It aims to be simple to follow and as such make this exciting new field of energy psychology available to you all.

The tapping does **NOT** claim to offer a cure for cancer, but is a powerful support for positive wellbeing. And you can do it for yourself, you can run with this, make changes and take back the power in your life, whatever that means to you. To me, this is the real joy of the tapping, the fact that we can all play a role in our own healing, whatever our beliefs, whatever our background, medical/ alternative, Western/ Eastern, or a combination of all of them. The tapping is there for us all.

A Bit About Me
I am **not** a doctor and I make no claim to medical knowledge. However, I have the deepest respect for the medical profession and their incredible work. I come from a medical family. My father was a cardiologist, and my father-in-law a general practitioner. My hope is to offer an extra tool to support you in your healing mission. I see the tapping as a bridge between the medical and complementary fields. Perhaps by combining the two approaches we are finally able to truly demonstrate the phenomena of Yin and Yang in action. My greatest wish is to see the tapping and other Energy Psychologies fully integrated and accepted within the medical field, as a powerful additional healing aid.

My background is in Ericksonian Clinical Hypnotherapy, NLP (Neuro-Linguistic Programming) and Psychology, but in the last 8 years I have become fascinated by the newly emerging field of Energy Psychology, and in particular the tapping techniques. My initial curiosity, when introduced to tapping during a supervision session, was aroused by the apparent simplicity of the technique and the fact that it seemed to be getting results where the skills I currently had were challenged.

My interest in any form of therapy has always been result based, if something seems to work I want to know why and to test it out for myself! Tapping presented that challenge, so I set about immersing myself in learning about it, attending training courses and studying Gary Craig's DVDs for many hundreds of hours. Then I progressed to trying it out on myself, then family and friends, before introducing it to my existing client base. The results were not only often amazing, but also lasting.

In 2005, I became the ninth person in the world to qualify as an EFT Master in an intensive and challenging programme designed by Gary Craig (see www.eftmastersworldwide.com/eftmaster.html). My work at this level with the tapping has led me to running groups in a leading UK cancer charity, Breast Cancer Haven, as well as working with individual cancer clients regularly as part of my private London practice. I have witnessed things happening that are just not meant to be possible, physical changes and healing which seem to defy medical convention. This makes me question what we are capable of when we really believe something is possible and commit to creating our new reality, when we begin to embrace the responsibility for our healing. I believe that the combination of Western and Eastern medical approaches represents the most powerful and exciting possibility for healing available. If we can put our differences aside now and work in a truly integrated fashion to move to the next level of healing I believe a whole new world of possibility will open to us.

And one of the first steps in this is reclaiming your power as the patient... Tapping helps you to do that. I am passionate about this work, about the changes, about the potential and I hope that you will feel equally inspired to own it for yourself.

I have worked with a large number of cancer patients and this book is an accumulation of their teachings. I have met people at all stages of the disease, from initial diagnosis, to remission, to total health, and also to hospice care and death. At every part of this spectrum, using the tapping has shown itself to be both comforting and beneficial, regardless of outcome. To release fear and anxiety and experience true inner peace during such physical turmoil is truly humbling to witness. I am immensely grateful to the inspirational people who have taught me so much and shared their journeys with me. It has been a true honour. I hope now to be able to share some of these lessons with you so that you too can empower yourself as you follow your particular path with cancer. Cancer is a life changing journey which no one asks to take, but which for many turns out to be the start of something ultimately powerfully positive and transformational.

As yet, there is no scientific research available to evidence the effectiveness of the tapping in cancer treatment, although as I write this book, the beginnings of a programme exist. However, the National Health Service in the UK has funded a number of cancer nurses to train in the tapping techniques as part of their Continual Professional Development Programme.

The Mind Body Connection
Many people refer to the body/mind connection. I would suggest that rather than a connection they are one, flip sides of the same coin, and that when one is out

of balance, this has a direct effect on the other. In tapping terms we are all energy configurations, and a thought (mind) is merely a different density of energy than a physical symptom (body). How do you know you are experiencing an emotion? You know because you get a physical feeling somewhere in your body! Think of exam nerves and those stomach butterflies, anxiety about speaking publicly and the sweating and shaking sometimes experienced. Then think of feeling love for someone and experience the warmth of that emotion. In order to feel an emotion, it has to show up in our bodies, even if subtly.

It is hard to escape the connection between the mind and disease. We are aware of the effect of long term stress on our bodies and minds, whether that presents in depression, panic attacks, migraines, ulcers, or even heart attacks. Yet stress is not a physical thing in itself, it is an accumulation of negative thoughts created by our response to our environment and life experience. But it is all energy. Our thoughts have a direct effect on our physical being... what if we can change our thoughts, what possibilities might that offer? The mind, and what it believes, directly influences our healing abilities. This is no different with cancer. Disease is dis-ease. The body doesn't lie, we simply need to learn to listen to it, all the information for healing is there.

Dr David Hamilton, 'It's the Thought That Counts', writes that 'although there are many different causes of cancer, for instance, one factor that seems to have an influence is the suppression of negative emotion. It has been shown that cancer generally progresses fastest in people who hold in deep emotional pain which has often built up over many years. The great news is that releasing the pain can halt and even reverse the cancer.'

The really exciting part of that is that with the tapping techniques we have the tool to do this!

The Placebo Effect
Most of us are familiar with the placebo effect, the psychological phenomenon whereby patients are given a sugar pill instead of active medicine, whilst believing it is the medicine itself, and get positive changes in their symptomology, illustrating the power of belief and its effect on physical healing.

'One of the most puzzling facts of medicine is the placebo effect: namely, that a substantial proportion of patients report feeling better after receiving a "sugar pill," or some other treatment with no known benefit for their illness. Between 30 - 60% of patients with illnesses ranging from arthritis to depression report a substantial improvement in their symptoms after receiving a placebo. It is not clear that placebo can "cure" any illness, but the power of the placebo effect in improving symptoms and reducing suffering is impressive.'
http://www.placebo.ucla.edu/

50 years ago and more, my father in law, and his father and grandfather before him, were well aware of this phenomenon. They were all eminent country medics who were well liked and respected within their community. They recognized that this respect, and their ability to personally connect with their patients, constituted an important part of their healing practice, and that there were many times in their general practice when it was the comfort of their wisdom and manner, rather than the need for medicine, that was key to helping their patients recover quickly from minor complaints such as colds, headaches, insomnia and backaches, the things that make up the bulk of a general practitioner's surgery. They had a supply of different colour sugar pills which they would sometimes give

to these patients, resulting in remarkable recoveries. For example, blue for insomnia, red for headaches etc. Prescribed with confidence and compassion, the patients would create their own healing without any active ingredients! In fact, they would often self prescribe and come into the surgery for a 'pink pill' or whatever, dependent on the issue!

The tapping is sometimes said to be a placebo. There may be an element of the placebo involved, but if that was the case why wouldn't a pink sugar pill be effective in deep emotional change work? It is still relatively early days in the field of Energy Psychology, and we have much more to learn, but the initial signs would point to tapping being far more than a trick of the mind, however positive that trick might be, especially in more complex fields such as serious disease. However, whether it is placebo or other ... I would question whether it matters. All that really matters are results. My interest is in providing healing support, and I have witnessed the power of the tapping in this arena too often now to ignore it.

The Power of the Mind

Whilst there are other complex factors contributing to the disease state, the power of the mind simply cannot be ignored during the healing process. In the film 'The Secret' Dr. John Demartini says *'Incurable means curable from within.".* This means that we already have what it takes to heal within us. The difficulty comes in accessing this place, in finding the keys to unlock our healing power. I believe that the tapping can offer one such key. To heal from cancer requires a complete shift in consciousness, to create such deep change that the disease no longer identifies with you.

'The greatest mistake in the treatment of diseases is that there are physicians for the body and physicians for the soul, although the two cannot be separated.'
Plato

Whilst this undertaking may sound both overwhelming and frightening it is also exciting. If you choose to follow this path you will be setting out on a voyage of self discovery and are likely to experience deep inner change. You will learn who the real you is, the you at your core, your truth. It may require courage, and will definitely require persistence and determination, but it will also be rewarding and inspiring, whatever the physical outcome. Don't wait, start now... you can do it! To quote Obama, 'Yes You Can!!'

This book offers practical suggestions for working with many of the issues which may present around cancer. There is no particular order to working through it, it is important that you start at the section which feels right to you, which draws you to it right now. The words and statements offered are merely ideas, feel free to replace them with your own language at any point. The important thing here is to understand the framework and then allow it to work for you in the best way possible. This is all about you.

This is the frame in which I offer you this work, with a mind open to possibilities beyond those we already know. Some of you will find it challenging and will disagree with the ideas within this book. All I ask is for a willingness to explore and the hope that in doing so, your journey becomes easier, in whatever way is appropriate for you.

So What Is EFT, Or the Tapping Techniques...?

Emotional Freedom Techniques (EFT)® is one of a new group of Energy Psychology techniques which are increasingly coming to the fore in the therapy field, known generically as Meridian Tapping Techniques.

'These techniques may be the most exciting discovery in psychology since Freud discovered the unconscious mind'
Sue Beer, 2005

In a nutshell, EFT involves tapping on various points on your body whilst tuning into the specific problem of the moment and speaking particular words out loud to yourself at the same time ... yes, I know that sounds nuts, but bear with me on this, you will get over feeling silly very quickly once you realise the power of it and start getting results for yourself! So, as one client put it, EFT is a tapping and talking thing! Just do it!

EFT is a derivation and simplification of Thought Field Therapy (TFT), the discovery of an American psychologist, Dr Roger Callahan. Dr Callahan is a cognitive psychologist of many years experience who became interested in studying the Chinese meridian system.

In 1980, he was working with a patient, Mary, who had a severe water phobia. She had frequent headaches and terrifying nightmares, both of which were related to her fear of water. She had gone from therapist to therapist for years for no real improvement. Callahan had been working with her for a year and a half with only a slight change, using conventional psychological techniques. Out of curiosity he had been studying the body's energy system and decided to experiment with tapping under her eyes (the end point of the stomach meridian). This was prompted by her complaint of some stomach discomfort. To his astonishment, she announced immediately that her phobia was gone and she rushed down to his swimming pool and began splashing water on her face. The phobia seemed to disappear completely and never occurred again. She has been filmed 13 years later and is still clear.

How did that happen? It would seem that when Mary was experiencing her fear the energy flowing through her stomach meridian was disrupted. That energy imbalance was what was causing her emotional intensity. Tapping under her eye sent pulses through the meridian and fixed the disruption. It balanced it out. Once this energy meridian was balanced the emotional intensity, the fear, went away. Therein lies the most powerful thing you are ever likely to learn about your unwanted emotions: they are caused by energy disruptions.

Callahan continued to evolve TFT to create a series of different algorithms (or tapping protocols or combinations) for specific issues. We owe Dr Callahan an enormous debt of gratitude for his inspiration and dedication.

EFT is a simplification of the process and offers a universal tapping protocol which covers all meridians at once. It continues to evolve and develop as as practitioners from all schools incorporate these tools into their practices. There are many interesting and effective advancements growing from the basic technique, many of which are included in this book.

The tapping works with the body's energy system, a system mapped out by the Chinese approximately 5,000 years ago. Our energy is referred to in Eastern medicine as Qi, Ki, Chi or Prana and is the cornerstone of many Eastern therapeutic approaches such as Acupuncture, Reflexology, Reiki, and Qi Gong. In essence, the tapping is a form of emotional acupuncture except that we don't use needles.

According to Traditional Chinese Medicine, the body is 'wired' in energy circuits, known as meridians, with each meridian corresponding to a specific organ. In order to maintain optimal health your energy system needs to be balanced. We all go in and out of balance many times, during every day, and often the energy system rights itself without our even knowing about it. However, sometimes we develop blocks to this happening naturally, something gets in the way. If left untreated, these blocks can result in dis-ease, either emotional, physical, or both. The tapping offers us a simple and easy way to clear these blocks and rebalance our energy system, restoring our path to health.

Energy, by its very nature, is active. In health it flows freely throughout the body. When a blockage occurs the natural vitality and fluidity of the energy has nowhere to go, and it stagnates, causing dis-ease – a feeling of not being 100% well or happy. That is where the tapping comes in, we direct our work at the root causes of these blocks, collapsing them, and allowing the energy to return to flow again.

As I write this I already know the response of the medical field to the concept of energy. For those who are trained in strictly evidence-based medicine the idea of energy flow and meridians often seems ludicrous. I prefer to look at energy as a metaphor. For me it equates to consciousness itself, that which we know exists, yet cannot tangibly quantify. I think Freud would have been fascinated by the tapping and how it seems to provide a doorway into not only our unconscious minds but also the greater energy field, that of universal or world consciousness.

$E=MC2$, Einstein's famous equation, would seem to show that everything is energy, whether a single atom, or a more dense energy complex like the human body. It is all energy. This is the frame in which the tapping operates as a tool to change, redirect, free our energy flow. A thought is merely energy too.

The Story of the 100th Monkey would seem to illustrate this notion of group consciousness, this idea of putting an idea out there and it being received when there is no physical method of communication.

The Story of the 100th Monkey
Nobody is sure whether the 100th Monkey story is true or folklore and perhaps it doesn't matter, it's the concept behind it that is interesting. And I think it is a cute story which illustrates the idea of group consciousness, whether 100% factual or not!

The story says that in 1952 there were a group of Japanese scientists on the island of Koshima in the Pacific, who were doing some research and as part of this research they wanted to learn about the behaviour of young monkeys.

They started off by giving the monkeys sweet potatoes, which they had dropped in the sand first. The monkeys loved the taste of the sweet potatoes but didn't seem to like the sand. One young monkey called Imo decided to wash her sweet potato in the sea to clean it, getting a salty sweet potato, free of sand, delicious! Imo then taught this to her mother and her young playmates, who in turn taught their mothers too.

Over a period of time more and more young monkeys began to wash their sweet potatoes in the sea, with only some adult monkeys imitating them. Then, in the autumn of 1958, something strange happened. The 100th monkey learned to wash its sweet potatoes and at this point everyone in the tribe started washing their sweet potatoes at the same time.

Even more surprisingly, suddenly monkeys on other islands, that had no contact whatsoever with those on Kashima, all started to wash their sweet potatoes at the exactly the same time.

So how did this learnt behaviour suddenly spread across the water? How did the monkeys on these other islands all start washing their sweet potatoes at the same time?

This story would suggest that when a certain number achieves an awareness, this new awareness may be communicated from mind to mind.

'The Hundredth Monkey phenomenon means that when only a limited number of people know of a new way, it may remain the conscious property of just those people. But there is a point at which if only one more person tunes in to a new awareness, a field is strengthened so that this awareness is picked up by almost everyone!' (Ken Keyes Jr, The Hundredth Monkey)

This is a phenomenon that Sue Beer and I have observed this in our teaching. When we started teaching our Level 3 Advanced Training, mainly taken by therapists, we would introduce this concept of the 100th Monkey with a view to teaching the concept of intuition and the power of intention to our students. A few years ago, it would take us an entire morning, people just couldn't understand what we were talking about. Then gradually, one by one, students began to get it. Some of that can probably be put down to an improvement in our teaching, but I don't believe it is just that, the change was so dramatic. One course was still struggling, the next group understood immediately. Now when we introduce this concept of there being a universal consciousness, something bigger than us, students are already aware and familiar with the idea. In fact we have had to change our course because it was taking so little time to introduce that concept!

The Concept of Consciousness

Scientists have been fascinated with the concept of consciousness for many decades, along with that of intuition, medium-ship, channelling and many of the other seemingly 'woo woo' concepts of the alternative therapy world. Only recently, however, has the new science of metaphysics been beginning to validate that which most of us intuitively know, that there is something more to life than we can see, there is more than this. The concepts of the Higher Self, God, The Field, and Zero Point are more than mere ideas. I believe they are all interpretations of what I will refer to as the universal energy field.

The universal energy field is a vast energetic superhighway which contains every piece of information that has ever existed, every thought, every emotion. We are like radio receivers; we download different bits of this information all the time, not always to our gain. In the same way as a radio transmitter goes fuzzy between the specific channels, we download some of the less than useful fuzzy frequencies alongside those which we receive with clarity. To my mind, those fuzzy frequencies represent the background noise of self criticism, self doubt, self judgment which are familiar to so many of us. With the tapping we have a way of clearing the negative fuzzy airwaves not just for ourselves, but, also, for the wider field. I believe that every piece of tapping we do to release ourselves from our negative binds also has a positive effect on universal consciousness. We find ourselves in a very exciting place as we enter the new century, we are witnessing major shifts in consciousness and all we have to do is work with ourselves.

One of my dearest friends is a scientist, suggests that there is no hard evidence as to the existence of an energy system, or indeed meridians. However, I would recommend anyone interested in this aspect of my work to read David Feinstein's excellent article, Six Pillars of Energy Medicine, which refers to research indicating this (http://innersource.net/em/publishedarticlescat/283-sixpillarsofem.html). Despite his cynicism, my friend doesn't dispute the validity of my work and the results people achieve through the tapping. So please take a leap of faith and find out for yourself the power of this amazing tool we call tapping.

How Can The Tapping Help With Cancer?

'When you treat a disease, first treat the mind.'
Chen Jen

The EFT tapping is a powerful and practical tool which works alongside both traditional medical approaches to cancer care and other complementary therapies. It is a valuable support to the healing process, clearing the body's energetic blocks to healing at a physical, emotional and spiritual level. The body is designed for health. When illness occurs it is because something is blocking that process. With cancer, and other serious disease, this block is likely to be multi-factorial, with contributors such as life style, genetic make up, life experience, nutrition and emotional wellbeing all having a potential role. Tapping can be used to support change in all these areas. It can provide you with immediate emotional support (often without the need for a therapist) and be a complement to whatever other treatment you choose, mainstream or otherwise.

With the tapping we work alongside the cancer, treating it with respect and humanity. We recognise that it serves a purpose, it has not appeared randomly, but has a message for us (albeit often heavily encoded). Understanding that deeper meaning behind the cancer, perhaps looking at it as a metaphor for change, may transform our relationship to the disease and open a new door for healing. We work **with** the internal disease state, coming from a place of communication and willingness to understand, which frees up our energy to focus on the job of healing.

In this holistic approach, we accept the cancer as a valuable part of you which is using an inappropriate method of communicating something positive to you, the misunderstood teenager who goes on a destructive spree in order to command attention. Once understood, the need to behave in such a way is removed and healing can begin.

A Course in Miracles states: 'Our constant thoughts create our reality.' We will discover the power of our thoughts and how to transform them from negative to focussing on the positive. How much more useful is it to think positively about the cancer as a learning experience than to respond to it with fear and negativity? The aim is to accept the disease and work with it to heal the body and let it go. Right now, this may sound like a pipe dream. How can you possibly feel positive about cancer? We will work together to consciously create a positive empowering future in whatever way is appropriate for you.

Teaching yourself to tap gives you a way of taking back some control and actively engaging in your own healing process. This in itself is empowering and positive. It does not offer a cure for cancer, but it will facilitate emotional healing and an increased sense of wellbeing. How that healing is experienced is different in everyone, the tapping offers a support to accepting that healing, in whatever way it occurs. In some cases this will not be a physical healing, but when a true shift in consciousness and emotional understanding are experienced then even death loses its fear and a deep inner peace occurs. This book offers a systematic structure to work within. This structure is applicable to all forms of cancer, and for all sufferers, regardless of age, environment etc. The aim of this book is to ease the journey, whatever direction it may be in.

We will look at all the physical components of cancer, working with the tumours themselves, the cancer cells, the immune system, and the various other physical aspects including healing post surgery, pain relief and dealing with the side effects of drug treatment. We will also work with resolving the trauma of cancer diagnosis, the belief systems that abound around the big 'C' and the many emotional issues that arise during this time.

Occasionally I am asked whether this work is safe, whether it is giving false hope and as such is unkind at least, cruel at most. My response is to ask what is 'false hope' - is there really such a thing? Does anyone really know 100% what is, and is not, possible with serious disease? How do you explain the many examples of spontaneous healing that we hear about, across continents and cultures? How much better might it be to experience cancer through the eyes of hope and possibility, than through the eyes of fear?

Safety is one of my highest values, both in my life and in my work, and I have no wish to create further hurt in an area already rife with sadness and pain. My simple intention with this work is to offer a valuable and emotionally healing support for those with this terrible disease. The worst that can happen from working with the tapping is that nothing will happen. In reality, so much more occurs when people take charge of their own journey in this way and that on its own is reason enough for me to want to get this work out there.

In the words of Norman Vincent Peale:

> 'Become a possibilitarian. No matter how dark things seem to be or actually are, raise your sights and see possibilities - always see them, for they're always there.'
> Norman Vincent Peale

Fear and dread will not change the disappointment if the outcome is not positive, why make the journey harder and more treacherous? I am not always working towards physical healing, it may not be appropriate with some clients, all I can do is get myself 'out of the way' and respect the journey of the person I am working with, and this journey may include preparing for a peaceful death, I am only the vehicle for the healing to go through, I am not the healer, you are, and healing is a word which means something different to each and every one of us. This work is about respect and love.

How to Use This Book

> 'Take your life in your own hands, and what happens?
> A terrible thing: no one to blame.'
> Erica Jong

There is no right or wrong way to use this book. The only true instruction is to familiarise yourself fully with the tapping protocols in the following chapter so that you are easily able to follow the routines in the book. For simplicity's sake the book is divided into a number of chapters, which cover many of the different aspects which may arise with cancer. Once you are confident with the tapping

9

itself, particularly the Short Cut Version, then begin your work where you are at right now. You can either work through each chapter systematically or dip in an out as is appropriate. It is possible that not every chapter will be relevant for you. If you are in pain, you may wish to begin there, if you are anxious about treatment start with that. It really does not matter, it will all help!

Research shows that when people are asked what is important to them in their medical care, they rate the manner in which their care is delivered at least as high as or higher than technical quality of care (Feletti, Firman, & SansonFisher, 1986; Scarpaci, 1988; Ware et al., 1978). Your role during this work is to treat yourself with the utmost respect and care and to look after yourself during this process. Be kind! You are your own healer, your own support.

Begin where you are right now, whatever stage you are at. Perhaps you have just received your diagnosis, are beginning your treatment, your journey, perhaps it is a recurrence or perhaps you are already free of it. Wherever you're at, right now is the perfect time to begin and to support your healing process in a whole new way.

Physical symptoms are often a metaphor for our emotional states. Indeed, American Indians believe that our physical and emotional worlds mirror each other. With the tapping it doesn't matter what you work with, the physical symptom or an emotional symptom, they are two sides of the same coin and affect each other accordingly. Clear a negative emotion and you will often find a change in physical symptoms and/or pain and vice versa.

When working with tapping, it is vital to address any negative emotions or thoughts and clear the energetic impact they may be creating on our system.

At first you may find this challenging. It goes contrary to the many books and audio programs out there on the power of positive thinking. People sometimes say 'But aren't you just reinforcing the negative?' The answer is no... we are addressing the negative (it is there anyway, whether you like it or not) and releasing it, instead of pushing it back inside for it to continue to grow. Do you know the saying 'What you resist persists'? Well this is no different for negative thoughts and feelings, the more we resist them, the more powerful they become, and the greater their hold on us. It is pointless to try and force positives, but far more empowering to watch and experience them growing naturally as you break through the negative thought patterns which so many of us carry, with or without cancer.

With the tapping we say it as it is, address it head on, and work to release it from our energetic thought field. This is not to say you will not have a particular thought again, but that it will not carry the same charge, and therefore not have such an effect on you. My colleague in Australia, Steve Wells (www.eftdownunder.com) talks of 'running the negative thought/emotion up the flagpole and saluting it'!

I would agree with him completely, welcome the negative thoughts only as an opportunity to release them and move forward. As you work through this book you will become increasingly aware of the power of your thinking and its effect on your health. You will also experience the results of releasing negative thought processes at an energetic level, and the joy of being able to get in touch with the 'real you', the you that is so much more than the sum of negative thoughts that may have created your reality to date.

My immense gratitude goes to the many pioneers in this field of Energy Psychology who have shared their discoveries with the world to allow each and every one of us the chance to explore these powerful healing tools for ourselves. The field is expanding all the time and the general spirit of sharing and support amongst practitioners is wonderful to experience.

Before Beginning This Work

Before beginning to work through the exercises in the following chapters, and take charge of your own healing, it is important to have a back-up support from an experienced EFT Practitioner, if required. I suggest checking the following listings and making preliminary contact with a practitioner near you. It may be that you never need their assistance, but if you find you do, it will save time and energy to have already found the right person to meet your needs. Take time to interview people and get a feel for them and their therapeutic approach.

www.theeftcentre.com
www.eftmastersworldwide.com
www.Energy-Therapist.net
www.aamet.org
www.thetappingsolution.com
www.mtt.com

So now, let's get tapping!

CHAPTER 2

THE TECHNIQUE

*'Your work is to discover your work
and then with all your heart to give yourself to it'*
Buddha

The tapping is a very practical, hands-on (literally!) approach to healing. Also known as 'that tapping thing' it uses a gentle tapping technique to clear the energy blocks in our system that may be interrupting our healing process, both physically and emotionally. The points we tap are the end points of the body's energy meridians, where they are closest to the surface of the skin. The aim is to send a vibration along each of them whilst tuned in to a specific problem to release the ongoing emotional charge.

In this book we are mainly going to use 9 tapping points which constitute an easy to remember, easy to apply routine, known as the Short Cut version of the tapping. However, to be thorough, I will include the Full Basic Recipe as well as it is equally effective and you may prefer to use it. Most seasoned practitioners tend to stick with the Short Cut version nowadays as it is effective the majority of the time, but with tapping it is all about results and if you find the Full Basic Recipe works better for you, then adapt the tapping protocols accordingly.

It is worth taking time to learn the tapping sequences below thoroughly so that you have them on automatic pilot. Tapping is best learnt in small building blocks, starting simply and building your confidence until you are able to experiment and become more flexible on your own. I would suggest beginning by working with a problem that is easily measurable for results, such as level of anxiety or a physical symptom.

There are two parts to the tapping sequence we are using here. The first part is called The Set-up.

Step 1: The Set-up
The Set-up is a very important component of the tapping, especially when working with serious diseases like cancer. It seems to align the energy system in such a way that it can then respond to the rest of the tapping. There is something powerful that happens in our subconscious minds with the juxtaposition of the negative and the positive statements. The combination of acknowledging the problem and allowing the possibility of self-acceptance anyway seems to allow the system to begin to relax and respond to the further tapping. It opens up the lines of communication.

The Set-up is designed to counteract unconscious self-sabotage (referred to as Psychological Reversal in Energy Psychology terms). Psychological Reversal comes and goes all the time and there is no way of telling if it is there at any one time. However, if it is there, the tapping routine will not be effective so just do the set-up anyway, if it is not there you will do no harm, and it only takes a minute or so to do.

Psychological Reversal is that unconscious saboteur that we are all familiar with. The part of us that makes us eat the chocolate cake when we are on a diet, the powerful part of us that can distract us from achieving our goals etc. Sometimes it is obvious, often it is more subtle and we are just left with a sense of frustration at our seeming 'stuckness'. I like to think of correcting Psychological Reversal as ensuring that our batteries are aligned in the correct way so that when we press our buttons and apply the tapping it works smoothly.

Doing the Set Up:
Take two fingers of either hand and tap on the side of your other hand where you would deliver a karate chop to someone. You need to apply some pressure but take care not to hurt yourself, remember, you are only sending a vibration of energy down that point.

As you tap on this point repeat a Set-up statement aloud as follows:

Even though I have '**this problem**' I deeply and completely love and accept myself

I have put '**this problem**' in bold because you will learn as you progress through this book to direct that piece of the Set-up statement to whatever specific issue you are working with.

Repeat this process three times.

As you discover more about the tapping you will learn about another option for the Set up called the Sore Spot. Whilst this point is equally as powerful as the Karate Chop point, I do not recommend that you use it during cancer treatment as it is a point of lymphatic congestion, and in some cases, the lymphatic system may be affected by the disease. Whilst there is no concrete evidence to say this is unsafe I would veer on the side of caution and leave well alone here.

Whilst it may seem strange to say these words out loud, and you may not believe them (most people don't) just **SAY THEM ANYWAY!** If you are really struggling to do this, begin with 'I am OK' or 'I am good' or 'I am cool', but always with a view to working towards self acceptance.

There is much documented evidence to suggest that self-acceptance and forgiveness are key factors in working with cancer. This is borne out not only in my work with the tapping, but also in the work of Louise Hay and Brandon Bays amongst others.

'People with cancer are also very self-critical. To me, learning to love and accept the self is the key to healing cancers.'
Louise Hay, You Can Heal Your Life

Whether you share this view or not, the concepts of self-acceptance and forgiveness form the basis of many different healing modalities. This takes us to the core of the energy psychologies and the set-up statement, I deeply and completely love and accept myself. From the very beginning of the work we are starting to clear a path to self-acceptance and forgiveness.

'True forgiveness is the ultimate aim of all healing'
Gary Craig

Forgiveness is about loving oneself *whoever* we are and *wherever* we are. It is about releasing the consequences of holding onto angers, guilts and resentments, and our self-judgments. I truly believe that whatever we do, it is always the best or only option available to us in the moment, according to our immediate perceptions and beliefs.

The tapping is about freeing ourselves from the ongoing impact of trauma, both physically and emotionally. This is not a forgiveness steeped in religious dogma or other moral implications. This is about self-forgiveness, which paves the way to experiencing inner peace and trust in one's inner self, despite the turmoil of a cancer diagnosis. It is the ultimate healing gift, and we can all receive it.

However, it is not about making the unacceptable acceptable, or condoning wrongdoing, but about **letting it go** so that we are no longer carrying it around with us in the present. The person who was abused as a child can begin to use the tapping techniques to let go of the ongoing responses to the abuse, as they show up in real time, such as feelings of self blame, self disgust etc, but this does not make what originally happened OK in any sense. But without gaining freedom from the abuse, the suffering continues, and the abuser still has the power. Letting it go, using tapping as a bridge to this, ultimately leads to forgiveness and acceptance of self, and healing. In no way does it condone the abusive behaviour, and nor should it.

When we are able to free ourselves from negative beliefs resulting from past experiences and the decisions we made, often in childhood, we are able to experience a sense of inner peace. This, in turn, can facilitate our physical healing. Mother Teresa said 'Peace begins with a smile.'

I invite you to take this idea and hold onto it, being curious as to how it will unfold for you, and then to check back in when you have completed the exercises in this book and see how you feel.

So, to repeat:

Step 1: The Set-up:
Tap on the Karate Chop point whilst repeating the Set-up Statement x 3

Even though I xxxxxxx I deeply and completely love and accept myself

The 14 meridian points used in this book are as follows:

1. **KC (Karate Chop):** In the middle of the fleshy part on the outside of the hand between the top of the wrist bone and the base of the baby finger.

2. **EB (Eye Brow):** At the beginning of the eyebrow, just above and to one side of the nose.

3. **SE (Side of the Eye):** On the bone bordering the outside corner of the eye.

4. **UE (Under the Eye):** On the bone under either eye, about 1 inch below the pupil.

5. **UN (Under the Nose):** On the small area between the bottom of the nose and the top of the upper lip.

6. **Ch (Chin):** Midway between the point of the chin and the bottom of the lower lip.

7. **CB (Collar Bone):** Take a fist and tap at the base of the throat where you would knot a tie

8. **US (Under Arm):** On the side of the body, at a point even with the nipple (for men) or in the middle of the bra strap (for women).

9. **BN (Below the Nipple):** For men, one inch below the nipple. For ladies, where the underskin of the breast meets the chest wall. We do not include this point in our regular tapping protocols as it is awkward to access. However, there are times when it will appear.

10. **ToH (Top of the Head):** On the crown of the head, spanning both hemispheres.

11. **Th (Thumb):** On the outside edge of the thumb on the side of the nailed.

12. **IF (Index Finger):** On the side of the index finger (the side nearest the thumb) on the side of the nailed.

13. **MF (Middle Finger):** On the side of the middle finger (the side nearest the thumb) on the side of the nailed.

14. **BF (Baby Finger):** On the inside of the baby finger (the side nearest the thumb) on the side of the nail bed.

Step 2: The Points:
Each energy meridian has two end points. For the purposes of The Basic Recipe, you need only tap on one end to balance out any disruptions that may exist in it.

Using a couple of fingers, tap approx 7 times on each of the following points, using whatever pressure feels right for you, but not hard enough to bruise yourself! These points represent the end points of the energy meridians, where they are closest to the surface of the skin, and you are only sending a vibration down them to clear blockages and rebalance the system.

The Abbreviations For These Points Are Summarized Below In The Same Order As Given Above:

KC:	Karate Chop
EB:	Beginning of the EyeBrow
SE:	Side of the Eye
UE:	Under the Eye
UN:	Under the Nose
Ch:	Chin
CB:	Beginning of the CollarBone
UA:	Under the Arm
BN:	(Below the Nipple)
ToH:	Top of the Head
Th:	Thumb
IF:	Index Finger
MF:	Middle Finger
BF:	Baby Finger

Please note that these tapping points proceed *down the* body, making them easy to memorise. However, it does not seem to matter if you change the order, or even forget a point. Tapping is a very forgiving process!

Note that while the BN point has been included for completeness, it is usually left out of the Sequence as it is an awkward point for ladies to access and the tapping results have been superb without it. The BN point relates to the Liver Meridian, and there may be occasions, however, where it is necessary to tap on it. For example it can be a very useful addition to the tapping when working with anger, or when supporting the body whilst it deals with the toxic effects of chemotherapy when the liver has to work overtime.

MERIDIAN TAPPING POINTS

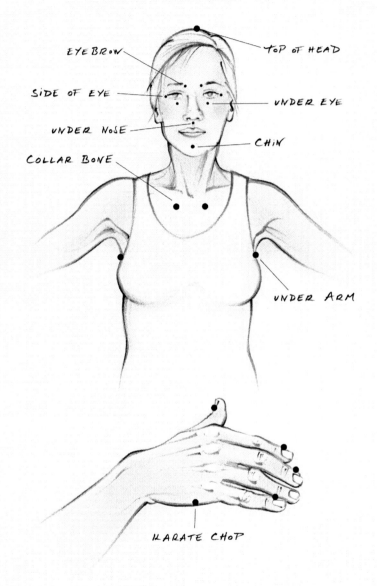

EYE BROW

TOP OF HEAD

SIDE OF EYE

UNDER EYE

UNDER NOSE

CHIN

COLLAR BONE

UNDER ARM

KARATE CHOP

Meridian Points

For information only, the points relate to the following meridians. It is not necessary to know these in order for the tapping to work.

EB:	Bladder Meridian
SE:	Gall Bladder Meridian
UE:	Stomach Meridian
UN:	Governing Vessel
Ch:	Central Vessel
CB:	Kidney Meridian
UA:	Spleen Meridian
BN:	Liver Meridian
ToH:	Meeting of 100 Pathways, covers all the meridians
Th:	Lung Meridian
IF:	Large Intestine Meridian
MF:	Heart Protector
LF:	Heart Meridian
KC:	Small Intestine Meridian
GS:	Triple Warmer Meridian

The 9 Gamut Procedure

Just when you think it can't get any stranger I want to introduce you now to the 9 Gamut procedure. The 9 Gamut is, perhaps, the most bizarre looking process within the tapping techniques. Its purpose is to 'fine tune' the brain and it does so via some eye movements and some humming and counting. Through connecting nerves, certain parts of the brain are stimulated when the eyes are moved. Likewise the right side of the brain (the creative side) is engaged when you hum a song and the left side (the digital or logical side) is engaged when you count.

The 9 Gamut procedure is a 10 second process wherein 9 of these 'brain-stimulating' actions are performed while continuously tapping on one of the body's energy points... the Gamut point. It has been found that this routine can add efficiency to the tapping and hastens your progress towards emotional freedom, especially when *sandwiched* between 2 trips through The Sequence.

To do the 9 Gamut Procedure you must first locate the Gamut point. It is on the back of either hand and is _ inch behind the midpoint between the knuckles at the base of the ring finger and the little finger.

Gamut Point

Next you perform 9 different actions while tapping the Gamut point continuously.

The 9 Gamut actions are:

1. Eyes closed
2. Eyes open
3. Eyes hard down right while holding the head steady
4. Eyes hard down left while holding the head steady
5. Roll eyes in a circle as though your nose was at the centre of a clock and you were trying to see all the numbers in order
6. Same as #5 but in reverse direction
7. Hum 2 seconds of a song (suggest Happy Birthday)
8. Count rapidly from 1 to 5
9. Hum 2 seconds of a song again

These 9 actions are presented in a specific order and we suggest you memorize them in the order given. However, you can mix up the order if you wish as long as you do all 9....**and**....you perform 7, 8 and 9 as a unit.
Also, note that for some people the tune Happy Birthday can bring up unhappy memories so it may be appropriate to use another song, and to work with those unhappy memories using the tapping.

EFT So Far:

The Setup...

followed by...

THE TAPPING SANDWICH

which is...

Sequence
9 Gamut
Sequence

Step 3: The Short Cut Sequence:
Using a couple of fingers, tap approx 7 times on each of the following points, using whatever pressure feels right for you, but not hard enough to bruise yourself! These points represent the end points of the energy meridians, where they are closest to the surface of the skin, and you are only sending a vibration down them to clear blockages and rebalance the system. The pressure may vary according to the issue you are working with. All that matters is that it feels right to you in the moment.

1. Beginning of the EyeBrow
2. Side of the Eye
3. Under the Eye
4. Under the Nose
5. Chin
6. Beginning of the CollarBone
7. Under the Arm
8. Top of the Head

19

Tapping Tips:
- You can tap with either hand but will probably find it more comfortable to use your dominant one
- Tap with the fingertips of your index finger and middle finger in order to cover the points more easily
- Tap solidly but never hard enough to hurt
- Tap approximately 7 times on each point (although it doesn't matter whether this is a little more or less)

It does not matter which side of the body you tap, the meridians are mirrored on each side. If you feel adventurous you can tap on both sides at the same time!

The Reminder Phrase
The Reminder Phrase is the phrase that you will use to keep your unconscious mind tuned in to the negative thought/ emotion/ memory that you are working with, in each tapping round. This is a vital part of the tapping process and initially needs to be spoken aloud wherever possible.

Tuning in to a problem can be done by simply thinking about it and repeating the words out loud. Thinking about the problem will bring about the energy disruptions involved which then, and only then, can be rebalanced by the tapping. Without tuning into the problem, and therefore creating those energy disruptions, the tapping does very little. However, this does not mean you have to go back into disturbing memories and re-experience them. In fact, quite the opposite; the aim is to make this as safe and easy as possible. It seems that using a keyword as a brief reminder will allow the unconscious to locate the relevant 'file' in your memory bank and work with it, just like hovering the mouse over a folder in the computer and seeing the dropdown menu, but not opening the specific file. All you need to do is be in the thought field of the experience to achieve results.

As an example, if I were to ask you if you had seen the movie 'Gone with the Wind' you would not have to run the entire movie to give me a yes or no response. In the same way, the unconscious mind can locate a memory without running the entire movie. With tapping we utilise this means of disassociating ourselves from a memory in a couple of very simple, easy to follow, ways: Tearless Trauma and The Movie Technique.

Tuning in is seemingly a very simple process, in theory. However, you may find it a bit difficult to consciously think about the problem while you are tapping, especially when you first learn. Do you remember learning to drive? How impossible it seemed to remember which foot to put where, to look in the mirror, and to steer all at the same time? Listening to the radio would have been overwhelming! And yet now it is automatic, you can drive, have a conversation and even eat at the same time!

So we say a Reminder Phrase aloud while we tap the points to keep our unconscious mind continually tuned into the problem state.

The Reminder Phrase is simply a word or short phrase that describes the problem and that you repeat aloud each time you tap one of the points in the Sequence. In this way you continually 'remind' your system about the problem you are working on.

The best Reminder Phrase is usually identical to the words you choose for the affirmation you use in the Setup. For example, if you are working on a headache, the Setup affirmation would go like this:

> Even though I have **this dull headache** I deeply and completely love and accept myself

> And the Reminder Phrase would be: **This dull headache**

You may find that some points are a little sensitive to the touch, and that this may vary between rounds. People often find a particular point especially powerful too, and locate it as their point, sometimes only needing to tap on that one point to get release. It is important to remember that we are working with energy here, and energy moves around – it is literally energetic! A point that is powerful one day may not be the same the next time you tap! Ideally, use all the points, but if you are somewhere where you feel self conscious, like on the bus, tap any point you can reach!

There are also points on the side of the fingers, along the nail bed. Hold one hand in front of you, horizontally, and using a couple of fingers from the other hand, tap on the side of the nail bed nearest to you, a few times on each finger, whilst repeating the Reminder Phrase. Whilst in my experience this is not as powerful as the main sequence, it is a very good way of keeping the energy system balanced when you are in place where it might be awkward to tap properly.

As you become more experienced with this technique you will naturally become more relaxed and the language you use will become less formulaic. There are examples of this throughout this book and I would encourage you to experiment with your own words to find the phrases that resonate strongest with you at any one time.

Affirmations and EFT - the Positive and the Negative
In a world which sells the benefits of positive affirmations, you may find it strange, initially, to be focusing on the negative in this way. However, stick with it, it is the negative which is causing the dis-ease state, physical or emotional, and when you have cleared your negative thoughts and feelings, the ones we all try and keep hidden away, the ugly ones, then your natural state of joy and love will rise to the surface... it is always there, just squashed under the weight of negative thoughts and life experiences. You will also feel more energized which in turn allows your body to turn its focus to physical healing. Begin with the mind and the body WILL follow.

One of the main errors that students of tapping make initially is putting positives into their tapping statements too early. If in doubt, keep to the negatives until they seem humorous and just don't resonate with you at all – as though that thought/ memory belongs with someone else, not you. You might find that you are arguing with the words you are using, or just forget what you are saying.

Positive affirmations DO work, but only when they have no negative undercurrent. So when making a positive affirmation always ask yourself 'Are there any 'yes buts' attached to my words?'. I like to think of the 'yes buts' as coat hangers, hanging underneath the clothes rail of the affirmation. You can unhook them easily with tapping and a little detective work. In tapping terms, these are referred to as tail-enders.

For example:
> **Positive affirmation:** I can heal easily

> **Possible yes buts:**

- It will be difficult
- It's not possible
- I am too old
- I can't do it
- No one heals from this
- I am not strong enough

Your yes buts will be your 'truth' at this moment... you will find that this will change as you work through this book. You will open a door to possibilities, and in turn emotional healing and in many cases physical healing.

The SUDS Scale

In order to keep track of the effectiveness of your work I recommend you rate the level of intensity of the emotion at the beginning of each round using a scale of 0 – 10, where 0 is no intensity at all (usually the ultimate aim of the work) and 10 is the highest intensity possible. This is known as the SUDS scale. All you need to know is that it is a way of measuring the emotional charge on a feeling, or the intensity of a physical pain or symptom.

SUDS stands for **S**ubjective **U**nits of **D**isturbance **S**cale, and the key word in this is SUBJECTIVE. One person's 3 could be another's 9. This scale is only useful when rating your own intensity, you cannot guess for another person.

It is also useful to keep a journal so you can return to your work and both test it, and also recognise what you have achieved. Keeping a diary can be very self-affirming. Buy a beautiful book, in your favourite colour or design, and write down not just the work you have done, but also the positive experiences of the day. Even in the darkest places it is possible to find snippets of pleasure, perhaps a beautiful flower, or a piece of music. Write them down to remind yourself of them when you need to find that joy during any dark times. Let them be a reminder that you are not alone.

'Every time you smile at someone, it is an action of love, a gift to that person, a beautiful thing.'
Mother Teresa

The Heart Anchor

My friend and colleague, Sue Beer, has developed a way of working with the Heart Anchor (Healing the Addicted Heart, the Five Stages of Transformation). Harnessing and building on the energetic vibration of the heart, our emotional centre and the seat of our truth, is not only extremely powerful, but gives us a gift which is with us wherever we are, whether in hospital, during treatment, doctor's appointments or any other times when we are in need of bringing ourselves back to centre and peacefulness.

Whilst Sue's work takes this well beyond the scope of this book and is the result of years of studying and research, I offer you this variation which you can start with today.

Place one hand over your heart Chakra (in the centre of your chest) and begin to create a collection of things that give you pleasure, as with your journal. It may be that you want to bring your favourite colour into this space, perhaps someone you love, a look on their face, the sound of their voice. It could be a beautiful rose, or a work of art. It doesn't matter, collect these and bring them into your heart. Keep your hand there as you enjoy these feelings and you will find the more you do it the quicker your heart responds. I like to think of it as having a basket of beauty held into my heart, which I add to as often as I like.

'It's the little things I want, those are what matter, the sunshine, a rose, my granddaughter's laugh. The big things like money and cars and holidays just don't seem to matter now.
Holding my hand over my heart and building a library of 'little things' I have them with me at any time I choose. What a gift to myself during this often harsh journey of cancer.'
Rachel, a breast cancer client

Aspects
In order to get complete relief from an issue it is important to get all the aspects, or pieces of the puzzle, that go into making that problem so effective. If a problem does not clear, it is usually because there is some other aspect interfering with the work. Your job is to become a detective and to unearth all these aspects and eliminate them. If tapping doesn't seem to work it is almost always due to undiscovered aspects, not the technique itself.

For example, you may work with your fear of spiders and seem to eliminate it, and then a spider scuttles across the room and the fear comes back. In this case, the aspect you have not covered will be a fear of spiders moving and you will need to tap specifically on this. The fear of a stationary spider and the fear of a moving spider are separate problems and need to be addressed separately by tapping.

Think of aspects as pieces of the puzzle that when treated individually with the tapping then allow the healing of the whole.

'There are no extra pieces in the universe.
Everyone is here because he or she has a place to fill,
and every piece must fit itself into the big jigsaw puzzle.'
Deepak Chopra

Different aspects are possible with just about any problem. Sometimes they take the form of a series of traumatic memories such as memories of war, abuse or rape. Each of those memories may be a separate problem, or aspect, and needs to be addressed individually before complete relief is obtained. Until all aspects are gone you may not feel you are getting relief even though you have taken care of one or more aspects. Persistence pays!

This chapter has covered the basic tapping protocol. In the following chapter we will look at further variations and innovations of the basic techniques, which I will use and refer to throughout this book.

CHAPTER 3

OTHER TAPPING TECHNIQUES

While much of this book will focus on the use of the basic EFT tapping technique, there are several variations and advancements, which are also useful to have in your toolbox. Some of these protocols have been developed by Gary Craig, others are the work of other similarly highly talented meridian therapists. Becoming familiar with these extra techniques will enhance and refine your own skilful use of the tapping.

- The Personal Peace Procedure/An Emotional Spring Clean
- The Movie Technique
- Tearless Trauma
- Telling the Story
- Chasing the Pain
- Choices Protocol
- Imaginary Tapping
- David Lake's Continuous Tapping
- Constricted Breathing Technique

The Personal Peace Procedure/An Emotional Spring Clean

I would like to introduce you now to the Personal Peace Procedure, developed by Gary Craig. For me, it is the basis of all our work with the tapping techniques. Effectively applied, the Personal Peace Procedure revolutionises our present by releasing the emotional baggage we all carry with us. It is a way of working through your residual emotional attachment to past events, and to all those memories that, when you bring them to mind now, still have a charge on them, still make you feel cross, embarrassed, shameful, sad etc. And you can do it for yourself!

Some memories, when you bring them to mind now, feel genuinely over and done with. You know something happened, but you don't feel disturbed when you remember it now. It really is over. And it isn't disturbing your energy system.

However other ones, maybe your first romance, something like that, may still have a charge when you pull them to mind now. For example, you may feel embarrassed, or hot, or shaky, or scared. Those memories that 'get' you in some way today, yet are over in real time, are those which are still creating a disruption in your energy system today.

These are the memories that you need to work through and clear using the PPP. This accumulation of our unresolved history leads to the more global manifestations of dis-ease, such as depression, panic attacks, general malaise and serious disease.

You may be asking whether it's normal to have an emotional response to something bad. Well, yes of course it is normal. Working like this is not going to make you an emotionless zombie, but it will allow you greater emotional freedom. Your unconscious mind will only clear whatever it deems to be 'excess emotion' for you.

For example, if someone died it is inevitably sad, but if they died twenty years ago and you are still crying about them every day, that is possibly an excessive emotional response. Those are the responses we are looking to change here, those which 'get' you in some way in the here and now but which belong on the shelf with the other history books.

With cancer, whilst there is no scientific research to substantiate this, my experience would indicate that a specific trauma in the 5 years preceding diagnosis **may** trigger an inappropriate immune system response, which in turn allows the cancer to develop. I say **may** because whilst intuitively, and through my observations in client work, I believe this to be true, I am in no position to prove it and it is always important to keep a very open mind.

However, true or otherwise, what I do know for sure is that doing your Personal Peace Process and letting go of all your old emotional baggage will absolutely bring you a sense of calmness and peace. For me, it is a vital part of everyone's healing path, cancer or otherwise.

Again, I would like to stress that experiencing trauma does NOT inevitably lead to cancer. However, those I work with who have a cancer diagnosis have almost invariably experienced some form of traumatic sudden shock in the preceding years.

Social Psychologist, Robert Caldini, uses the metaphor of the tabletop to help us understand the effect of specific life events on our more general (or global) feeling of wellbeing.

For an example, if we take depression. You are not born depressed, things happen that lead you to that state. Depression becomes the table top which is supported by the power we give to the specific negative events (table legs) which created it. Take out enough legs and the table top will collapse.

Most of us will not know exactly what things those are so, but by working with our own PPP we will work through all our negative history anyway, without the need to be diagnostic or self analytical.

At some point you will find that the depression lifts and you just feel better. You won't have to go through every single memory on your list because there is likely to be a generalisation effect. This means that the unconscious mind seems to find links between different memories, similarities of sorts, and by clearing the emotional charge on one very often the charge on others, even seemingly unrelated, will diminish too. However, it is worth being systematic, particularly when dealing with something as serious as cancer.

To create serious physical or emotional dis-ease there are likely to be many contributors, and these will not necessarily always be obvious. You will learn to become your own detective, but an easy way to ensure you are covering all the emotional bases is to be meticulous in your application of the tapping, searching out each and every memory that still carries an emotional charge. You are looking for those memories which, when you bring them to mind, still 'get' you in some way, still make you feel angry, sad, guilty, lonely etc.

Another useful metaphor for this is to think of the game '*Jenga*', where you pile bricks up one on top of the other in a tall tower. Then each player takes a brick out, then the next until at some point that tower of bricks collapses. If you think of those bricks as a wall that is between you and total health, I wonder how many bricks you will need to remove from that wall in order to feel very much better. Even removing just one will allow you to get a glimpse!

Whatever your thoughts on the above, systematically working through your own Personal Peace Process as follows will allow you to begin to feel better generally, and less likely to be triggered to ongoing stressors in your life today.

So:

Buy yourself another notebook

Divide it into sections, each one representing a decade of your life

Under each decade bring to mind any memory which still has a charge on it today – if you are not sure, write it down anyway. List both obvious traumas and the little 't' traumas, the everyday traumas, they are all valuable to work through.

If there are some things that happened which you can't remember but others tell you about and you feel you **SHOULD** have a response to, put them down on the list anyway.

You may want to divide each decade into relevant sections such as:

- School
- Home
- Siblings
- Parents
- Family
- Husband/wife/partner
- Children
- Romantic Relationships
- Work
- Friends
- Other

Now apply the Movie Technique or Tearless Trauma as follows:

The Movie Technique
Make each memory into a mini movie, as if you can watch it on the wall opposite, with you in it.

How long does it run?

To allow this to work easily you want a movie that is no more than 5 minutes, but preferably less. It may be that a specific movie contains many different pieces; that is fine but you will need to treat each one separately with the tapping.

Imagine that you have a camera in your mind and zoom into the piece of each memory that has an emotional charge; it may be a look on someone's face, it may be something somebody said, it may be the moment the accident happened. You want to find THAT moment, the moment out of the whole memory which contains the highest emotional charge.

Give that piece a short title that **specifically** represents the movie for you. The only reason for making it relatively short is that you will be tapping around all the points using it as the Reminder Phrase.

For example:

'Three years old, Dad hitting me in the kitchen'

as opposed to:

'Dad hitting me'

If your Dad hit you once the chances are he hit you several times and there are may be a number of memories that could fit under that title. You will need to treat each one as a separate incident.

Quickly rate each movie on a scale of 0 – 10 on how you feel about them **NOW**, not then but **NOW.** How does it make you feel when you think about it now?

If you don't know, guess.

If you don't feel anything about it but you think you should, just guess at how much you think you **SHOULD** feel about it and treat it in the same way.

Now start tapping as follows, simply following the movie title with either 'movie' or 'emotion'.

When you have tapped on it for maybe four or five rounds, if no emotional response reveals itself then you are clear on that particular memory, it is not contributing to the way you live your life in the here and now. If you were repressing or avoiding the emotions underneath it, and you start to get a sense of them continue tapping, following your emotional or physical responses.

Repeat 3 times while tapping the Karate Chop:

Even though I have this X movie I deeply and completely love and accept myself

Eyebrow:	*This 'X' movie*
Side of Eye:	*This 'X' movie*
Under Eye:	*This 'X' movie*
Under Nose:	*This 'X' movie*
Chin:	*This 'X' movie*
Collar Bone:	*This 'X' movie*

Under Arm:	*This 'X' movie*
Top of Head:	*This 'X' movie*

Repeat 3 times while tapping the Karate Chop:

Even though I have these X movie emotions I deeply and completely love and accept myself

Eyebrow:	*X movie emotions*
Side of Eye:	*X movie emotions*
Under Eye:	*X movie emotions*
Under Nose:	*X movie emotions*
Chin:	*X movie emotions*
Collar Bone:	*X movie emotions*
Under Arm:	*X movie emotions*
Top of Head:	*X movie emotions*

Repeat 3 times while tapping the Karate Chop:

Even though I have these X emotions I deeply and completely love and accept myself

Eyebrow:	*X emotions*
Side of Eye:	*X emotions*
Under Eye:	*X emotions*
Under Nose:	*X emotions*
Chin:	*X emotions*
Collar Bone:	*X emotions*
Under Arm:	*X emotions*
Top of Head:	*X emotions*

Continue like this until you feel comfortable enough to watch the movie. Check your SUDS scale of 0 – 10 and notice what your intensity is now, when you think about the movie. Continue tapping as above until you feel a significant reduction in the intensity.

Run it on the wall opposite you, noticing any piece that still has an emotional charge.

Stop at that piece and tap.

Repeat 3 times while tapping the Karate Chop:

Even though I feel 'X' at that bit I deeply and completely love and accept myself

Eye Brow:	*Feeling X at that bit*
Side of Eye:	*That bit*

Under Eye:	*Still getting me*
Under Nose:	*Still making me feel X*
Chin:	*Feeling X at that bit*
Collar Bone:	*That bit*
Under Arm:	*Still getting me*
Top of Head:	*Still making me feel X*

Repeat 3 times while tapping the Karate Chop:

Even though he said that I deeply and completely love and accept myself

Eyebrow:	*He said that*
Side of Eye:	*Those words*
Under Eye:	*His words*
Under Nose:	*He said that*
Chin:	*I can't believe he said that*
Collar Bone:	*Those words*
Under Arm:	*He said that*
Top of Head:	*His words*

Continue the process until you can run the entire movie in one go without getting any charge. At this point it may seem like you are watching someone else in that situation, it might turn into black and white, or it may have moved very far away. Sometimes you may not be able to see it at all anymore. It will not make what happened OK, but it will prevent you from feeling the pain of it in your life today.

When you feel that you can run the movie from start to finish without any emotional charge continue to the next step, which is telling the story.

Telling the Story Technique
Imagine telling someone the story of one of your negative memories.

How do you feel when you think about telling that story? Rate your intensity on the 0 – 10 SUDS scale.

Is it OK to share it or do you feel anxious, embarrassed, frightened or other? If so, before starting telling the story tap as follows:

Repeat 3 times while tapping the Karate Chop:

Even though I have this telling the story anxiety I deeply and completely love and accept myself

Eyebrow:	*Telling the story anxiety*
Side of Eye:	*Telling the story anxiety*
Under Eye:	*Telling the story anxiety*
Under Nose:	*Telling the story anxiety*

Chin:	*Telling the story anxiety*
Collar Bone:	*Telling the story anxiety*
Under Arm:	*Telling the story anxiety*
Top of Head:	*Telling the story anxiety*

When you have cleared your initial feelings about telling the story you can start to imagine telling it.

As with The Movie Technique, when you reach a point in the story that feels uncomfortable, for whatever reason, stop and tap on that bit.

For example:

Repeat 3 times while tapping the Karate Chop:

Even though I feel too embarrassed to talk about that bit I deeply and completely love and accept myself

Eyebrow:	*Embarrassed at that bit*
Side of Eye:	*This embarrassment*
Under Eye:	*Embarrassed at that bit*
Under Nose:	*This embarrassment*
Chin:	*Embarrassed at that bit*
Collar Bone:	*This embarrassment*
Under Arm:	*Embarrassed at that bit*
Top of Head:	*This embarrassment*

Repeat 3 times while tapping the Karate Chop:

Even though I feel ashamed when I think of that bit I deeply and completely love and accept myself

Eyebrow:	*This shame*
Side of Eye:	*Shame at that bit*
Under Eye:	*My shame*
Under Nose:	*Shame at that bit*
Chin:	*This shame*
Collar Bone:	*Shame at that bit*
Under Arm:	*My shame*
Top of Head:	*Shame at that bit*

Remember to keep checking in on your SUDS scale of 0 – 10. Continue until you can 'Tell the Story' without any emotional charge.

If you can actually test this by really talking it through with somebody, for instance a therapist or a good friend, somebody you can trust, then go ahead and do it. It is important to take care of yourself at all times though, and it may not be appropriate for other people to know these stories, they are private for whatever reason and that is fine, respect your privacy here. No one needs to know apart from you but you need to clear any ongoing emotional response.

Tearless Trauma Technique

The Tearless Trauma Technique should be used when the thought of even looking at the movie is too much.

In the Movie Technique you use dissociation to keep yourself at a safe distance from the memory you are working with by looking at it as a movie on the wall in front of you.

With Tearless Trauma you take the dissociation a step further by putting the movie out of sight and quickly guessing at how you would feel if you were to watch it, but without actually doing so.

Instructions for Tearless Trauma

- Choose the movie from your list.
- GUESS at what your emotional intensity would be (on a 0-10 scale) IF you were to vividly imagine the incident. DO NOT actually imagine it.
- Then do a few rounds on 'This X movie" as with the Movie Technique
- After a few rounds of tapping, **GUESS** how intense you would feel now were you to look at it, again without doing so.
- Continue until your **GUESS** is low on our scale of 0 – 10.
- Then start to watch the movie as with the Movie Technique, again stopping to tap on any piece of it that still holds a charge.

Chasing the Pain

There are three very simple things to monitor when working with pain with the tapping:

1. Location

Describe the exact location of the pain. Be specific. In the same way a postcode will direct you to a precise address whereas just saying London a letter would be unlikely to find you, you need to instruct your unconscious mind to the exact location of the discomfort, ie the tip of my left shoulder blade, the top of my right thigh etc

2. Quality

Pains have many different qualities. They can be sharp, dull, hot, constant etc. The word 'pain' itself may not be right, it could be an ache or a hurt etc.
Make sure your wording accurately reflects the symptom.

3. Intensity

Use the SUDS Scale of 0 – 10 to rate the intensity of the pain right now

Repeat 3 times while tapping the Karate Chop:

Even though I have this sharp pain on the right side of my neck I deeply and completely love and accept myself

Eyebrow:	*This sharp pain on the right side of my neck*
Side of Eye:	*This sharp pain on the right side of my neck*
Under Eye:	*This sharp pain on the right side of my neck*

Under Nose:	*This sharp pain on the right side of my neck*
Chin:	*This sharp pain on the right side of my neck*
Collar Bone:	*This sharp pain on the right side of my neck*
Under Arm:	*This sharp pain on the right side of my neck*
Top of Head:	*This sharp pain on the right side of my neck*

Then tune back into your symptom and see what has happened to the pain.

- **Check the location**
- **Check the quality**
- **Check the intensity**

If any of these have changed, alter your words accordingly.

It is very common for pains to change and move around the body. In tapping terms, we call this **Chasing the Pain**. Keep chasing the symptoms around your body until they are clear. It is a curious phenomenon that seemingly intractable problems with a genuine physical cause can change and even clear as you tap.

The Choices Method
Choices is a technique developed by Pat Carrington, PhD, aimed at realising positive goals with the tapping.

The method is based on the use of a 'Choice', a unique form of affirmation which differs from traditional affirmations in that the statement of desired outcome is preceded by the phrase 'I choose to...' instead of by a simple declarative phrase such as 'I am...' 'I have...,' etc. The Choice replaces the default affirmation of I deeply and completely love and accept myself.

Unlike traditional affirmations, Choices affirmations do not contradict a person's present view of reality. Think of the difference in how you feel when you hear the following two statements:

I have total health
I choose total health

One feels far less combative, and therefore more acceptable to both the conscious and unconscious minds.

The Choices Protocol
When using the Choices method, a formal Choice is substituted for the traditional self-acceptance affirmation ("I deeply and completely accept myself") in the Set Up Statement, and is then used in part of the subsequent reminder phrases. This Choice takes the form of a phrase which is, in general, the opposite of the negative statement contained in the first portion of the setup phrase process, the one which commences with the words 'Even though...'.

The Choice is an expression of what the person truly wants (a desired outcome) for the problem which the treatment is presently addressing. It is aimed at that specific problem rather than being a general affirmation. This change in the setup phrase is followed by similar alterations in the reminder phrases that follow.

The protocol for the Choices technique is known as **The Choices Trio** because it has three distinct components as follows.

Instructions for the Choices Trio
After you obtain an initial SUDS level, proceed as follows:
- Identify the negative thought/attitude/ feeling etc that you want to change.
- Create a Choice that is roughly the opposite, for example: 'I choose to feel at ease swimming in deep water' would be an appropriate opposite Choice for the negative statement: 'I'm afraid of swimming in deep water.'
- Combine the negative statement with the positive Choice to create a Choices Set-Up phrase. For example: 'Even though I'm afraid of swimming in deep water, I choose to feel at ease when swimming in deep water.'
- Tap the Karate Chop while repeating this Choices Set-Up phrase three times.

Follow this Set-Up with the Choices Trio:

Step 1
Do one complete **Short Cut** round of tapping on the negative thought only. For example: 'I'm afraid of swimming in deep water'.

Step 2
Follow immediately (without repeating the Set-Up) with one complete **Short Cut** round of tapping using the Choices statement only, as a Reminder Phrase. For example: 'I choose to feel at ease swimming in deep water'.

Step 3
Follow immediately (without repeating the Set-Up) by one complete **Short Cut** round of tapping using alternating phrases as follows:
- At the first point (Eyebrow) use the **negative thought** as a Reminder Phrase (in the above example, 'I am swimming in deep water.').
- At the next (Side of Eye), use the **positive choice** for the Reminder Phrase (e.g. 'I choose to feel at ease swimming in deep water.').
- At the next (Under Eye), use the **negative thought** for the Reminder Phrase, etc.

Continue this alternation of negative and positive for the entire round.

If more work is needed, repeat the Trio as many times as necessary.

It is very important to use the full Short Cut version as you MUST end with the positive choice at the end of the third round.

Imaginary Tapping
Your unconscious mind does not know the difference between fact and fiction. When you vividly imagine something you really do experience it. Many of you will already know that in the way past traumas can feel very real in the present.

For those of you who don't, vividly imagine holding half a lemon and then squeeze some of the juice into your mouth. Are you salivating? Do you have a lemon?

Imaginary tapping can be very effective at times when you can't physically tap, such as during an MRI scan. It is also useful at night (see Chapter on insomnia) when the physical body is too tired to tap.

Instructions for Imaginary Tapping
After identifying something you'd like to tap on:

- Close your eyes
- Imagine tapping around the points on the shortcut version as follows:

1. Eyebrow
2. Side of your eye
3. Under your eye
4. Under your nose
5. Chin
6. Collar Bone
7. Under one arm
8. Top of head

Dr David Lake's Continuous Tapping
Developed by Dr David Lake (www.eftdownunder.com), this technique is extremely helpful to use during treatment itself, and post surgery when mobility might be low. David refers to it as energy toning.

- Using the forefinger, tap on the inside of the thumb along the nail bed facing the body
- Then use the thumb to tap the same position on each of the four fingers
- Get a rhythm going and tap continuously
- There is no need to tune into anything specific

Constricted Breathing Technique:
Take a couple of deep breaths to stretch out the lungs.

Then take the fullest breath possible for you right now and rate it on a scale of 0 – 10 where 0 is no breath at all and 10 is the fullest breath you can imagine taking.

Repeat 3 times while tapping the Karate Chop:

Even though I have this constricted breathing I deeply and completely love and accept myself

Repeat 3 times while tapping the Karate Chop:

Even though something is blocking my fullest breath I deeply and completely love and accept myself

Eyebrow:	*This constricted breathing*
Side of Eye:	*This constricted breathing*
Under Eye:	*Something is blocking my breathing*
Under Nose:	*Something's in the way of my fullest breath*
Chin:	*This constricted breathing*

Collar Bone:	This constricted breathing
Under Arm:	This block to my fullest breath
Top of Head:	This constricted breathing

Tap using the following Reminder Phrases, or variations thereof:

Eyebrow:	This remaining constricted breathing
Side of Eye:	This remaining block to my fullest breath
Under Eye:	This remaining something blocking my breath
Under Nose:	This remaining constricted breathing
Chin:	The remaining block to my breathing
Collar Bone:	This remaining constricted breathing
Under Arm:	This remaining block to my fullest breath
Top of Head:	This remaining something blocking my breath

Reassess your breath. Chances are your breathing will be deeper, or more expansive, or have changed quality in some way. Sometimes a snippet of a memory, or an emotion, may surface. If this is the case, make a note to work with that as it will be important and relevant in some way, even if that is not clear now.

In the following chapters we will be looking at applying the tapping technique specifically to work through the immediate emotions that can arise with a cancer diagnosis. We will also look at the impact the word 'cancer' can have on your physiology and energy system.

CHAPTER 4

THE EMOTIONS OF DIAGNOSIS

'You may not yet be able to bring your unconscious mind activity into awareness as thoughts, but it will always be reflected in the body as an emotion, and of this you can become aware.'

Eckhart Tolle

A cancer diagnosis is the beginning of an emotional rollercoaster, no matter how prepared you may be. It is, as a good friend said, a pivotal moment in life. Some emotions may be obvious, whilst others may catch you unawares. In this chapter, I shall list the primary emotions which I see in my practice, and illustrate how to work with these with EFT. However, this is by no means an exclusive list, whatever you are feeling you can work with it with EFT, just replace my words with yours as necessary. Remember, it is all about **YOU**.

The main emotions around cancer seem to be:

- Shock
- Fear (of different sorts)
- Anger (again, of different sorts)
- Resentment
- Sadness
- Anxiety
- Panic
- Self pity

Many clients, at some point, will end up seeing their cancer as, ultimately, a life enhancing experience. Something had to stop them in their tracks and make them take a long hard look at the way they were leading their lives. Once through the healing process, people often find themselves in a position to truly embrace their life in a way that is congruent for them – no more pretending to be someone they are not, no more doing things which don't fit with their life ethos. People often find that during their cancer journey they have learnt to really enjoy being in the moment, appreciating life in a new way, no longer stuck on the stressful treadmill they were once on. They view the world, and their role in it, with new, clearer eyes.

Cancer offered them the opportunity to change in a way they would otherwise have ignored. The diagnosis forced them into a place where they had to deeply examine their innermost, and often darkest, thoughts, feelings and beliefs. Whilst reaching into these uncomfortable extremes, they learnt what worked for them and what didn't, and how to find the courage to make the healing changes. Not an easy call - and I am always filled with awe by the courage and determination of those who are able to face their demons and work through their most intimate and painful thoughts and behaviours.

Without exception, these amazing individuals reap their rewards, sometimes with health, sometimes with spiritual growth, often with both. Whatever the outcome, the connection to self and the understandings of who they really are, and can be, far outweigh the trauma of doing the work.

As I write this I can feel the goosebumps rising. I feel so privileged to have witnessed these journeys first hand. It is incredibly humbling to be part of and I am so grateful for the lessons they have taught me, which I am able to share with you here.

However, initially you are more likely to resonate with Simon as he describes receiving his cancer diagnosis as follows:

'The world stopped, like a roller coaster that gets stuck when you are at the top hanging upside down, you can see everything, it has form in shapes and colours, you know it is real, yet you have no connection to it anymore. I felt like I was the observer, yet I was the observed. I was manacled to a world I was no longer a part of. Nothing was the same, nothing ever will be'.
Simon

His words say everything to me, and I often hear clients say that the world is the same, yet the colour has faded, nothing that once was important matters any more. The shock of a cancer diagnosis brings our vulnerability and role in the world into sharp focus.

The Awareness of Negative Thoughts and Feelings
From an Energy Psychology perspective, the manifestation of a negative feeling/ thought/ belief/ memory is something to be welcomed, because once it is in consciousness, in our awareness, we have the tools with which to release it. When we release these feelings, we are naturally clearing our blocks to emotional wellbeing and will feel more in control and positive. However, negative emotions have a tendency to hurl themselves back onto centre stage if we allow them to, and different things may seem to trigger a similar response. This does not mean that the work you have done has not been successful, it merely means there are more pieces to the jigsaw puzzle that need to be addressed.

Whilst we are beginning here by looking at the emotions themselves, this is only part of our work. In tapping terms, the emotions are global concepts, meaning that they are usually the result of many different specific thoughts and memories accumulating into the one feeling. EFT will help reduce the excess emotional responses we all experience easily. But in order to get complete permanent relief we also need to work with the specific events that led to the feeling in the first place, in this case, the diagnosis and anything connected to it.

The most commonly expressed immediate emotional responses to a cancer diagnosis are shock, fear, anger, anxiety, resentment, sadness and guilt.

Think about your diagnosis and ask yourself, making a note of your responses and the intensity of feeling using the SUDS Scale of 0 – 10.

- **'How do I feel right now when I think about it?'**
- **'What is the strongest emotion?'**
- **'Where in my body am I feeling it?'**

- **'What emotions still come up when I hear the word cancer?'**

Begin by assessing your strongest feelings on the scale of 0 to 10, one at the time, starting with the most intense and then work through them, tapping using the protocols that follow in this chapter.

Cancer – That Powerful Word

'Cancer is a word, not a sentence.'
John Diamond

Words have their own energetic frequency. Think of how you feel when you hear the following words: laughter, depression, fun, love, fear. Each has its individual energy, doesn't it? In EFT we refer to this energy as a vibration. And the vibration of the word reflects in our own energetic vibration. This is why when we spend time with someone who is depressed we may feel low ourselves, we can begin vibrating at their frequency.

The word '*cancer*' can, in itself, create fear, even in those with no history of the disease. Merely reading or hearing the word seems to access the vibration of the disease itself at some level in some people. When training other therapists to work with tapping and cancer I will ask them to close their eyes and hear the word 'cancer', and to notice their immediate response. Sometimes this can be very surprising, with tears, shaking and other physiological responses such as extreme body heat/cold, sometimes memories pop up, and often they will experience at least a change in their breathing as they resonate with that word. They are tuning into the vibration of cancer as they experience the meaning of that word to them. This is a subjective response, dependent on individual thoughts and beliefs, and does NOT mean they will go on to develop cancer; merely is an example of how a word can have a negative effect on our energy system, creating a disruption which we can rebalance with the tapping.

When you are diagnosed with cancer it is going to be a word that appears frequently in your world, both externally and internally, in your thoughts, and your interactions with other people, especially the doctors. It is wise to recognise the potential energetic disruption this causes and to take remedial action.

Say 'Cancer' out loud to yourself and notice your response. This is the starting point of your work and of addressing cancer. You may want to get your friends and family to do this exercise with you so that they too are able to achieve a calm balanced response to the word.

Keep coming back to the word until you are no longer experiencing any excessive emotional or physical response to it. You may not like the word, but it becomes just another word, with the same degree of emotion attached to it as the word 'cold' or 'cough', releasing any intense charge.

Your response to the word is likely to vary as you work through the different chapters in this book, and it is quite normal to need to keep coming back to tapping on the word itself over a period of time.

Remember to use the SUDS scale of 0 – 10 to measure your levels of intensity and your progress.

What is the strongest emotion that you feel when you hear the word 'cancer'? For most people it is fear. Tap as follows, replacing the words 'fear' and 'frightening' with your own choice of words if that is more appropriate for you.

Tapping Section: *The Word Cancer*

Repeat 3 times while tapping the Karate Chop:

Even though I'm frightened of that word I deeply and completely love and accept myself

Eyebrow:	*That frightening word*
Side of Eye:	*This cancer*
Under Eye:	*This fear*
Under Nose:	*This frightening cancer*
Chin:	*This frightening word*
Collar Bone:	*This cancer fear*
Under Arm:	*That word*
Top of Head:	*Cancer*

What emotions does this evoke? How intense are they on a scale of 1 – 10? Make a note.

Repeat 3 times while tapping the Karate Chop:

Even though there is something about the word cancer I deeply and completely love and accept myself

Eyebrow:	*Cancer*
Side of Eye:	*Cancer*
Under Eye:	*Cancer*
Under Nose:	*Cancer*
Chin:	*Cancer*
Collar Bone:	*Cancer*
Under Arm:	*Cancer*
Top of Head:	*Cancer*

What emotions does this evoke? How intense are they on a scale of 1 – 10? Make a note.

Repeat 3 times while tapping the Karate Chop:

Even though I have cancer I deeply and completely love and accept myself

Eyebrow:	*Cancer*

Side of Eye:	*This cancer*
Under Eye:	*Cancer*
Under Nose:	*Cancer*
Chin:	*Cancer*
Collar Bone:	*This cancer*
Under Arm:	*Cancer*
Top of Head:	*Cancer*

Do a round shouting the word at each point:

Repeat 3 times while tapping the Karate Chop:

Even though I still have this cancer response I deeply and completely love and accept myself

Eyebrow:	*This response*
Side of Eye:	*This word*
Under Eye:	*Cancer*
Under Nose:	*This scary word*
Chin:	*I don't want it*
Collar Bone:	*I don't like it*
Under Arm:	*This cancer feeling*
Top of Head:	*Cancer*

Repeat 3 times while tapping the Karate Chop:

Even though there is still something about that word that gets me I deeply and completely love and accept myself

Eyebrow:	*Cancer*
Side of Eye:	*That word*
Under Eye:	*C*
Under Nose:	*A*
Chin:	*N*
Collar Bone:	*C*
Under Arm:	*E*
Top of Head:	*R*

Continue:

Eyebrow:	*That jumble of letters*
Side of Eye:	*That word*
Under Eye:	*Cancer*
Under Nose:	*Those letters*
Chin:	*C A N C E R*
Collar Bone:	*My remaining response*
Under Arm:	*Cancer*
Top of Head:	*Cancer*

Whilst it is possible to release all emotions around the word 'Cancer' so that it impacts you like any other word, ie dog or cat, it is more likely that it will still hold a little intensity and that is OK. Check to make sure that you feel comfortable as you say the word aloud and that any physical response has cleared. It is not always necessary or possible to reduce an issue to zero. However, whilst it is natural to hold a little feeling about the word itself, not to like it, it is not useful to feel much intensity. Different emotions may be triggered at different times during your cancer journey. Whenever you notice yourself having a strong reaction to the word, return to these protocols and tap to clear it. Working this way already begins to change the power of the disease and its emotional hold on you.

Julia, who has ovarian cancer, having tapped as described above, said she felt liberated! She said it was as if the monster had turned into an imp, which she could see looking up at her trying to be endearing. The structure of her representation of the cancer had totally changed, she surprised herself by feeling compassion for it, and also humour. And it only took 5 minutes of tapping! This powerful image has stayed with her and she speaks fondly of training her imp!

The Language of Cancer

'The thought manifests as the word. The word manifests as the deed. The deed develops into habit. And the habit hardens into character. So watch the thought and its ways with care. And let it spring from love, born out of concern for all beings.'
Buddha

During traditional medical intervention you can feel very disempowered and out of control. It can feel as if something is attacking you from the inside, while you are also being 'attacked' externally during treatment. Much of the language used around cancer is hostile and negative. We are at war with the disease. It is often viewed as the enemy to be fought against, beaten, destroyed, killed. The body becomes a battlefield. It can feel like being an onlooker in a war zone over which you have little control. Does anything or anyone thrive in war?

If instead we work **with** the internal disease state, coming from a place of communication and willingness to understand, it frees up our energy to focus on the job of healing.

41

Are you constantly speaking in this way? Flooding your unconscious mind with violence and war metaphors, thoughts of struggles and attack? These are strong words, but not healing ones. If any of these resonate with you and your beliefs it is important to tap to clear them. Whilst healing from cancer (in any sense) may be a long journey, the aim of this book is to take it step by step and ease that path, offering your unconscious mind, and your body, other options than warfare.

Use and adapt the following tapping protocols until you feel a change in the way you feel about the words. You might feel lighter, they may carry less charge, you might not be able to focus on them...

Struggle Battle Fight Kill Destroy Beat Win Lose War

Perhaps some of the following advertising taglines from around the world get to you:

- "You can never have too many outfits. Or too many breast checks"
- Thyroid cancer is growing 6 times faster than prostate cancer. Ask your doctor to check your neck. It could save your life.
- "Prostate cancer surgery so effective, even women can feel the difference"
- "My sister accidentally killed herself. She died of skin cancer"
- "Don't take the sun lightly"
- "Obituary. He was waiting for symptoms. Colon cancer screening saves lives."
- "Watch your mouth"
- "If only women paid as much attention to their breasts as men do"
- "It's in your breast interest to have both"
- "Smokers never become old"
- "Touch A Tit, Save A Tit"
- "The Marlboro Man Died of Lung Cancer"
- "Smoking doesn't only hurt you."
- "Free2Be"
- "If you're going to stare at my breasts, ... you could at least donate a dollar to save them."
- "Be Bold. Check them"
- "If you can't stop smoking, cancer will."
- "Winston Tastes Good, Like a Carcinogen Should"
- "Support our Boobs!"
- "Join the fight for women's survival"
- "Living with cancer"

Tapping Section: *How you feel about cancer?*

Use/adapt the following tapping protocols until you feel a change in the way you feel about the words. You might feel lighter, they may carry less charge, you might not be able to focus on them….

Repeat 3 times while tapping the Karate Chop:

Even though healing has to be a struggle I deeply and completely love and accept myself

Eyebrow:	*It has to be a struggle*
Side of Eye:	*It has to be difficult*
Under Eye:	*It can't be easy*
Under Nose:	*This cancer struggle*
Chin:	*This difficult struggle*
Collar Bone:	*This cancer battle*
Under Arm:	*This cancer fight*
Top of Head:	*It can't be easy*

Repeat 3 times while tapping the Karate Chop:

Even though I am battling with cancer I deeply and completely love and accept myself

Eyebrow:	*Battling with cancer*
Side of Eye:	*This battle*
Under Eye:	*Cancer battle*
Under Nose:	*Battling with cancer*
Chin:	*This battle*
Collar Bone:	*Cancer battle*
Under Arm:	*Cancer battle*
Top of Head:	*Battling with cancer*

Repeat 3 times while tapping the Karate Chop:

Even though it is going to be a real struggle I deeply and completely love and accept myself

Eyebrow:	*This struggle*
Side of Eye:	*It has to be a struggle*
Under Eye:	*Cancer struggle*

Under Nose:	It is going to be such a struggle
Chin:	Cancer struggle
Collar Bone:	Cancer struggle
Under Arm:	My struggle
Top of Head:	Cancer struggle

Watch your language! Do any of the following statements form part of your everyday language:

- Sick of living this way
- Sick to death
- Dead to the world
- Feel like death warmed up
- Going to catch my death
- Laugh myself sick
- Worried sick
- Bored to death
- Sick and tired

If they are, just notice, and tap to clear them. These statements are so much a part of everyday language that they often go undetected, yet they are giving specific instructions to the unconscious mind.

Tap on them as and when you catch yourself saying or thinking any of them:

Repeat 3 times while tapping the Karate Chop:

Even though I am sick to death of X I deeply and completely love and accept myself

Eyebrow:	Sick to death
Side of Eye:	Those words
Under Eye:	Sick to death
Under Nose:	I am sick to death
Chin:	Sick to death of X
Collar Bone:	Those words
Under Arm:	Sick to death
Top of Head:	Sick to death of X

Shock

'We shall not fail or falter; we shall not weaken or tire. Neither the sudden shock of battle nor the long-drawn trials of vigilance and exertion will wear us down. Give us the tools and we will finish the job.'
Sir Winston Churchill, Radio speech, 1941

Assess the intensity of the shock as you think of it now. Give it a number on the SUDS intensity scale. How do you know? What tells you? The answer to these questions will be that you have, to one degree or another, a physical sensation which is telling you the strength of the shock for you now. When you have assessed this and given it a number begin to tap:

Tapping Section: Tapping for shock

Repeat 3 times while tapping the Karate Chop:

Even though I have this diagnosis shock I deeply and completely love and accept myself

Eyebrow:	*This diagnosis shock*
Side of Eye:	*This shocking diagnosis*
Under Eye:	*This diagnosis shock*
Under Nose:	*Diagnosis shock*
Chin:	*Diagnosis shock in my body*
Collar Bone:	*Diagnosis shock in my cells*
Under Arm:	*Diagnosis shock*
Top of Head:	*Diagnosis shock*

Repeat 3 times while tapping the Karate Chop:

Even though I have this cancer shock I deeply and completely love and accept myself

Eyebrow:	*This cancer shock*
Side of Eye:	*Cancer shock*
Under Eye:	*Cancer shock*
Under Nose:	*This cancer shock*
Chin:	*Cancer shock*
Collar Bone:	*Cancer shock*
Under Arm:	*Cancer shock*
Top of Head:	*This cancer shock*

Tap for 3 – 4 rounds and then tune into to the shock feeling again and notice what has happened. You can expect the sensations to have reduced, or changed. Unless they have completely cleared continue to tap with them, altering your words to fit the new intensity of feeling, for example:

Repeat 3 times while tapping the Karate Chop:

Even though I still have some of this diagnosis shock I deeply and completely love and accept myself

Eyebrow:	*Remaining diagnosis shock*
Side of Eye:	*Remaining diagnosis shock*
Under Eye:	*Just there in my body*
Under Nose:	*Remaining diagnosis shock*
Chin:	*Remaining diagnosis shock*
Collar Bone:	*Just there in my body*
Under Arm:	*Remaining diagnosis shock*
Top of Head:	*Remaining diagnosis shock*

Continue until you can think of the cancer diagnosis in general without feeling shock in your body. I am not expecting you to like the diagnosis, but we are working to rebalance your mind and body to the thought of it so it releases its hold on you and you can begin focussing on your healing.

Fear

> *'How very little can be done under the spirit of fear.'*
> *Florence Nightingale*

A very small number of people experience no fear when first faced with a cancer diagnosis. For the vast majority, it is a terrifying experience which brings with it a sudden sense of one's own mortality, something most of us avoid looking at. There are many potentially frightening aspects to a cancer diagnosis, the treatment, the prognosis, the change of lifestyle, the loss of income, the possibility of death, and more. To be able to reduce your fear with EFT will allow you to make important decisions from a clearer headspace. Notice the thought that brings the fear to the fore and insert 'that thought' into your Set Up Statement and Reminder Phrase. For example:

Tapping Section: Tapping for fear

Repeat 3 times while tapping the Karate Chop:

Even though I have that frightening thought I deeply and completely love and accept myself

Eyebrow:	*That thought*

46

Side of Eye:	*That frightening thought*
Under Eye:	*That powerful thought*
Under Nose:	*That thought*
Chin:	*That thought*
Collar Bone:	*That terrifying thought*
Under Arm:	*That thought*
Top of Head:	*That frightening thought*

Fear of the Cancer

There will be those who will go into coping mode, and embrace the cancer and ensuing treatment as a project to be completed, shutting off any emotional response. Ask yourself, is that me? If so, where are those emotions, where have you shut them away? Why? It is likely to be because they feel too overwhelming and frightening to deal with. And that is OK right now, but they will need to be addressed and worked through. The unconscious mind is like a leaky sieve, it will release the emotions at some point.

Suzy, on receiving a diagnosis of cervical cancer, said that it felt like being run over by a bus, not just the once, but continually, by a stream of buses. Every time she got up again another bus came along and knocked her over again. Eventually she decided just to lie down and be run over, and at this point the buses started to miss her and she had time to catch her breath and focus on survival.

I think this is such an apt description of the many exhausting rounds of tests, specialists and results that occur after the initial diagnosis.

Begin by assessing the intensity of your generalised fear right now. On a scale of 0 -10 how strong is that fear as you tune into it now? Once again, notice how that feels in your body. We will start by working with the global fear – the general all encompassing fear that a diagnosis can bring. Then we will look at applying the tapping to more specific fear topics such as fear of what is going to happen, fear of the treatment, fear of the future, fear of dying etc. I see a multitude of different, very real, fears in my practice and have selected a few of the most common. Please feel free to adapt the wording to suit whatever is going on for you.

Repeat 3 times while tapping the Karate Chop:

Even though I have this cancer fear I deeply and completely love and accept myself

Eyebrow:	*This cancer fear*
Side of Eye:	*This cancer fear*
Under Eye:	*This cancer fear*
Under Nose:	*This cancer fear*
Chin:	*This cancer fear*
Collar Bone:	*This cancer fear*

Under Arm:	This cancer fear
Top of Head:	This cancer fear

One of the most frightening things about a cancer diagnosis is that nothing is the same as it was before and you are confronted with mounds of information and decisions that need making when you are still in shock. This often brings with it a fear of what is going to happen. As humans we like to feel in control, to know what the future holds. A fear of the unknown is present in most of us at some level, even without a cancer diagnosis.

Fear can create a disruption to our ability to think clearly, we can feel muddled and confused. This is an actual energetic interference, like the static you can get on a television screen when you lose reception. We are literally losing our reception, our ability to download information from the outside world with clarity. The receivers are disrupted through our fear and our anxieties.

> *'The only thing we have to fear is fear itself.'*
> *Franklin D. Roosevelt*

Repeat 3 times while tapping the Karate Chop:

Even though I'm really scared, I don't know what's going to happen, I deeply and completely love and accept myself anyway

Eyebrow:	This cancer fear
Side of Eye:	I'm really frightened
Under Eye:	I'm scared
Under Nose:	I don't know what can happen
Chin:	This cancer fear
Collar Bone:	I'm really scared
Under Arm:	This fear
Top of Head:	This cancer fear

Continue:

Eyebrow:	Fear of the future
Side of Eye:	I don't know what is going to happen
Under Eye:	This fear of the unknown
Under Nose:	This fear
Chin:	Fear of what might happen
Collar Bone:	Fear of what this means
Under Arm:	Fear of the cancer
Top of Head:	Fear of my cancer

Check back with your scale of 0 – 10 and notice what has happened.

- **Is it the same?**
- **Has it changed?**
- **Less or more?**

Unless it has totally released continue tapping as follows:

Repeat 3 times while tapping the Karate Chop:

Even though I still have some of this cancer fear I deeply and completely love and accept myself

Eyebrow:	*This remaining fear*
Side of Eye:	*Remaining cancer fear*
Under Eye:	*Remaining fear of the unknown*
Under Nose:	*Remaining cancer fear*
Chin:	*Remaining feeling scared*
Collar Bone:	*Remaining fear of the unknown*
Under Arm:	*Remaining cancer fear*
Top of Head:	*Remaining feeling scared*

Repeat 3 times while tapping the Karate Chop:

Even though I am still scared I deeply and completely love and accept myself anyway

Eyebrow:	*Remaining scared feelings*
Side of Eye:	*Remaining fear*
Under Eye:	*Remaining feeling scared*
Under Nose:	*Remaining cancer fear*
Chin:	*Remaining scared feelings*
Collar Bone:	*Remaining fear*
Under Arm:	*Remaining feeling scared*
Top of Head:	*Remaining cancer fear*

Fear of Treatment and its Side Effects

'Poisons and medicine are oftentimes the same substance given with different intents.'
Peter Mere Latham

There is so much information available about the various cancer treatments and their potential side effects that it is almost impossible not to have created some

49

beliefs around this area, whether or not you have cancer. We hear about the 'terrible side effects', the nausea, the hair loss, impotence etc.

We will address supporting the medical model of treatment and working to reduce any potential side effects in detail in Chapter 14, but it is useful to begin to reduce the fear even in the early stages post diagnosis in order to preserve your energy for the healing process. My clients have found that by working to reduce the fear and anxiety around the treatment itself side effects are lessened and the entire experience of treatment becomes a little easier.

Are you afraid of taking drug treatment? That is reasonable, no one would volunteer for it.

How strong is that fear, on our SUDS scale? Again, notice how you know?

Repeat 3 times while tapping the Karate Chop:

Even though I'm frightened by the treatment and the side effects I deeply and completely love and accept myself

Eyebrow:	*Fear of the treatment*
Side of Eye:	*Fear of the treatment*
Under Eye:	*Fear of the side effects*
Under Nose:	*Fear of the side effects*
Chin:	*Fear of the treatment*
Collar Bone:	*Fear of the treatment*
Under Arm:	*Fear of the side effects*
Top of Head:	*Fear of the treatment*

Repeat 3 times while tapping the Karate Chop:

Even though I am scared of taking the drugs I deeply and completely love and accept myself

Eyebrow:	*This fear of the drugs*
Side of Eye:	*This fear*
Under Eye:	*This fear of the drugs*
Under Nose:	*This fear*
Chin:	*This fear of the drugs*
Collar Bone:	*This fear*
Top of Head:	*This fear of the drugs*
Top of Head:	*This fear*

After 3 – 4 rounds, check in on the specific fearful thought about the treatment or side effects and notice what happens in your body now. How strong is the fear?

Do you need to do more rounds? Do you need to adapt your words to the new feeling? Is it still a fear, or would a word such as anxiety or concern work better?

Tapping is a fantastic tool to use when faced with the brain fog that often comes with internal conflict, that inner chaos that seems to so effectively interrupt our clarity at times when we most need it. You will notice that the more you use the tapping, no matter what on, the clearer your thinking will become in all areas.

When you work directly with the treatment options you have chosen, later in this book, you will discover ways of enhancing the healing properties of chemotherapy and/or other drugs by learning how to accept, even welcome, the positive healing aspects of them, as well as radiotherapy and surgery.

Fear of Death and Dying

> *'The day which we fear as our last is but the birthday of eternity.'*
> *Seneca*

A very obvious fear, or fearful thought, which inevitably accompanies a cancer diagnosis is that of death and dying. A few decades ago cancer often meant a death sentence. This is not the case now, and medical science is making major exciting breakthroughs all the time. Treatment is now tailor made to the individual and many of those diagnosed with cancer today will go on to live long and fulfilling lives after treatment. However, naturally the fear lingers for many people and is definitely worth working with here.

Is there a specific thought that makes the fear particularly strong for you? What do you have to think to bring that fear back? Perhaps you are hearing someone saying something? Perhaps you have read something? Perhaps you have seen something in the media? If you can extract the specific thought processes that are contributing to the fear then include them in your Set Up Statements and Reminder Phrases until you have reduced the fear to a low intensity, or preferably have let it go completely.

It may sound like a strange question, but what specifically is it about dying/death that is most frightening?

Repeat 3 times while tapping the Karate Chop:

Even though I am terrified of dying I deeply and completely love and accept myself

Eyebrow:	*This terror of dying*
Side of Eye:	*I'm so frightened*
Under Eye:	*This fear of dying*
Under Nose:	*This terror of dying*
Chin:	*This fear of death*
Collar Bone:	*This terror of dying*
Under Arm:	*This terrifying thought*
Top of Head:	*This terrifying thought*

It may be leaving your loved ones, it may be the thought of pain, it may be any number of things. If you are able to establish the true meaning of dying for you, and what the fear is most attached to, tap to clear it.

Nicky's story
Nicky was terrified of dying. She began having nightmares about it, in her nightmares she was always alone, and cold, and frightened. When we discussed her dreams, whilst tapping as she spoke, Nicky realised that the main peak of her fear was connected to dying alone in a strange place. She desperately wanted to die at home, in her own bed, with her family close by. She wanted to feel 'normal' in death. Once she realised this, she asked her husband to promise her that he would do his best to facilitate this for her, also making it clear to the nursing staff who were supporting her. Having got this sorted in her mind, Nicky felt relaxed and calmer about the prospect of dying, and was able to fully turn her attention in the direction of healing. As yet, her husband has not had to carry out her wishes, nor does it look likely that he will have to at this point.

Depending on your particular cancer and prognosis, death may seem a very real possibility. If this is the case it is possible to use EFT to clear the fears that may arise and in the event of this becoming your reality, allow the transition to be peaceful for both you and those close to you. I will return to this in subsequent chapters.

Fear of The Future

> *'I've developed a new philosophy... I only dread one day at a time.'*
> *Charlie Brown*

Another fear you may experience is a fear of the future, in some ways a fear of living or a dread of how that might be. Once you have had a cancer diagnosis life will never be the same. By the time you have moved through it and are free of cancer you are unlikely to be the same person you were before becoming ill. The world will seem like a different place. For some people, this will feel really exciting and as they progress through their cancer journey the new reality that they see, the wisdom that they acquire is transformational within itself. For others it will be unfathomable and terrifying, bringing with the thought a sense of dread. It may seem impossible to imagine. How will you ever escape the shadow of cancer? How can something so terrifying ever take a back seat in your life? In Chapter 20 you will learn how to begin to consciously create your future, but at this point focus on the fear itself as follows:

Tapping Section: Fear of the future

Repeat 3 times while tapping the Karate Chop:

Even though I am afraid of the future I deeply and completely love and accept myself

Eyebrow:	*Fear of the future*
Side of Eye:	*Fear of the future*
Under Eye:	*Fear of the future*

Under Nose:	*Fear of the future*
Chin:	*Fear of the future*
Collar Bone:	*Fear of the future*
Under Arm:	*Fear of the future*
Top of Head:	*Fear of the future*

Repeat 3 times while tapping the Karate Chop:

Even though I don't know what the future holds I deeply and completely love and accept myself

Eyebrow:	*Fear of the unknown*
Side of Eye:	*Fear of the future*
Under Eye:	*Fear of what might happen*
Under Nose:	*Fear of the unknown*
Chin:	*Fear of the future*
Collar Bone:	*Fear of what might happen*
Under Arm:	*Fear of the unknown*
Top of Head:	*Fear of the future*

Repeat 3 times while tapping the Karate Chop:

Even though I can't see beyond the cancer I deeply and completely love and accept myself

Eyebrow:	*Can't see past the cancer*
Under Eye:	*Can't imagine my future*
Under Eye:	*Don't know what will happen*
Under Nose:	*Fear of the future*
Chin:	*Can't see past the cancer*
Collar Bone:	*Can't imagine my future*
Under Arm:	*Don't know what will happen*
Top of Head:	*Fear of the future*

Continue tapping on the above protocols until your fear subsides and you are able to consider the possibility of your future, post cancer. Then, if you want to begin to create that future at this point, turn to Chapter 20 and continue your work.

Anger

'Holding on to anger is like grasping a hot coal with the intent of throwing it at someone else; you are the one getting burned.'
Buddha

This is where we begin to address some of the emotions many of us do not allow ourselves to express, or even admit to. In the UK we have the expression 'keeping a stiff upper lip' and we are known for our ability at suppressing our emotions. This is not healthy, and we are going to begin learning how to change that now... And it can be fun!

Anger can have a very positive energy and sometimes it is appropriate and reasonable. However, anger at having cancer creates further dis-ease and conflict within one's physiology and is disempowering. Expressing anger can sometimes be healthy; however, anger at yourself and your dis-ease is not only a waste of valuable energetic resources, but also harmful and negative. There is a big difference between a 'clean' anger, which would be anger at a one-off incident, and a lingering malignant anger, which is continually reactivated by your thought processes.

For example, it may be appropriate to be angry at the way you are given your diagnosis, but if that anger continues to fester long after the event then it is no longer either useful or healthy. In the following tapping phrases we are looking at self anger, and anger at the cancer itself, both of which need to be cleared in order to facilitate healing. They are a waste of valuable energy, however reasonable they may seem to you right now.

Are you afraid of opening a can of worms by looking at anger issues? I often hear people say that if they take the lid off their anger they won't be able to control it and are frightened of where it may lead. And I agree that the prospect of being out of control around anger is both scary and un-therapeutic. However, with the tapping you have the option of letting the anger go 'one worm at a time', safely. By tapping around on a general feeling of anger, or sense that there is anger inside you, you will be able to lower the overall intensity of the emotion before looking at the specifics your anger is directed at. In this way, when you do decide to look at the specific issues you will be able to take them at your own pace, one at a time, worm by worm! You can always put the lid back on, it is still there!

In Chinese medicine, as with tapping, our physical and emotional states are considered entwined, and with each emotion connecting to a specific organ. Whilst I am disinclined to look at this in depth as I am not qualified in TCM (Traditional Chinese Medicine) and am wary of either misdiagnosis, or of missing something by focussing on a particular area whilst ignoring others, with anger I find it useful to bear this in mind. In Chinese medicine, anger is said to be connected to the liver. In EFT terms the liver point is Below the Nipple point, on either side of the body. Rather than confuse our tapping protocol, I think it can be useful to do each round below twice, once as normal, and once merely tapping on the BN point for each Reminder Phrase.

Tapping Section: Tapping for anger

Repeat 3 times while tapping the Karate Chop:

Even though I'm really angry about this, it's not fair, and I don't deserve it, I deeply and completely love and accept myself, I am OK

Eyebrow:	*This anger*
Side of Eye:	*This deep anger*
Under Eye:	*It's not fair*
Under Nose:	*Why me*
Chin:	*I don't deserve this*
Collar Bone:	*It's really not fair*
Under Arm:	*This anger*
Top of Head:	*This anger*

Now tapping only on the Below the Nipple point continue:

- *This deep anger*
- *It's not fair*
- *Why me*
- *I don't deserve this*
- *It's really not fair*
- *This anger*
- *This cancer anger*
- *This cancer anger*

Don't hold back, say it how it is … Shout, rant, cry, swear, rant, speak the unspeakable … Let all the frustration and anger out… Fill in the stars below!

Eyebrow:	*I am REALLY angry*
Side of Eye:	*I am so ********
Under Eye:	*This enormous anger*
Under Nose:	*This ******* cancer*
Chin:	*This cancer anger*
Collar Bone:	*This overwhelming anger*
Under Arm:	*This enormous anger*
Top of Head:	*I am SO SO angry*

Again tapping on the Below the Nipple point:

- *I am REALLY angry*

- *I am so ********
- *This enormous anger*
- *This ******* cancer*
- *This cancer anger*
- *This overwhelming anger*
- *This enormous anger*
- *I am SO SO angry*

Self-Anger

> *'For every minute you are angry, you lose sixty seconds of happiness.'*
> *Author Unknown*

Are you beating yourself up over your diagnosis? Is this a general theme for you? Is it useful? How much time do you waste in self-abuse? When working through your self-anger complete the following:

I am angry with myself because...

You may have a multitude of 'becauses', and you will need to incorporate them within your tapping.

- Because I should have taken more care of myself
- Because I ignored x
- Because I didn't go for health checks earlier
- Because I should have gone to the gym more
- Because I should have stopped smoking/drinking/etc

So when you tap now, fill in the gaps with your own should and could haves (I should have 'gone to the gym more often').

Repeat 3 times while tapping the Karate Chop:

Even though I am angry with myself because ... I deeply and completely love and accept myself anyway

Eyebrow:	*This anger*
Side of Eye:	*I should have....*
Under Eye:	*I could have......*
Under Nose:	*This anger.....*
Chin:	*I should have.....*
Collar Bone:	*I could have.....*
Under Arm:	*This anger.....*

Top of Head: *This self anger*

And on the Below the Nipple point:

- *This anger*
- *I should have....*
- *I could have......*
- *This anger.....*
- *I should have.....*
- *I could have.....*
- *This anger.....*
- *This self anger*

Suppressed Anger

> *'Do not teach your children never to be angry; teach them how to be angry.'*
> *Lyman Abbott*

In my work with cancer patients, I frequently see a pattern of suppressed anger. I am not saying that suppressed anger has to be there when you have cancer, that is definitely not always the case, but I have seen it many, many times. It often shows up after a number of sessions, when my client has gained enough trust in me to feel safe to start expressing it. It may be that when they were children they had not been able to express anger it may have got them into trouble, anger was not an acceptable emotion, in many households that used to be the case, hopefully less so now.

Anger in itself is actually a positive emotion provided it doesn't linger with you. To express anger at something, an injustice, or hurt or whatever is fine, it is a normal emotion. To bury it inside because you are not allowed to express it - *'It's wrong I shouldn't be feeling like that'* - is when the danger starts. Whilst I am not expecting you necessarily to be aware of any suppressed anger, think about your attitude towards anger itself and make notes in your notebook.

- Does anger frighten you?
- Are you afraid of loud voices?
- Do you hate people shouting?

Ask yourself the following questions:

- Is it safe for you to express anger?
- Is it safe for others if you express anger?
- If not, why not?
- According to whom?
- What would have happened?

- Would you have been punished?

If you have any memories come up at this point, rate them on a scale of 0 – 10 and using the Movie Technique work through them. Then choose any or all of the following protocols and work with them until you feel yourself responding differently to the idea of expressing anger.

Repeat 3 times while tapping the Karate Chop:

Even though it is not safe to express anger I deeply and completely love and accept myself

Eyebrow:	*It isn't safe to express my anger*
Side of Eye:	*Anger isn't safe for me*
Under Eye:	*I can't express anger*
Under Nose:	*I am not allowed to express anger*
Chin:	*It's not safe to express anger*
Collar Bone:	*Anger isn't safe for me*
Under Arm:	*I can't express anger*
Top of Head:	*I am not allowed to express anger*

And the Below the Nipple point:

- *It isn't safe to express my anger*
- *Anger isn't safe for me*
- *I can't express anger*
- *I am not allowed to express anger*
- *It's not safe to express anger*
- *Anger isn't safe for me*
- *I can't express anger*

Repeat 3 times while tapping the Karate Chop:

Even though I can't be angry I deeply and completely love and accept myself

Eyebrow:	*I can't be angry*
Side of Eye:	*It is not OK to be angry*
Under Eye:	*Anger is unacceptable*
Under Nose:	*I am not allowed to be angry*
Chin:	*I can't be angry*
Collar Bone:	*It is not OK to be angry*

Under Arm:	Anger is unacceptable
Top of Head:	I am not allowed to be angry

And the Below the Nipple point:

- I can't be angry
- It is not OK to be angry
- Anger is unacceptable
- I am not allowed to be angry
- I can't be angry
- It is not OK to be angry
- Anger is unacceptable

What might happen if you express your anger?

Repeat 3 times while tapping the Karate Chop:

Even though I can't be angry because... I deeply and completely love and accept myself

Eyebrow:	It's too frightening
Side of Eye:	I'll get into trouble
Under Eye:	X will happen
Under Nose:	It's too frightening
Chin:	It's too frightening
Collar Bone:	I'll get into trouble
Under Arm:	X will happen
Top of Head:	It's too frightening

Zoe's story

Zoe was clearly scared of even touching on the subject of anger, although she said she knew she had 'anger issues' but was hiding from them. She said she felt like she was burning up inside with rage but couldn't do anything about it. She realised that she needed to release her anger now, as her cancer diagnosis seemed like a tipping point and she found herself silently fuming over comparatively minor everyday occurrences such as running out of milk.

I asked her what it was about her anger that was so terrifying to her and she said she was afraid of causing pain to people, that her anger was dangerous to others and should never be shown the light of day. I asked her where she had learned that, how was anger managed when she was growing up, was she allowed to express it then. She looked surprised and told me that to her anger was a noisy emotion, it had to be expressed in the way a toddler throws a tantrum, and that her mother suffered from appalling migraines brought on by the slightest sound.

When she got a migraine she would take to her bed for days and the finger of blame would be pointed at the children by their father and nanny and their disapproval would feel devastating to Zoe. As a result, Zoe and her siblings had spent their childhood tiptoeing around, scared to open their mouths yet alone shout or scream, or indeed be loud and have fun. One of her siblings had got around this by turning to amateur dramatics and the other was a singer, but Zoe had never been able to break free of her fear of emotional expression, especially anger. The tiny Zoe believed that if she got angry it would kill her mother and whilst rationally she now recognised this was not the case she was still frozen in her fear of her anger.

We began by edging up on the problem with tapping rounds using the following Set Up Statement. Please tap along too.

Repeat 3 times while tapping the Karate Chop:

Even though it is not safe to be angry I deeply and completely love and accept myself

Eyebrow:	*Not safe to be angry*
Side of Eye:	*Not safe to be angry*
Under Eye:	*Anger is not safe for me*
Under Nose:	*Not safe to be angry*
Chin:	*Not safe to be angry*
Collar Bone:	*Not safe to be angry*
Under Arm:	*Anger is not safe for me*
Top of Head:	*Not safe to be angry*

Repeat 3 times while tapping the Karate Chop:

Even though I will hurt Mummy if I get cross I deeply and completely love and accept myself

Eyebrow:	*I'll hurt her*
Side of Eye:	*I can't get cross*
Under Eye:	*I will hurt Mummy*
Under Nose:	*It is not OK to be cross*
Chin:	*I'll hurt her*
Collar Bone:	*I can't get cross*
Under Arm:	*I will hurt Mummy*
Top of Head:	*It is not OK to be cross*

Repeat 3 times while tapping the Karate Chop:

Even though they will blame me I deeply and completely love and accept myself

Eyebrow:	*They will blame me*
Side of Eye:	*It will be my fault*
Under Eye:	*It is always my fault*
Under Nose:	*Fear of being blamed*
Chin:	*Fear of being blamed*
Collar Bone:	*Fear of it being my fault*
Under Arm:	*Fear of being blamed*
Top of Head:	*All these fears*

Repeat 3 times while tapping the Karate Chop:

Even though I will get into trouble if I get angry I deeply and completely love and accept myself

Eyebrow:	*It's not OK to be angry*
Side of Eye:	*I'll get into trouble*
Under Eye:	*Something bad will happen*
Under Nose:	*I am not allowed to be angry*
Chin:	*It's not OK to be angry*
Collar Bone:	*I'll get into trouble*
Under Arm:	*Something bad will happen*
Top of Head:	*I am not allowed to be angry*

Repeat 3 times while tapping the Karate Chop:

Even though they won't love me if I am angry I deeply and completely love and accept myself anyway

Eyebrow:	*They won't love me*
Side of Eye:	*Fear of not being loved*
Under Eye:	*I won't be loved if I am angry*
Under Nose:	*Fear of not being loved*
Chin:	*They won't love me*
Collar Bone:	*Fear of not being loved*
Under Arm:	*I won't be loved if I am angry*
Top of Head:	*Fear of not being loved*

Gradually Zoe's terror of being angry started to change, bringing with it compassion for the younger her:

Repeat 3 times while tapping the Karate Chop:

Even though I decided anger wasn't safe I deeply and completely love and accept myself, I did the best I could

Eyebrow:	*I decided that*
Side of Eye:	*Anger wasn't safe*
Under Eye:	*That decision*
Under Nose:	*It's not safe to be angry*
Chin:	*I decided that then*
Collar Bone:	*Anger wasn't safe then*
Under Arm:	*That decision*
Top of Head:	*It's just not safe to be angry*

Repeat 3 times while tapping the Karate Chop:

Even though I learned to suppress my anger I am open to the possibility that they didn't intend me to be so afraid now

Eyebrow:	*That learning*
Side of Eye:	*Suppressing anger*
Under Eye:	*I learnt that*
Under Nose:	*And I'm good at it*
Chin:	*But what if I made a mistake?*
Collar Bone:	*What if they didn't mean me to be afraid now?*
Under Arm:	*I was only a little girl*
Top of Head:	*What if I made a mistake about this?*

Repeat 3 times while tapping the Karate Chop:

Even though they made us keep quiet I am open to the possibility that they only wanted to make Mummy better

Eyebrow:	*They did that*
Side of Eye:	*And I decided it wasn't safe*
Under Eye:	*We had to keep quiet*

Under Nose:	It wasn't safe to have emotions
Chin:	I am open to the possibility
Collar Bone:	They were only trying to make Mummy better
Under Arm:	What if it wasn't really about us?
Top of Head:	I am open to that possibility

Repeat 3 times while tapping the Karate Chop:

Even though it wasn't safe to be angry then I am open to the possibility that I can safely release my old angers now, little by little, in baby steps

Eyebrow:	It wasn't safe then
Side of Eye:	What if it is safe now?
Under Eye:	I am open to the possibility that I can safely release my old angers now
Under Nose:	In baby steps
Chin:	I am open to that possibility
Collar Bone:	I choose to begin to release my old angers safely now
Under Arm:	Gently, in baby steps
Top of Head:	I choose to begin now

Finally, we created a Choice for Zoe which took into account her anxiety about hurting others with her anger:

Repeat 3 times while tapping the Karate Chop:

Even though I am scared of being angry I choose to learn to release my anger safely and healthily with tapping now, for me and for others

Eyebrow:	Remaining fear of being angry
Side of Eye:	I choose to let it go
Under Eye:	I choose to learn to release my anger
Under Nose:	Safely and healthily with tapping now
Chin:	For me and for others
Collar Bone:	Remaining fear of being angry
Under Arm:	I choose to learn to release my anger
Top of Head:	Safely and healthily with tapping now

Does Zoe's story resonate with you? If so, continue to tap as follows:

Repeat 3 times while tapping the Karate Chop:

Even though it is not safe for X if I am angry I deeply and completely love and accept myself

Eyebrow:	*Not safe for X*
Side of Eye:	*Fear of hurting X*
Under Eye:	*My anger is not safe for X*
Under Nose:	*Fear of hurting others*
Chin:	*Not safe for X*
Collar Bone:	*Fear of hurting X*
Under Arm:	*My anger is not safe for X*
Top of Head:	*Fear of hurting others*

When the intensity of your fear has reduced, or even gone, introduce a Choice as above, making sure the wording is appropriate for you and feels right.

Repeat 3 times while tapping the Karate Chop:

Even though my anger is still not completely safe for X I choose to learn to release it safely and healthily with tapping, for me and for X

Eyebrow:	*Remaining not safe for X emotions*
Side of Eye:	*Remaining fear of hurting X*
Under Eye:	*Remaining fear of my anger*
Under Nose:	*Remaining not safe stuff*
Chin:	*Remaining not safe for X emotions*
Collar Bone:	*Remaining fear of hurting X*
Under Arm:	*Remaining fear of my anger*
Top of Head:	*Remaining not safe stuff*

Continue:

Eyebrow:	*I choose to release my anger safely and healthily now*
Side of Eye:	*I choose to learn how to*
Under Eye:	*I choose to release my anger safely and healthily now*
Under Nose:	*For me and for X*
Chin:	*I choose to release my anger safely and healthily now*
Collar Bone:	*I choose to learn how to*

Under Arm:	*I choose to release my anger safely and healthily now*
Top of Head:	*For me and for X*

Continue:

Eyebrow:	*Remaining not safe for X emotions*
Side of Eye:	*I choose to release my anger safely and healthily now*
Under Eye:	*Remaining fear of hurting X*
Under Nose:	*I choose to learn to release my anger safely now for everyone*
Chin:	*Remaining not safe for X emotions*
Collar Bone:	*I choose to release my anger safely and healthily now*
Under Arm:	*Remaining fear of hurting X*
Top of Head:	*I choose to learn to release my anger safely now for everyone*

One of my favourite ways of clearing anger, tap and rant!

Tap around all the points ranting, letting the anger flow, again speaking the unspeakable, as my friend Sue would say, 'Give it some welly!', meaning say it as though you mean it, give it expression, bring it to life. Keep going until you feel calmer. If you think you should be feeling angry but you can't access it then make it up, just tap anyway.

It can also feel very therapeutic to tap and rant whilst solely tapping on the BN (liver point).

Ranting means saying how you feel out loud, on your own, over and over again, however unreasonable you may judge it, however you may feel about it. Get the energy of the anger up and tap to clear it. For example:

Repeat 3 times while tapping the Karate Chop:

Even though I am angry at the world I deeply and completely love and accept myself

Eyebrow:	*This anger*
Side of Eye:	*He did this*
Under Eye:	*She did this*
Under Nose:	*How dare they*
Chin:	*I feel like screaming at them*
Collar Bone:	*I am angry at the world*
Under Arm:	*This anger*
Top of Head:	*My anger*

Continue without censoring your words at all as long as you feel is necessary. You will find it very cathartic and releasing, and also possibly very tiring! Releasing anger can be both safe, and ultimately fun.

Finally, tap a few rounds on the following Choices focussing on the positive only at this point. Tap on all the points with the following two phrases:

I choose to release any suppressed anger easily now

I choose to release any old anger from my cellular memory now.

As you go through the process of your journey with cancer, the highs and the lows and the various treatments and checkups, you may find anger releasing gradually as you tap through different layers. If and when it does, the important thing is just to go with it, even if you don't understand where it is coming from - it doesn't matter. If it's being released just tap to assist it on its way, acknowledge it and let it go. We don't always need to know the origins of things, often it is enough to just go with what presents itself in the moment.

Resentment

> *'Resentment is like taking poison and waiting for the other person to die.'*
> *Malachy McCourt*

Many people resent their cancer, certainly initially, and why wouldn't they? I am often told 'I don't have time for this' or 'I am too busy to be sick'. Cancer has the ability to interrupt and disrupt your life in a way that forces you to pay attention to it. It stops you in your tracks and forces a reassessment of both lifestyle and values. Because of the nature of the dis-ease it may appear suddenly, without symptoms, possibly during a routine health test, with no warning. Once you have recovered from the initial shock, resentment often appears. At this point, we are solely working with any resentment of the cancer itself, we will look at other resentments further on.

Listen to your self-talk, the things you are saying quietly in your head, the thoughts you are judging and expecting others to judge, such as 'It's not fair'. If those thoughts are there, accept them and tap to release them. Resentment is a toxic emotion which feeds itself – the more you resist it the more it permeates your thoughts. Get rid of it, it is unhealthy and blocks the healing process.

Clearing resentment can be one of the most challenging areas to work with. It requires frankness and honesty. The energetic vibration of resentment is both heavy and draining, and it requires a lot of effort to suppress it. Once released you will be surprised at how much better you feel, and how much more focussed you can become on your healing process.

Tapping Section: Tapping for resentment

Repeat 3 times while tapping the Karate Chop:

Even though I have this cancer resentment I deeply and completely love and accept myself

Eyebrow:	*This cancer resentment*
Side of Eye:	*This resentment*
Under Eye:	*This cancer resentment*
Under Nose:	*This resentment*
Chin:	*This cancer resentment*
Collar Bone:	*This resentment*
Under Arm:	*This cancer resentment*
Top of Head:	*This resentment*

George's story

George stormed into my office, full of anger and resentment. His first words were 'I don't have time for this'. 'This' turned out to be cancer.

George was in his mid fifties and self employed. He had gone to the doctor for routine blood tests which had shown a rise in his PSA levels, and therefore the possibility of prostate cancer. After a biopsy this diagnosis had been confirmed and George had been advised to have a course of radiation, visiting the hospital for a short time five days a week for 6 weeks. As a large part of George's work was out of town this was clearly going to have an effect on his ability to earn and support his family. However, for George it wasn't so much the financial implications of the treatment as the fact that in his words 'I have so much to do, I don't have time for this'. He was veering towards ignoring it and continuing as though nothing was wrong. I challenged him as to whether this would be truly possible for him and he admitted that it was unlikely, it was always be lurking in the background, it would be hard to forget about it completely.

We began by working on the anger and resentment about the diagnosis, as above, and his not having time for it.

Repeat 3 times while tapping the Karate Chop:

Even though I don't have time for this I deeply and completely love and accept myself

Eyebrow:	*I don't have time for this*
Side of Eye:	*I have too much to do*
Under Eye:	*I'm too busy for this*
Under Nose:	*I don't have time for this*
Chin:	*I have too much to do*
Collar Bone:	*I'm too busy for this*
Under Arm:	*I don't have time for cancer*
Top of Head:	*I am too busy*

Repeat 3 times while tapping the Karate Chop:

Even though I am too busy to have treatment I deeply and completely love and accept myself

Eyebrow:	I am just too busy
Side of Eye:	I can't spare the time
Under Eye:	I have too much to do
Under Nose:	I can't give up that time
Chin:	I am just too busy
Collar Bone:	I can't spare the time
Under Arm:	I have too much to do
Top of Head:	I can't give up that time

Continuing:

Eyebrow:	I am just going to forget about it
Side of Eye:	I don't have time for it
Under Eye:	It will just go away
Under Nose:	I will pretend it never happened
Chin:	I don't have time for it
Collar Bone:	I'm going to ignore it
Under Arm:	Maybe
Top of Head:	Maybe not

Continue:

Eyebrow:	I am open to the possibility that ignoring it might not work for me
Side of Eye:	Maybe it won't go away
Under Eye:	Yes it will, I am going to ignore it
Under Nose:	No I'm not
Chin:	I am open to the possibility that I need to do the treatment
Collar Bone:	That I can find the time
Under Arm:	That I need to find the time
Top of Head:	That it is important for me

At this point George was beginning to recognise that he did need to do the radiation treatment, that he couldn't ignore it, as in the long run this would not serve him, his family nor his clients. Having released the resentment he started to explore ways in which he could combine working and the radiation and its possible side effects. He realised that by making a few minor adjustments to his routine, he could continue to work during the treatment. He worked out a way of making minor changes in his lifestyle and working life and came up with his own solution for the situation. I think it would have taken him far longer to do this, if at all, had he not been able to tap through the cloud of negativity and resentment that had encapsulated him on diagnosis.

Sadness

Turn your face to the sun and the shadows fall behind you.
Maori Proverb

As anger and resentment subside you may feel an overwhelming sense of sadness. Maybe the tears will feel unpredictable and uncontrollable. This is a completely normal response to a shock. Allow yourself to cry, but when possible tap at the same time. There is no need to speak at this point, your system knows exactly what thoughts and feelings you are tuned into, a reminder phrase is not necessary and would possibly interrupt the clearing. Just go with the tears and tap.

Raj's story
Raj had been diagnosed with Non-Hodgkins Lymphoma and was in a state of denial. He was carrying on with his life as though nothing had happened, although he was preparing for treatment. He just didn't seem to have any feelings about the diagnosis. He came to see me because his wife had told him the tapping would help him with his healing, but he only wanted to learn the tapping points, not do any work. Obviously I respected this and began to teach him the background to EFT and the Short Cut version, sticking very specifically to working with physical pain and discomfort and how Raj could apply it for himself in these areas.

We needed something to work with to give Raj the experience of tapping for himself but as he was in no obvious discomfort at the time it was tricky to know where to begin. I decided, with his agreement, to work with his breath, using the Constricted Breathing Technique (see Chapter 3).

Raj rated his breathing currently at a 6 on the scale of 0 – 10 and was very willing to tap to improve it. He also fully accepted that breathing freely was a good marker of lack of stress in the body (note, only in the body, he was not prepared to go with breathing as an indicator of anxiety levels and I certainly was not going to push it).

After a couple of rounds Raj's breathing moved to an 8 and he was visibly more relaxed. He wanted to see if he could get it to a 10 so we continued, tapping very simply on 'my constricted breathing' and 'this block to my fullest breath'.

After a further couple of rounds I noticed that Raj had a tear rolling down one cheek and that he was clearly experiencing some sort of internal conflict. His breathing had suddenly become quicker and his skin tone had changed. I asked him what was happening and he said he felt like crying and he didn't like it. I asked him how he felt about crying and he said that in his culture tears were a sign of weakness, and that he hadn't cried since he was a very little boy. The last time he had cried his older brothers had taunted him and told all his friends and it had been very humiliating for him. He was 7 years old. The phrase 'Big boys don't cry' seemed to echo his belief.

We started tapping, using the Movie Technique (and I invite you to tap along):

Tapping Section: Tapping for sadness

Repeat 3 times while tapping the Karate Chop:

Even though I have this 'Crying' movie I deeply and completely love and accept myself

Eyebrow:	*Crying movie*
Side of Eye:	*This crying movie*
Under Eye:	*My crying movie*
Under Nose:	*Crying movie*
Chin:	*Crying movie emotions*
Collar Bone:	*Crying movie emotions*
Under Arm:	*Crying movie emotions*
Top of Head:	*My crying movie emotions*

Even though I'm not allowed to cry I deeply and completely love and accept myself

Eyebrow:	*Not allowed to cry*
Side of Eye:	*It's not OK to cry*
Under Eye:	*Big boys don't cry*
Under Nose:	*I can't cry*
Chin:	*Not allowed to cry*
Collar Bone:	*It's not OK to cry*
Under Arm:	*Big boys don't cry*
Top of Head:	*I can't cry*

Even though I learnt that then I deeply and completely love and accept myself anyway

Eyebrow:	*I'm not allowed to cry*
Side of Eye:	*I mustn't cry*
Under Eye:	*They said that*
Under Nose:	*And I believed them*
Chin:	*Crying is bad*

Collar Bone:	I mustn't cry
Under Arm:	I learned that then
Top of Head:	They said that

Very gradually Raj began to cry softly, and I kept tapping, changing the words allowing him to give himself permission to cry now, to express and release his feelings.

Repeat 3 times while tapping the Karate Chop:

Even though I learnt not to cry I am open to the possibility that I can release my tears healthily now

Eyebrow:	I mustn't cry
Side of Eye:	Crying is bad
Under Eye:	Maybe
Under Nose:	Maybe not
Chin:	I am open to the possibility that I am allowed to cry now
Collar Bone:	I am open to the possibility that it is safe for me
Under Arm:	I am open to the possibility that I can allow myself to release my tears
Top of Head:	What if it is safe now?

Repeat 3 times while tapping the Karate Chop:

Even though I learnt that then what if I made a mistake, what if it is OK to cry now

Eyebrow:	I learnt that then
Side of Eye:	They taught me that
Under Eye:	What if I made a mistake
Under Nose:	What if that little me made a mistake
Chin:	What if it is safe to cry now
Collar Bone:	For me, and for others
Under Arm:	I am open to that possibility
Top of Head:	What if it is safe to cry

Gradually Raj began to smile through the tears. I asked him what was happening and he said he was feeling love for the little him. He said he had been fighting his emotions all his life and felt like someone had just switched the light on. By fighting his emotions he had been suppressing all of them, positive and loving as

71

well as negative and he felt very excited by the possibility of voicing them. He had never even told his wife or children he loved them, although he had shown it to them by his actions and working hard. He said that unlocking the tears made him feel both light and free.

We continued to work over a number of sessions to clear the trauma of the diagnosis, plus other negative memories as he allowed them to surface and be felt. At no point did Raj feel overwhelmed, he greeted each memory and emotion as an experience and seemed to be thoroughly enjoying his emotional journey despite the occasional painful moment! He looked on it as an adventure.

By giving himself permission to 'feel' and to cry in this way Raj was able to fully embrace life, both the positives and the negatives, including his cancer, and was able to support himself on his healing journey in a new way. As I write he is in remission following a strong course of chemotherapy, and continues to tap enthusiastically!

Allow yourself to cry, allow yourself to grieve for your health, allow yourself to truly feel, however scary. But as you do, keep tapping all the points at the same time, until the upset calms. Tears are nature's way of emotional release.

The bottom line is that a cancer diagnosis is sad, and it is healthy to acknowledge that. However, acknowledging it whilst tapping on it will help prevent the sadness from becoming pervasive and allow you to get an emotional foothold and be able to focus on your healing.

Below are some general protocols for sadness. Work with the ones that feel appropriate for you, and change the words to more suitable ones should you need to.

Repeat 3 times while tapping the Karate Chop:

Even though I feel really sad I deeply and completely love and accept myself

Eyebrow:	*This sadness*
Side of Eye:	*This awful sadness*
Under Eye:	*This overwhelming sadness*
Under Nose:	*This sadness*
Chin:	*This awful sadness*
Collar Bone:	*This overwhelming awful sadness*
Under Arm:	*This deep, deep sadness*
Top of Head:	*This overwhelming deep sadness*

Repeat 3 times while tapping the Karate Chop:

Even though it is sad I deeply and completely love and accept myself

Eyebrow:	*This sadness*
Side of Eye:	*It's really sad*
Under Eye:	*This terrible sadness*

Under Nose:	It's really, really sad
Chin:	This awful sadness
Collar Bone:	It's really, really sad
Under Arm:	This awful sadness
Top of Head:	This really awful overwhelming sadness

Repeat 3 times while tapping the Karate Chop:

Even though I can't stop crying I deeply and completely love and accept myself anyway

Eyebrow:	I can't stop crying
Side of Eye:	I can't stop the tears
Under Eye:	Feeling really sad
Under Nose:	This sadness
Chin:	I can't stop crying
Collar Bone:	I can't stop the tears
Under Arm:	Feeling really sad
Top of Head:	This sadness

Helplessness

> *'When you come to the end of your rope, tie a knot and hang on.'*
> *Franklin D. Roosevelt*

An initial response to a cancer diagnosis is often one of helplessness. You may feel like your life is being taken over, it is no longer in your hands, people are telling you what to do, putting you under pressure to make quick decisions and you feel powerless to help yourself.

This is where the tapping comes into its own. It gives you a way of beginning to take back the controls, managing your own situation and, even at this point, to begin managing your healing. So, if you are feeling helpless or powerless just begin by noticing that feeling and tapping with it.

Hakim's story
Ever since his melanoma diagnosis Hakim's life had been going in a downward spiral and he just could not seem to pull himself back on track. He had had surgery but had developed blood poisoning so stayed in hospital for nearly 3 weeks. During this time, he had been visited by many family, friends and colleagues, who were growing more and more concerned at his mental state.

Hakim ran his own hedge fund business and was known to be a dynamic team leader and successful entrepreneur. People referred to his 'Midas touch' meaning that everything he applied himself to turned to gold. But now he seemed a shadow of his former self, almost shrunken.

His prognosis was positive, the mole had been caught early and there was no spread. He had every reason to feel optimistic. Yet he was very withdrawn. His wife brought him to see me and we only did the one session, which enabled Hakim to regain his former charisma and drive.

Hakim had always been in control in his life. His father had died when he was very young and he had taken over the role of head of the household. From as early as he could remember he was the organiser, the problem solver, the solution finder – that was his identity, and what had led him to his fantastic business success. People respected him and followed his orders. This included his wife and family.

But suddenly he found himself in a position where he had zero authority, and zero choice over his treatment. The blood poisoning had caused him to drift in and out of consciousness for a couple of weeks and he had little recollection of what had happened during that time. What he did know was that he had been bathed, catheterised, dressed etc by the nursing staff while he was ill and that he had not had the strength to stop them and do it himself.

Hakim simply couldn't cope with his vulnerability at that time and his lack of control over his body, and also his environment. Rather than dwell on it he had found safety in withdrawing and building a wall around him. He imagined everyone was laughing at his weaknesses. He thought he had lost their respect as many people had seen him in this state. His pride in his role as a figurehead had been severely knocked and he felt helpless to change how he felt about what had happened.

Please follow along with this tapping that I did with Hakim:

Tapping Section: Tapping for helplessness

Repeat 3 times while tapping the Karate Chop:

Even though I feel helpless I deeply and completely love and accept myself

Eyebrow:	*Feeling helpless*
Side of Eye:	*I can't do anything about this*
Under Eye:	*Feeling helpless*
Under Nose:	*Feeling helpless*
Chin:	*This helplessness*
Collar Bone:	*Feeling really helpless*
Under Arm:	*Feeling out of control*
Top of Head:	*Feeling helpless*

Repeat 3 times while tapping the Karate Chop:

Even though I have lost their respect I deeply and completely love and accept myself

Eyebrow:	*Losing respect*
Side of Eye:	*Losing their respect*
Under Eye:	*They won't respect me now*
Under Nose:	*They'll never respect me*
Chin:	*Losing their respect*
Collar Bone:	*And everything I feel about it*
Under Arm:	*Losing their respect*
Top of Head:	*They'll never respect me now*

After a couple of rounds of tapping I checked in with Hakim by asking him how he felt and whether it was really true that he has lost their respect. He smiled and said no, but they might still tease him – but that was OK, he could handle that.

I asked him how he felt about regaining his old self now, stepping into his power again as head of his company, and his family. How strong were those old helpless feelings now?

He had no emotional response to this, but did feel a tightening in his stomach so we did a couple of rounds on that until it eased. Then I asked him again. This time his voice changed and he sounded far more confident and strong. He said he felt completely able to take on whatever role he wanted to, and for it to be successful. He also said that he never again wanted to be in such a helpless place and made a vow to reassess his life/work balance and to take more care of his health.

Anxiety

> *'Anxiety is a thin stream of fear trickling through the mind. If encouraged, it cuts a channel into which all other thoughts are drained.'*
> Arthur Somers Roche

A cancer diagnosis will inevitably bring with it some degree of anxiety: anxiety about the future, anxiety about the treatment, anxiety about making the right choices, anxiety about others coping, and more. This may range from intermittent anxious thoughts to a constant low level anxiety, or for some people a continual high level anxiety.

In tapping terms, anxiety is a global issue. It is usually the generalised effect of a number of specific events, which accumulate to create the anxiety response. However, in the case of post diagnosis anxiety it is not necessary to go further than the immediate presenting feelings. The accumulated thoughts and beliefs, which often appear in quick succession at this time, need quick and immediate relief with tapping.

However, that concept in itself is often enough to create further anxiety with thoughts such as 'Where do I begin?' 'Am I doing this right?' quickly rising to the surface. The quick answer to both those questions is:

Begin where you are at: as with anything with EFT, begin with what is presenting in the moment. With anxiety this may well be a physical response, perhaps sweating or pounding heart. Start there. If there is no physical response then ask yourself 'How do I know I am anxious?' If a thought or memory appears, then tap on that.

It is always easiest to work with the physical responses, as described below, and it may be that that is **all** that you need to do to collapse the anxiety response. In fact, all emotions have a physical manifestation, otherwise how would we know we were feeling them? However, these are often well concealed from us. With anxiety they can be very clear and if they are for you it might be more useful to start your tapping with the physical symptoms (See Chapter 5).

The immediate aftermath of a cancer diagnosis can also be very confusing. There will usually be a further series of tests, some of which may be invasive, and different options of treatment. Different people will have contrasting views and everyone will be keen to give you their advice. It can feel overwhelming and decisions may seem to be taken out of your hands. And these decisions often need to be taken immediately; the sense of urgency and pressure can be enormous.

You may feel a conflict between mainstream and complementary treatments. Perhaps you have never taken drugs, or followed a medical approach to health. Cancer suddenly brings these decisions into sharp focus and challenges even the strongest held beliefs. You may feel pulled in many different directions, and unable to think clearly. You may feel like you have no time to think, and that you have to become a medical expert in minutes, grasping all the terms and implications of your diagnosis. All this on top of being in shock...

Frank's story
Frank, on receiving a diagnosis of testicular cancer, likened this experience to being very small on a roundabout in the playground with someone else spinning it round too fast and all you want to do is stick a foot on the ground to stop it and regain your balance, but you can't, it is going too quickly.

Be compassionate to yourself, you have had a shock and now you have to make some life changing decisions, in any other circumstances you would be given time to pick yourself up. Imagine you can press the pause button (as on your DVD player) and allow yourself some time out to gather your thoughts.

The first step of our work is to get a reduction in your anxiety levels. It is near impossible to make a well considered decision from a place of high anxiety, so the calmer you become, the clearer you will be. Then you will be able to calmly do your research and decide the right course of action. Until then, everyone will be giving you their views, snippets of information, their beliefs and more. Whilst well meaning, this only serves to increase confusion.

Rate your anxiety levels right now, when you think of the diagnosis, using the SUDS scale of 0 – 10 and tap:

Tapping Section: Tapping for anxiety

Repeat 3 times while tapping the Karate Chop:

Even though I'm anxious the cancer I deeply and completely love and accept myself

> *Eyebrow:*   *Cancer anxiety*

Side of Eye:	*Cancer anxiety*
Under Eye:	*Cancer anxiety*
Under Nose:	*Cancer anxiety*
Chin:	*Cancer anxiety*
Collar Bone:	*Cancer anxiety*
Under Arm:	*Cancer anxiety*
Top of Head:	*Cancer anxiety*

When you feel you have a foot in the door and the SUDS levels around the anxiety have lowered sufficiently (0 – 4 perhaps) continue as follows:

Repeat 3 times while tapping the Karate Chop:

Even though I'm anxious about the diagnosis I deeply and completely love and accept myself

Eyebrow:	*Cancer anxiety*
Side of Eye:	*Diagnosis anxiety*
Under Eye:	*Anxiety*
Under Nose:	*Diagnosis anxiety*
Chin:	*Remaining diagnosis anxiety*
Collar Bone:	*Remaining anxiety*
Under Arm:	*I choose to let it go*
Top of Head:	*It's safe to let it go*

Continue:

Eyebrow:	*Remaining anxiety*
Side of Eye:	*I choose peace instead of this*
Under Eye:	*Remaining anxiety*
Under Nose:	*I choose peace instead of this*
Chin:	*It's possible for me to have peace instead of this*
Collar Bone:	*And I choose peace instead of this*
Under Arm:	*Remaining anxiety*
Top of Head:	*I choose peace instead of this*

Panic Attacks

'Panic is a sudden desertion of us, and a going over to the enemy of our imagination.'
Christian Nevell Bovee

Panic attacks are very frightening and can seem to come out of nowhere. They have strong physical symptoms such as rapid heartbeat, sweating, perhaps even dizziness and shallow quick breathing. Sufferers can feel out of control and very fearful.

If you have a very high level of anxiety and are experiencing the symptoms of a panic attack **BEGIN TAPPING** immediately – forget about any words!

TAP all the points, or any points you can reach, round and round, quickly at first, and then slowing the tapping down as the panic subsides. At this point words are superfluous, just tap.

If you are with someone who is having a panic attack, the same approach applies. If you are unable to safely access their face, tap on the following points:

- **Top of the Head**
- **The Inside of one Wrist (about 2" from the base of the hand)**
- **The Inside of one Calf (about 2" above the ankle)**

The combination of these three points covers all the meridians. You need to create maximum meridian stimulation as the body releases the panic. Keep talking to the person, reassuring them with your voice tone and your own breathing.

Some people are more prone to anxiety than others and some may already have a history of panic attacks. Panic attacks very often resolve by tapping on the memory of the first or worst attack and clearing that from your energy system. By neutralising the fear of another panic attack and the memory of the first/ worst one, the focus changes and you will feel calmer.

With many people panic and fear about having a panic attack is often as bad as the attack itself. It is useful to do some tapping around this when you are not in the panic itself. Otherwise it can become a loop, with the anxiety about a panic attack and the focus on an attack bringing on an actual attack. So, if this resonates, tap as follows:

Tapping Section: Tapping for panic

Repeat 3 times while tapping the Karate Chop:

Even though I have this panic about the panic I deeply and completely love and accept myself

Eyebrow:	*Panic about the panic*
Side of Eye:	*Panic about the panic*
Under Eye:	*Panic about the panic*

Under Nose:	*Panic about the panic*
Chin:	*Panic about the panic*
Collar Bone:	*Panic about the panic*
Under Arm:	*Panic about the panic*
Top of Head:	*Panic about the panic*

Sophie's story

Sophie, who has a long history of panic attacks and fearfulness, said that for her it was not even a panic about the panic attack, she didn't get that close to them. It was more that occasionally she remembered her fear of them she felt fearful of the fear itself, more than the actual attack. To her the fear was the frightening part. So we tapped as follows, and I asked Sophie to continue tapping as if by rote on the same protocol when she was at home. When I next saw her she said she could now think of her fear of the panic attacks objectively, she didn't actually experience it when she remembered it. The fear of the fear itself had cleared. She was still fearful of the panic attacks themselves, and this was the next layer to work with. Very gently we worked to clear the excess fear around them, and eventually we were able to work on the panic attacks themselves. We are continuing to work together on her other anxieties both current and historical, and she is making fantastic progress. She is visibly more relaxed within herself and to date the panic attacks have gone.

Repeat 3 times while tapping the Karate Chop:

Even though I have this fear of the fear of panic attacks I deeply and completely love and accept myself

Eyebrow:	*Fear of the fear*
Side of Eye:	*Fear of the fear*
Under Eye:	*Fear of the fear*
Under Nose:	*Fear of the fear*
Chin:	*Fear of the fear*
Collar Bone:	*Fear of the fear*
Under Arm:	*Fear of the fear*
Top of Head:	*Fear of the fear*

When you feel calmer you may want to look at this in more depth. I would recommend ideally having someone with you as you do this, or going to an EFT Practitioner so that you feel completely safe doing the work. However, if this is not possible for you, your job here is to monitor yourself very carefully and at the slightest sign of any of the old physiological responses you used to have, stop there and tap until they have reduced.

The most important thing is to keep tapping, even if the symptoms may seem to increase, this will be temporary and the more you tap the quicker you will clear them and whatever thoughts they are connected to, conscious or unconscious. I repeat, it is of utmost importance to KEEP TAPPING - you need maximum meridian stimulation.

Ask yourself the following questions:

- **When did I first feel like this?**
- **What was happening at that time?**
- **When was the worst time?**

When you have the answers, begin with the memory that has the highest intensity on your SUDS scale when you bring it to mind now. Using the Movie Technique (see Chapter 2), tap to clear the intensity around that memory. Then systematically work through the next one, and any others that still have some emotional charge for you.

Stick rigidly to the wording below, so that you are in the thought field of the movie but, as with Gone with the Wind, are not running it in your mind.

Repeat 3 times while tapping the Karate Chop:

Even though I have this first panic attack movie I deeply and completely love and accept myself

Eyebrow:	*First panic attack movie*
Side of Eye:	*First panic attack movie*
Under Eye:	*First panic attack movie*
Under Nose:	*First panic attack movie*
Chin:	*First panic attack movie*
Collar Bone:	*First panic attack movie*
Under Arm:	*First panic attack movie*
Top of Head:	*First panic attack movie*

Continue immediately with:

Eyebrow:	*First panic attack emotions*
Side of Eye:	*First panic attack emotions*
Under Eye:	*First panic attack emotions*
Under Nose:	*First panic attack emotions*
Chin:	*First panic attack emotions*
Collar Bone:	*First panic attack emotions*
Under Arm:	*First panic attack emotions*
Top of Head:	*First panic attack emotions*

Now check in and see how intense you feel when you think of looking at your original movie. If there is still some excess emotion (I am not expecting you to love the movie!) then continue tapping as above, adding the word 'remaining'.

Eyebrow:	*Remaining first panic attack emotions*
Side of Eye:	*Remaining first panic attack emotions*
Under Eye:	*Remaining first panic attack emotions*
Under Nose:	*Remaining first panic attack emotions*
Chin:	*Remaining first panic attack emotions*
Collar Bone:	*Remaining first panic attack emotions*
Under Arm:	*Remaining first panic attack emotions*
Top of Head:	*Remaining first panic attack emotions*

Continue:

Eyebrow:	*Remaining first panic attack emotions*
Side of Eye:	*Remaining first panic attack emotions*
Under Eye:	*Remaining first panic attack emotions*
Under Nose:	*Remaining first panic attack emotions*
Chin:	*Remaining first panic attack emotions*
Collar Bone:	*Remaining first panic attack emotions*
Under Arm:	*Remaining first panic attack emotions*
Top of Head:	*Remaining first panic attack emotions*

Check in again. Continue until you have reached a zero or feel it is OK to watch the movie.

Then run the movie.

What happens?

If any particular piece still gets you, pause the movie and tap to clear it. It may be the tone of someone's voice, the look on someone's face, I don't know.

Repeat 3 times while tapping the Karate Chop:

Even though I still feel X at that bit I deeply and completely love and accept myself

Eyebrow:	*That bit*
Side of Eye:	*That X bit*
Under Eye:	*That bit*
Under Nose:	*That X bit*
Chin:	*That bit*

Collar Bone:	That X bit
Under Arm:	That bit
Top of Head:	That X bit

Continue:

Eyebrow:	Remaining emotions connected to that bit
Side of Eye:	Remaining emotions connected to that bit
Under Eye:	Remaining x connected to that bit
Under Nose:	And everything it means to me
Chin:	Remaining emotions connected to that bit
Collar Bone:	Remaining emotions connected to that bit
Under Arm:	Remaining x connected to that bit
Top of Head:	And everything it means to me

When you can run the entire movie without any emotional intensity move onto the next one and check if you still feel the way you used to about it. Chances are that the intensity on that one will have reduced too.

Continue working in this way until you have cleared the emotional charge on any memories that feel connected to the panic.

How are you creating your panic attacks?

'Some patients I see are actually draining into their bodies the diseased thoughts of their minds.'
Zacharty Bercovitz

Ask yourself the following questions:

- **What do you have to think about to create a panic attack?**
- **Are you seeing an image?**
- **Are you hearing something?**
- **What /who does that remind you of? (You may need to use the Movie Technique to clear a related memory)**

Once you have isolated the main contributory factors tap around on each of them until they no longer have any impact on you.

Maybe you have a thought that recurs and creates the panic response. If so, what is that thought? What would it be like if you couldn't think it anymore? Tap on that thought:

Repeat 3 times while tapping the Karate Chop:

82

Even though I have this X thought I deeply and completely love and accept myself

Eyebrow:	*This thought*
Side of Eye:	*This powerful thought*
Under Eye:	*This X thought*
Under Nose:	*This powerful thought*
Chin:	*This thought*
Collar Bone:	*This powerful thought*
Under Arm:	*This X thought*
Top of Head:	*This powerful thought*

Continue:

Eyebrow:	*That thought*
Side of Eye:	*What if I couldn't think it*
Under Eye:	*That thought*
Under Nose:	*What if it wasn't there anymore*
Chin:	*That thought*
Collar Bone:	*What if I could think it*
Under Arm:	*That powerful thought*
Top of Head:	*What if I could let it go*

Continue:

Eyebrow:	*I choose to let this old thought go*
Side of Eye:	*It isn't useful to me*
Under Eye:	*I don't need it*
Under Nose:	*I don't deserve it*
Chin:	*I choose to release this old thought from my energy system*
Collar Bone:	*I choose to let it go*
Under Arm:	*And I choose for that to be surprisingly easy*
Top of Head:	*I choose to release that old thought from my energy field*

Whilst panic attacks can be slow and difficult to resolve with other therapeutic modalities with EFT they can be surprisingly easy to change. You may need to be a little persistent, but if you systematically follow the formulaic approach above, noticing where it leads you and making a note of it in case you need to work on another aspect later, you should be able to prevent further panic attacks surprisingly easily.

Marlene's story
Marlene had suffered from panic attacks as long as she could remember. Her mother said she had always been an anxious child but had no idea why, she had had a seemingly happy childhood.

Sometimes needing to find the root cause of a condition is not useful, particularly around panic, it can be self-fulfilling and create a panic about the panic, much the same as I spoke of in the story above with Sophie.

Marlene did not believe that she could be any other way, she had long periods without the attacks, usually 3 – 4 months, but when they started, apparently out of nowhere, they came in quick succession. They were debilitating and exhausting, and stopped as suddenly as they started.

I asked Marlene what happened physically when they started and we tapped through each of the physical symptoms separately, even though they weren't actually present at the time. I then asked her whether, during the times she was free of them, she ever thought about them. She said not often, but when she did she then couldn't get rid of the thought and the fear that it brought with it. Then a few days later the attacks would start up. When they were over she said she usually felt relieved and that she knew she could then relax, safely enjoy life and forget about them again for a while.

It seemed like she only felt able to fully embrace life when she had just had a series of panic attacks. In a strange way, panic attacks allowed her to participate in life safely. All these insights were coming from Marlene herself, I was just tapping on her, following her train of thought and observing the changes in her physiology as she explored these ideas.

Marlene was able to recognise how she had stitched herself up by needing the panic attacks at some level, again without needing to know why she had created that mechanism unconsciously. Once she could see that clearly for herself she was able to tap on letting go of the need for panic attacks, and was able to authentically choose peace instead.

We never knew why she experienced so many attacks so quickly, but it has been over a year since that session and to date Marlene has had no more panic attacks!

Overwhelm and Confusion

> *'Think left and think right and think low and think high.*
> *Oh, the thinks you can think up if only you try!'*
> *Dr. Seuss, Oh, the Thinks You Can Think!*

After diagnosis, the professionals, and the people who care for you, will probably bombard you with facts, knowledge, lack of knowledge and opinions. This is hugely tempting for them and allows those close to you to feel useful. And of course, it is the responsibility of the medical field to give you the facts and treatment options. Everyone is only doing the best they can, but it may not always feel like that! The result of all this input may be an overwhelm of thoughts, leading to confusion and anxiety.

Everyone will have their own opinion, surgeons will want to operate, radiographers radiate, and so on. Rightly, each specialist will have very strong beliefs in their own modality. Take a step backwards and do your own research, or at least clear your anxiety and notice how you are thinking, what feels right for you. Our gut instincts are rarely wrong, but we tend to dismiss them or often not even notice them. Whatever treatment or selection of treatments you opt for, it is important that you feel as positive as possible about them and their healing potential.

Caroline's story
Caroline described the sense of overwhelm as similar to how she felt when, in her highly pressurised grammar school, she had been asked, aged 13, not only to select her GCSEs and A Levels, but also to decide what career she wanted to pursue, and therefore tailor her exam choices accordingly. She was then asked to complete a computerized programme which gave her a long list of possible career options, many of which she had never heard of, and she was expected to make a choice there and then! She laughed and said she wished she had known about EFT then as she would have spent hours tapping on things akin to 'Even though I don't know what an ophthalmologist is…!'.

Whilst she was amused by the memory now we still took a few minutes tapping through it to make sure it was totally clear and not contributing to the current overwhelm. Caroline then said 'I felt so stupid, like I should have known, and that is exactly how I feel now. How can I have such a serious illness and not know what the various options mean, what all these long words are actually saying?'

So we did a couple of rounds on feeling stupid, bringing in humour with phrases such as

Repeat 3 times while tapping the Karate Chop:

Even though I didn't know what she was talking about I deeply and completely love and accept myself

Eyebrow:	*I didn't know*
Side of Eye:	*I didn't understand her*
Under Eye:	*I just didn't get it*
Under Nose:	*I didn't know*
Chin:	*How could I have known?*
Collar Bone:	*I didn't know*
Under Arm:	*I didn't understand her*
Top of Head:	*I didn't know*

Repeat 3 times while tapping the Karate Chop:

Even though I should have known what an ophthalmologist was, every 13 year old knows that..... maybe....I deeply and completely love and accept myself

Eyebrow:	*I should have known*
Side of Eye:	*I should have known*
Under Eye:	*Maybe*
Under Nose:	*Every 13 year old knows that*
Chin:	*Don't they?*
Collar Bone:	*Maybe not*
Under Arm:	*I should have known*
Top of Head:	*No I shouldn't have*

Caroline started laughing again. She realised that if anyone was stupid here it had been the careers advisor who clearly had no understanding of 13 year old girls! However, whilst in that instance she realised it wasn't really important whether she understood or not, now it was possibly a matter of life or death.

I tested her again by asking her how stupid she was now, as an adult, knowing that she was a very successful lawyer. Was it possible that a top oncologist coming to see her might not understand her legalese immediately? Was it as simple as having not needed to know the particular language before? Was she capable of learning now?

Again Caroline laughed and realised that she was more than capable of doing her own research, understanding her choices and gaining clarity. As she really 'got' this her entire physiology changed, it was as if a weight was lifted. She sat upright, her complexion changed colour and she looked almost excited by the prospect of new learning. She had stepped back into the resourceful person her colleagues and family knew so well.

Below are a variety of tapping protocols which may resonate with you. Take whichever ones feel right in this moment and begin working with them. Ultimately, when the overwhelm and confusion subsides you can introduce the Choices at the bottom of this piece, but only as and when you feel it is appropriate for you.

Tapping Section: Tapping for overwhelm and confusion

Repeat 3 times while tapping the Karate Chop:

Even though I feel overwhelmed by information I deeply and completely love and accept myself

Eyebrow:	*This overwhelm*
Side of Eye:	*Too much information*
Under Eye:	*I can't take it all in*
Under Nose:	*Feeling overwhelmed*

Chin:	This overwhelm
Collar Bone:	Too much information
Under Arm:	I can't take it all in
Top of Head:	Feeling overwhelmed

Repeat 3 times while tapping the Karate Chop:

Even though I don't know which course of treatment to follow I deeply and completely love and accept myself

Eyebrow:	I don't know what to do
Side of Eye:	Which treatment should I have
Under Eye:	This treatment anxiety
Under Nose:	I don't know what is right for me
Chin:	I don't know what to do
Collar Bone:	Which treatment should I have
Under Arm:	This treatment anxiety
Top of Head:	I don't know what is right for me

'The hardest thing to learn in life is which bridge to cross and which to burn.'
David Russell

Repeat 3 times while tapping the Karate Chop:

Even though I am frightened of making the wrong decision I deeply and completely love and accept myself

Eyebrow:	Fear of making the wrong decision
Side of Eye:	What if I do the wrong thing
Under Eye:	What if I choose the wrong course of treatment
Under Nose:	Fear of making the wrong choice
Chin:	Fear of getting it wrong
Collar Bone:	What if I do the wrong thing
Under Arm:	What if I choose the wrong course of treatment
Top of Head:	Fear of making the wrong choice

Repeat 3 times while tapping the Karate Chop:

Even though they are all telling me what to do and I feel so confused I deeply and completely love and accept myself

Eyebrow:	This confusion
Side of Eye:	Too much information
Under Eye:	This confusion
Under Nose:	I can't take it all in
Chin:	This confusion
Collar Bone:	I don't know what to do
Under Arm:	This confusion
Top of Head:	Too much information

Repeat 3 times while tapping the Karate Chop:

Even though I wish they would all just shut up I deeply and completely love and accept myself

Eyebrow:	Just shut up
Side of Eye:	Leave me alone
Under Eye:	Go away
Under Nose:	I can't think straight
Chin:	Just shut up
Collar Bone:	Leave me alone
Under Arm:	Go away
Top of Head:	I can't think straight

For some people, the pressure to act immediately is immense. Your oncologist may feel that urgent surgery is required, and be putting you under immense pressure. He/she won't be doing that for fun, they will be acting according to their specialist knowledge and statistics and it is obviously very important to listen. However, the extra pressure adds to the already existing stress so it is useful to tap to clear it, and bring in some more positive Choices.

Suzy's story
Suzy was feeling panic struck by the need to make life saving decisions immediately. She was a person who liked to mull over her options, research thoroughly and have all the information in front of her before making her mind up about anything, from washing powder to relationships. So you can imagine how she felt when her oncologist admitted her into hospital straight from his consulting room.

She rang me from her bed in a blind panic, her mind was whirring and she could hardly speak, let alone think with any clarity. She felt like a small child, completely powerless and helpless to change her situation, completely at the hands of an authoritative adult in charge of her destiny. After tapping down the immediate panic we worked through the various layers of emotion presenting, fear, anxiety, helplessness etc. Eventually we were able to introduce the possibility that, even though she was under such pressure, she did still have a choice and she didn't have to sign the consent form. Recognising that truth, that ultimately she was still in charge, she was able to relax and trust in her ability to choose correctly for her. With her regained clarity and calmness she was able to accept the emergency surgery and following treatment and the oncologist was amazed by the speed with which she healed and continues to heal.

Repeat 3 times while tapping the Karate Chop:

Even though I need space and time to think, I am open to the possibility that I can trust myself to make the right decision for me

Eyebrow:	*Feeling pressurised*
Side of Eye:	*I need space*
Under Eye:	*I need time to think*
Under Nose:	*This incredible pressure to decide*
Chin:	*I need space to breathe*
Collar Bone:	*I need time to think*
Under Arm:	*Feeling pressurised*
Top of Head:	*This pressure to decide*

Keep checking in on the feelings, using the SUDS scale, and when you are feeling calmer introduce the following Choice:

Eyebrow:	*I choose to trust my judgment*
Side of Eye:	*I choose to trust my intuition*
Under Eye:	*I choose to trust my ability to decide*
Under Nose:	*I choose to make the perfect decision for me*
Chin:	*I choose to trust my judgment*
Collar Bone:	*I choose to trust my intuition*
Under Arm:	*I choose to trust my ability to decide*
Top of Head:	*I choose to make the perfect decision for me*

It's Not Fair!!

'Life's not always fair.
Sometimes you can get a splinter even sliding down a rainbow.'
Cherralea Morgen

At some point, most of you are likely to experience thoughts such as 'It's not fair' and 'Why me?'. You may feel you are not 'allowed' to have these thoughts; believing they are not adult, or that society scorns self-pity, etc. Be honest with yourself, if the thoughts are there - that is how it is for you at this point. Denying them will only perpetuate them. Trying not to think something only gives that thought more power.

Don't think of Elvis naked.... What do you have to do NOT to think of that? Yes, you have to think of it before cancelling it out!

And actually, it isn't fair, is it? Why is it you that has cancer? Why is it anyone? You may or may not have a wealth of answers for this, and some of them may be valid, such as having a less than healthy lifestyle. But not everyone with your lifestyle gets cancer, do they? We all know stories about people who have chain smoked and lived healthily into their nineties... Is that fair?

None of it is 'fair' in that sense. And you may believe that you have stacked the odds against you for whatever reason, but the concept of fairness implies that someone else is dealing the cards, you have no power over your hand... And you do, it is all about accessing it!

So bring those words out into the open, create a Set Up Statement around them, acknowledge them, accept them, and let them go. They may be a truth, and as such acceptable, but they are still a distraction from your healing path.
Say it as it is!

Ruth's story
Ruth was young and healthy and about to embark on a new career when she received a diagnosis of breast cancer. Instead of spending her time in her new office, getting to know her colleagues and her role she found herself having to face surgery and a gruelling course of chemotherapy. She was very angry at the world and could not accept what was happening to her. We worked together on her anger at being sabotaged by cancer which led us to 'It's not fair' and similar emotions.

She said she felt like a small child and just wanted to lie on the floor and scream and stamp her feet, but the adult in her was scornful of this. So we started with:

Please tap along if it suits you:

Tapping Section: Tapping for wanting to scream

Repeat 3 times while tapping the Karate Chop:

Even though I want to scream and shout I deeply and completely love and accept myself

Eyebrow:	*I want to scream and shout*
Side of Eye:	*It's not fair*
Under Eye:	*I want to scream*
Under Nose:	*I want to shout*
Chin:	*I want to kick out at life*
Collar Bone:	*It's not fair*
Under Arm:	*I want it to go away*
Top of Head:	*It's not fair*

Ruth's voice tone was level and quiet, and in no way matched the intensity of the feelings she had spoken about so I asked her to do another round, giving it some emphasis, even shouting.

Repeat 3 times while tapping the Karate Chop:

Even though I want to scream and shout I deeply and completely love and accept myself

Eyebrow:	*I want to scream and shout*
Side of Eye:	*It's not fair*
Under Eye:	*I want to scream*
Under Nose:	*I want to shout*
Chin:	*I want to kick out at life*
Collar Bone:	*It's not fair*
Under Arm:	*I want it to go away*
Top of Head:	*It's not fair*

Repeat 3 times while tapping the Karate Chop:

Even though it's not fair, why me? I deeply and completely love and accept myself

Eyebrow:	*It's not fair*
Side of Eye:	*Why me?*
Under Eye:	*I don't deserve this*
Under Nose:	*It's not fair*
Chin:	*Why me?*
Collar Bone:	*I don't deserve it*
Under Arm:	*No one deserves it*
Top of Head:	*Why me?*

Repeat 3 times while tapping the Karate Chop:

Even though I have these 'why me' emotions I deeply and completely love and accept myself

Eyebrow:	*Why me*
Side of Eye:	*It's not fair*
Under Eye:	*Why me*
Under Nose:	*I don't deserve this*
Chin:	*Why me*

Collar Bone:	*It isn't fair*
Under Arm:	*Why me*
Top of Head:	*I don't deserve it*

By adding some real feeling to her tapping Ruth was able to allow her anger and self pity to really vent themselves and after a few rounds she started to laugh. I asked her whether she still wanted to lie on the floor and have a tantrum and she said that whilst it might be fun she didn't feel she needed to now. She felt that whilst it still didn't feel fair, that was more just a fact that she was able to accept and not a strong feeling as such anymore. If you feel like shouting, shout, but tap at the same time!

If you feel like shouting, shout, but tap at the same time!

Continue by addressing any judgments you may have around self pity, feeling sorry for yourself. You are human – you are bound to experience these feelings on occasion. The trick is to notice them, let go of the judgments and tap to release them. Nothing is wrong, it is as it is, and a valid response, but not useful to hold on to.

Eyebrow:	*Poor me*
Side of Eye:	*It is sad*
Under Eye:	*I am having a difficult time*
Under Nose:	*That is a truth*
Chin:	*I choose to let go of any remaining self judgments*
Collar Bone:	*Remaining self pity*
Under Arm:	*Remaining poor me*
Top of Head:	*I accept how I feel and I choose to let the judgments go*

Repeat 3 times while tapping the Karate Chop:

Even though I shouldn't feel sorry for myself I deeply and completely love and accept myself

Eyebrow:	*This self pity*
Side of Eye:	*I shouldn't feel it*
Under Eye:	*Feeling sorry for myself*
Under Nose:	*Poor me*
Chin:	*This self pity and all my judgments about it*
Collar Bone:	*I choose to release it now*
Under Arm:	*Remaining judgements*
Top of Head:	*Remaining self pity*

As you have been tapping through the various rounds in this chapter you are likely to have been aware, at some level, of a physiological response. That is to say, some form of sensation or discomfort in your body at varying times: maybe butterflies in your stomach, or a shakiness or some other feeling. These are the bodily interpretations of your emotions, and you will be feeling something, even if you have not been aware of it. In order to experience an emotion there has to be some form of sensation in your body, otherwise how do you know you are having that emotion?

In the following chapter we will look at how it is possible to work with the physiological response to an emotion by changing our language to match the physical sensations. It doesn't matter which approach you take, emotional or physical, but sometimes it is easier to work with the body as it lets go of the need to analyse or label a particular emotion.

CHAPTER 5

HOW YOUR EMOTIONS SHOW UP IN YOUR BODY

*'Nerves and butterflies are fine - they're a physical sign that you're mentally ready
and eager. You have to get the butterflies to fly in formation, that's the trick.'*
Steve Bull

As evidenced with anxiety, emotional responses also manifest in physical
symptoms. How often have you had butterflies in your stomach when thinking of
sitting an exam? How many times have you felt your heart rate speed up when
you think of seeing the person you love? The tears when you feel sad? In fact,
we have to experience a physical response in order to know we are feeling an
emotion, we have just become very adept at ignoring the connection! It can be
so quick, or so subtle, we just miss it altogether. If you look for it, you **will** find
it!

Think of the 'Mary' story in Chapter 1. Whenever she thought of water she got a
feeling in her stomach. By tapping on that feeling, whilst tuned into it, she was
able to release a lifelong phobia. This is no different.

All thoughts bring with them some feeling, some emotional response. It is just
the way it is. Very often, these feelings pass through us without being flagged
up. We process them automatically, or they have no particular emotional charge
to them. This is often the case with habitual thinking. Even when they're
negative, we are so used to the thoughts and corresponding emotions we fail to
notice them. However, other thoughts will create obvious physical symptoms,
such as the butterflies mentioned above. This is the moment to start being alert
to this.

How do you feel when you think certain thoughts?
Begin asking yourself how you feel when you think a certain thought, or access a
particular memory, such as your diagnosis experience. It is easier to work with
the feelings as they arise than to ignore them and allow them to accumulate into
a more overwhelming physical or emotional response, as with the panic attacks
addressed earlier. Tapping on the physical or emotional response will allow 'your
butterflies to fly in formation'.

'Heavy thoughts bring on physical maladies;
when the soul is oppressed so is the body.'
Martin Luther

It is usually much easier to begin working with any physical symptoms than
analysing the thought processes that create them.

When you find yourself getting a physical response to a particular thought or
emotion, like in the stomach, tap as follows (we will look into physical responses
in more depth later on):

For now, think of your diagnosis and notice where you feel a response or reaction in your body.

Is it your stomach like Mary, is it your chest, your throat, or where is it showing up?

Rate its intensity on a scale of 0 – 10 and begin tapping, replacing the word *stomach* for the one most appropriate to you.

Tapping Section: Tapping for feelings in your body

Repeat 3 times while tapping the Karate Chop:

Even though I have this fear in my stomach I deeply and completely love and accept myself

Eyebrow:	*Fear in my stomach*
Side of Eye:	*Fear in my stomach*
Under Eye:	*Intense fear in my stomach*
Under Nose:	*Fear in my stomach*
Chin:	*Cancer fear in my stomach*
Collar Bone:	*Fear in my stomach*
Under Arm:	*Cancer fear in my stomach*
Top of Head:	*Fear in my stomach*

After a round or two check in with the fear and see what has happened. If it is still there ask yourself:

- Is it a pain, or an ache, or a hurt?
- What quality does it have?
- Is it heavy, hot, sickening, sharp, or something else?
- Is it a pain, or an ache, or a hurt?
- Which word most accurately describes it?

You might want to purely focus on the physical sensations. For example,

Repeat 3 times while tapping the Karate Chop:

Even though I have this hot (or equivalent) fear in my stomach I deeply and completely love and accept myself

Eyebrow:	*Hot fear in my stomach*
Side of Eye:	*Hot cancer fear just there*
Under Eye:	*Hot fear in my stomach*
Under Nose:	*Hot fear just there*

Chin:	*Hot fear in my stomach*
Collar Bone:	*Hot fear in my stomach*
Under Arm:	*Hot fear just there in my stomach*
Top of Head:	*Hot cancer fear just there*

Repeat 3 times while tapping the Karate Chop:

Even though I have butterflies in my stomach I deeply and completely love and accept myself

Eyebrow:	*Butterflies in my stomach*
Side of Eye:	*Awful butterflies in my stomach*
Under Eye:	*These butterflies in my stomach*
Under Nose:	*Butterflies in my stomach*
Chin:	*These butterflies in my stomach*
Collar Bone:	*These awful butterflies in my stomach*
Under Arm:	*These butterflies in my stomach*
Top of Head:	*These butterflies in my stomach*

Check in with it again and adjust your words to include any changes of quality or position. You may be curious to discover that the feeling moves around your body. This happens, and all you need to do is follow it until it releases. In tapping terms this is called Chasing the Pain (See Chapter 3).

How Emotions Show up in Our Body
The following are a few examples of some of the more obvious ways emotions show up in our physical body. You are probably familiar with most of them. If you feel any of them, tap on the physical symptoms, you don't necessarily need to know what they connect to.

Repeat 3 times while tapping the Karate Chop:

Even though I have this sharp pain in my stomach I deeply and completely love and accept myself

Eyebrow:	*Sharp pain in my stomach*
Side of Eye:	*Sharp pain in my stomach*
Under Eye:	*Sharp pain in my stomach*
Under Nose:	*Sharp pain in my stomach*
Chin:	*Sharp pain in my stomach*
Collar Bone:	*Sharp pain in my stomach*
Under Arm:	*Sharp pain in my stomach*
Top of Head:	*Sharp pain in my stomach*

Repeat 3 times while tapping the Karate Chop:

Even though I have this block in my throat I deeply and completely love and accept myself

Eyebrow:	*This block in my throat*
Side of Eye:	*This block in my throat*
Under Eye:	*This block in my throat*
Under Nose:	*This block in my throat*
Chin:	*This block in my throat*
Collar Bone:	*This block in my throat*
Under Arm:	*This block in my throat*
Top of Head:	*This block in my throat*

Repeat 3 times while tapping the Karate Chop:

Even though I have this tightness in my chest I deeply and completely love and accept myself

Eyebrow:	*Tightness in my chest*
Side of Eye:	*Tightness in my chest*
Under Eye:	*Tightness in my chest*
Under Nose:	*Tightness in my chest*
Chin:	*Tightness in my chest*
Collar Bone:	*Tightness in my chest*
Under Arm:	*Tightness in my chest*
Top of Head:	*Tightness in my chest*

You are now ready to explore and release the trauma and shock around the actual specific memory of the diagnosis itself. In the next chapter, I will be looking in depth at how you can do this safely. If at any time during your work you find you are stuck and can't move forward from a certain thought or emotion, that is the time to see an experienced practitioner to help you through that block. A full listing of practitioner resources is available in the appendix of this book. One of the wonderful things about the tapping and other Energy Psychologies is that you can work over the phone, allowing you access to top practitioners around the world.

CHAPTER 6

THE TRAUMA OF DIAGNOSIS

'Whatever words we utter should be chosen with care for people will hear them and be influenced by them for good or ill'
Buddha

Many of my clients can vividly remember the moment of their cancer diagnosis and still have varying degrees of upset about it. It is very important to begin this process by working through the trauma of the diagnosis. The diagnosis itself can be very frightening. As I said before, the very word 'Cancer' may bring with it fear and dread. Suddenly the future seems uncertain and everything familiar is challenged. A cancer diagnosis affects not just you, the patient, but also your family, friends and colleagues at work.

The Men in White Coats

'In nothing do men more nearly approach the gods than in giving health to men.'
Cicero

People often take the word of the consultant/surgeon as law. It is well documented that for a number of people their blood pressure rises at the sight of a doctor or in a hospital setting. This is known as White Coat Syndrome. Although nowadays most consultants/ surgeons wear suits or even less formal clothing in their practices, rather than the white coats of old, in order to avoid this unnecessary extra problem, many people consider them to be the ultimate authority and take their word as law, without question. This is not to say that consultants and surgeons are not authorities in their profession. They certainly are, and their wealth of knowledge is extremely valuable and needs to be taken seriously by the patient.

However, it is best if the patient/doctor relationship is based on mutual respect, rather than a fear of authority in some form. Probably unfairly, but nevertheless frequently, I hear patients referring to their consultant as 'They think they are God'. And in the same vein, some people will take their every word literally.

Even consultants get bad days. Remember these are highly trained top clinicians, but they may not have the best bedside manner all the time, and they are under considerable stress themselves. They are, above all, caring individuals who are doing their best, but they do not necessarily have all the answers... yet.

This can be where the patient can form dangerous beliefs around outcome and the future. It is very important to tap to clear any emotional attachment to the diagnosis and prognosis, like fears and sadness. There is often anger and disbelief; and denial can come before realisation of the reality of the diagnosis and its implications. I will discuss this in detail later.

Whilst people in the medical profession are becoming increasingly aware of the power of their words on the patients and how a diagnosis is delivered, we have to remember that consultants are delivering bad news day in and day out. Whilst it won't be easy for them, as with anyone that is doing something regularly, there may be an element of automatic pilot, which may translate as uncaring to the patient.

Tapping Section: Tapping for emotions about diagnosis

Repeat 3 times while tapping the Karate Chop:

Even though I have these diagnosis emotions I deeply and completely love and accept myself

Eyebrow:	*Diagnosis emotions*
Side of Eye:	*Diagnosis emotions*
Under Eye:	*Diagnosis emotions*
Under Nose:	*Diagnosis emotions*
Chin:	*Diagnosis emotions*
Collar Bone:	*Diagnosis emotions*
Under Arm:	*Diagnosis emotions*
Top of Head:	*Diagnosis emotions*

Repeat 3 times while tapping the Karate Chop:

Even though he/she told me that I deeply and completely love and accept myself

Eyebrow:	*He/she said that*
Side of Eye:	*He/she told me that*
Under Eye:	*His/her words*
Under Nose:	*He/she said that*
Chin:	*He/she said that*
Collar Bone:	*He/she told me that*
Under Arm:	*His/her words*
Top of Head:	*He/she said that*

Repeat 3 times while tapping the Karate Chop:

Even though he/she gave me that diagnosis   I deeply and completely love and accept myself

Eyebrow:	*That diagnosis*
Side of Eye:	*His/her words*
Under Eye:	*Everything I feel about it*

Under Nose:	*Everything he/she said*
Chin:	*That diagnosis*
Collar Bone:	*His/her words*
Under Arm:	*Everything I feel about it*
Top of Head:	*Everything he/she said*

Repeat 3 times while tapping the Karate Chop:

Even though he/she said that and it must be true, he/she's the expert, I deeply and completely love and accept myself

Eyebrow:	*He/she's the expert*
Side of Eye:	*It must be true*
Under Eye:	*He/she must know*
Under Nose:	*He/she's the expert*
Chin:	*He/she's the expert*
Collar Bone:	*It must be true*
Under Arm:	*He/she must know*
Top of Head:	*He/she's the expert*

Keep tapping until you can hear their words and feel calm about them. Then introduce one of the following Choices:

I choose to keep an open mind about my prognosis

I choose to trust in my body's healing capacity

I choose to surprise him/her with my healing ability

I choose health and healing instead of this

Researchers at the University of Wisconsin found that empathic doctors speeded up the healing process. In a randomised controlled trial they found that patients who were attended by caring doctors recovered faster than those whose physicians were thoroughly professional but distant.

According to the study, the patients, who were suffering from coughs and colds, took an average of seven days to recover under a sympathetic doctor while others took an extra day in recovery.

The doctor's empathy also boosted the patients' immune system, the Journal of Family Medicine reported.

http://bps-research-digest.blogspot.com/2009/11/patients-with-empathic-attentive.html

'It's not denial. I'm just selective about the reality I accept'.
Bill Watterson

100

Denial

Some consultants are concerned about their patients being in denial, when they seem to refuse to face the reality of their diagnosis and situation - where patients are just not connecting to or understanding the seriousness of their diagnosis. My sense is that as long as those patients are able to make a decision, to come to a choice about their treatment, there is time for them to absorb the full facts around it and the prognosis later.

Many people are unable to take all the information on board at the same time so they compartmentalise. They put the full meaning of what is being said to them away, just for a short time, whilst they get on with the immediate decision-making. Denial is a common unconscious defence mechanism that allows the patient time to fully come to terms with the impact of the trauma, giving them time to adjust. In this respect, it can be a healthy response. Where it runs into danger is when the patient stays in denial, to the extent that it affects their decision-making and treatment choices, where they are unable to face reality for a longer period of time and the disease progresses unhindered.

'It takes courage to grow up and become who you really are.'
e.e. cummings

Tapping Section: Tapping for denial

Repeat 3 times while tapping the Karate Chop:

Even though I just can't go there I deeply and completely love and accept myself

Eyebrow:	*Don't want to think about it*
Side of Eye:	*Can't go there*
Under Eye:	*Can't think about it*
Under Nose:	*Don't want to go there*
Chin:	*Don't want to think about it*
Collar Bone:	*Can't go there*
Under Arm:	*Can't think about it*
Top of Head:	*Don't want to go there*

Repeat 3 times while tapping the Karate Chop:

Even though I am not going to think about it I deeply and completely love and accept myself

Eyebrow:	*I refuse to go there*
Side of Eye:	*It is just not happening*
Under Eye:	*I refuse to think about it*
Under Nose:	*It isn't real*
Chin:	*I refuse to go there*

Collar Bone:	*It is just not happening*
Under Arm:	*I refuse to think about it*
Top of Head:	*It isn't real*

When you reach a point where it seems possible to look at the diagnosis and prognosis, introduce one or more of the following Choices:

- **I choose calmness and clarity instead of this**
- **I choose to calmly assess my healing options**
- **I choose to clearly understand my healing choices**
- **I choose to think clearly about this now**

Charlie's story

Charlie was fantastic at compartmentalising. He was a very busy man and well rehearsed in separating out the different areas of his life which needed his attention into separate 'files' in his mind, accessing them only when necessary. He claimed this allowed him to give full focus to one thing at a time, without distraction.

With his cancer he had, in his words, created a mini filing cabinet of the different aspects of it which needed to be addressed in time.

Charlie had a diagnosis of lung cancer, a very serious diagnosis. He had multiple tumours in both lungs. Charlie's way of coping with the enormity of this was to focus on one area at a time until he felt he had 'a handle' on that piece and could turn his attention to the next. To quote him he had compartments for:

- *Oncologist*
- *Cancer*
- *Hospital*
- *Pain*
- *Chemotherapy*
- *Healing/remission*
- *Future*
- *Prognosis*

And he had not gone into all of them yet.

He had a very good relationship with his oncologist, he respected him and he was fond of him. Even more importantly, he trusted him. He had to see him fortnightly for monitoring. He was on oral chemotherapy at home.

This particular fortnight Charlie had started focussing on supporting his healing process. He had taken up swimming and had already noticed a marked improvement in his lung capacity and breathing.

At his next appointment he was very excited to report that he thought there was progress, that the chemotherapy and his swimming seemed to be working, that he really felt he was beginning to heal now. On hearing this, the first thing Charlie's oncologist said to him was 'You do understand there is no cure for this don't you'.

Charlie did know this, and he had chosen to focus on remission rather than cure. He was optimistic that he could live with the disease for a long time and that it did not have to kill him. As such he was allowing himself to keep positive and work hard at healing. He believed anything was possible and had refused to focus on the medical prognosis. However, it was not that he was denying it, but in his view the prognosis was only that way until it wasn't; until someone, or a series of people, had proved a different outcome to be possible.

The oncologist's need to stress the reality of the situation, again, knocked Charlie badly. He told me 'I thought he would be pleased with my efforts, that I was doing something positive to support his work with me, instead he pulled the rug out from under me. It seemed as though he thought nothing was going to change the outcome, and that I was wasting my time trying to get stronger. In that one sentence, he managed to totally deflate me and I feel back at square one.'

Having used this example I would like to go back to **stressing** that in the majority of cases the diagnosis is delivered with empathy and compassion and people feel very safe and looked after but if this has happened to you or you can relate to the above stories then create your own movie and tap as follows:

Tapping Section: Tapping for 'reality' news from doctor

Repeat 3 times while tapping the Karate Chop:

Even though I have this 'X' movie emotion I deeply and completely love and accept myself

Eyebrow:	*X movie emotion*
Side of Eye:	*X movie emotion*
Under Eye:	*X movie emotion*
Under Nose:	*X movie emotion*
Chin:	*X movie emotion*
Collar Bone:	*X movie emotion*
Under Arm:	*X movie emotion*
Top of Head:	*X movie emotion*

Repeat 3 times while tapping the Karate Chop:

Even though he/she said this (if you want to, add the doctor's name) I deeply and completely love and accept myself

Eyebrow:	*He/she said this*
Side of Eye:	*His/her words*
Under Eye:	*Feeling 'X'*
Under Nose:	*He/she said 'X'*
Chin:	*His/her words*

Collar Bone:	*Those words*
Under Arm:	*Feeling 'X'*
Top of Head:	*Those words*

Continue working with those specific words until you are able to speak them aloud without any emotional charge. You may need to work through the specific feelings they bring up for you too. For example:

Repeat 3 times while tapping the Karate Chop:

Even though I am really angry about this I deeply and completely love and accept myself

Eyebrow:	*This anger*
Side of Eye:	*This anger*
Under Eye:	*I'm really angry*
Under Nose:	*This anger*
Chin:	*How dare he/she say that*
Collar Bone:	*This anger*
Under Arm:	*Those words*
Top of Head:	*My anger*

In the following tapping protocol, I want you to tune into the specific words that the doctor used when delivering your diagnosis. What exactly did he/she say? How does hearing those words make you feel now? Insert the appropriate emotion below if 'anger' feels wrong for you.

Repeat 3 times while tapping the Karate Chop:

Even though I have this anger in my chest I deeply and completely love and accept myself

Eyebrow:	*Anger in my chest*
Side of Eye:	*Anger in my chest*
Under Eye:	*Those words*
Under Nose:	*Anger at those words*
Chin:	*Anger in my chest*
Collar Bone:	*Anger in my chest*
Under Arm:	*This anger*
Top of Head:	*Anger in my chest*

Repeat 3 times while tapping the Karate Chop:

Even though I am terrified of those words I deeply and completely love and accept myself

Eyebrow:	*Those terrifying words*
Side of Eye:	*Terror*
Under Eye:	*Terror*
Under Nose:	*This terror*
Chin:	*Those terrifying words*
Collar Bone:	*This terror*
Under Arm:	*Terror*
Top of Head:	*Word terror*

If you are struggling to release the emotions, tune into your body and ask yourself where you feel that anger/terror etc. Adapt the following protocol and tap as below:

Repeat 3 times while tapping the Karate Chop:

Even though I have this fear in my stomach I deeply and completely love and accept myself

Eyebrow:	*Fear in my stomach*
Side of Eye:	*Fear in my stomach*
Under Eye:	*Those words*
Under Nose:	*Stuck in my stomach*
Chin:	*Fear in my stomach*
Collar Bone:	*Fear in my stomach*
Under Arm:	*This fear*
Top of Head:	*Fear in my stomach*

> *'A conclusion is the place where you got tired of thinking.'*
> *Attributed to Arthur McBride Bloch*

Despite their best intentions...
In my work, I hear all sorts of stories, both good and bad, about consultants. Whatever I hear, I strongly believe that they are all coming from a very positive place, ultimately they are all healers, they just want the best for you and their aim is to begin their work on your healing as quickly as possible. This is absolutely not 'a dig' at the medical profession. They do an amazing and very difficult job and we would be in a much worse place without their expertise. Just for a moment, step into a consultant's shoes. I cannot imagine what it must be like to have to continually impart bad news to patients (inasmuch as a cancer diagnosis itself is unlikely ever to be considered good news). They must have to

dig deep into their own resources to be able to do this, and there will be an emotional toll on them too. Is it any wonder that sometimes they are unaware of the impact of their choice of words?

However, there are inevitably some patients who have been delivered a diagnosis in an unsuitable or distressing way. If that is you, you will need to work to clear the charge on that specific memory, especially bearing in mind that you are likely to be spending more time with your consultant and your relationship with him/her is very important. You don't want to go into the next session with a negative attitude towards him/her, after all you are putting your life in his/her hands.

Frances' story

Frances and I were working on the trauma following her diagnosis for breast cancer. She had had a biopsy, a mammogram and ultrasound, and was coming back to get her results. Before telling her however, the consultant wanted do one further check. When the oncologist had finished checking and Frances was about to get dressed he chose to deliver the news that she had malignant breast cancer. Now if that wasn't traumatic enough, being delivered the bombshell by a man, when she was standing there feeling very vulnerable practically naked, only wearing her knickers, added an extra layer to the diagnosis trauma. It took many sessions to fully clear that traumatic memory as Frances felt abused and humiliated, both of which were familiar feelings to her with past resonances which needed to be addressed as well.

We began specifically addressing the diagnosis itself, using the following protocols until Frances was able to talk it through without emotion. It would never be a great memory, but the humiliation and upset had resolved and she was able to focus on her consultant's medical wisdom and expertise instead.

Tapping Section: Tapping for diagnosis emotions

Repeat 3 times while tapping the Karate Chop:

Even though I have these diagnosis emotions I deeply and completely love and accept myself

Eyebrow:	*Diagnosis emotions*
Side of Eye:	*Diagnosis emotions*
Under Eye:	*Diagnosis emotions*
Under Nose:	*Diagnosis emotions*
Chin:	*Diagnosis emotions*
Collar Bone:	*Diagnosis emotions*
Under Arm:	*Diagnosis emotions*
Top of Head:	*Diagnosis emotions*

Repeat 3 times while tapping the Karate Chop:

Even though I wasn't even dressed I deeply and completely love and accept myself

Eyebrow:	*I wasn't even dressed*

Side of Eye:	*He said that*
Under Eye:	*And I wasn't even dressed*
Under Nose:	*I was vulnerable*
Chin:	*Feeling vulnerable*
Collar Bone:	*I wasn't even dressed*
Under Arm:	*He said that*
Top of Head:	*And I was vulnerable*

Repeat 3 times while tapping the Karate Chop:

Even though he said that and I was naked I deeply and completely love and accept myself

Eyebrow:	*I wasn't even dressed*
Side of Eye:	*He said that and I was naked*
Under Eye:	*His words and I was naked*
Under Nose:	*Naked emotions*
Chin:	*I wasn't even dressed*
Collar Bone:	*I was in my knickers*
Under Arm:	*He said that and I was naked*
Top of Head:	*Naked emotions*

Repeat 3 times while tapping the Karate Chop:

Even though it was humiliating I deeply and completely love and accept myself

Eyebrow:	*Humiliation*
Side of Eye:	*Diagnosis humiliation*
Under Eye:	*Mr X humiliation*
Under Nose:	*It was humiliating*
Chin:	*Humiliation*
Collar Bone:	*Diagnosis humiliation*
Under Arm:	*Mr X humiliation*
Top of Head:	*It was humiliating*

When considering your diagnosis, keep these questions in mind:

- Who delivered it?
- What did they say?

- What was their tone like?
- Did they seem in a rush?
- Did you feel heard?
- Who was with you?
- How did they react?

Other pieces about the diagnosis experience
There may be many pieces connected to the diagnosis which need working on, perhaps finding a lump, seeing the doctor, having a biopsy, scan etc. Make a list of all of these in the same way as you have worked with the diagnosis itself and work systematically through them, using the Movie Technique.

Notice where it takes you, you may get fragments of other memories connected with past illnesses, etc. If this happens, write them down and come back to them. Tapping seems to allow your unconscious mind to deliver the next piece for you to consider working with, all you have to do is recognise it!

Carol's story
Carol had gone back to her consultant a few days after her initial breast cancer surgery to discuss options for the next stage of her treatment. She was being put under a lot of pressure to go ahead and have chemotherapy and she was not at all sure she wanted to take that route.

Carol is a very happy smiley person, she smiles when she is happy but she also smiles and laughs when she is nervous or stressed. She was sitting in her consultant's office being put under pressure to make a decision about her treatment and she smiled and laughed, in this case with nervousness.

Her consultant turned to her and said 'I don't know why you are smiling, this is VERY serious'. Clearly, the consultant needed to get his message across and perhaps thought that Carol was in denial, but this made Carol defensive. She was already frightened and now she was also upset that her consultant wasn't capable of seeing that her laughter was an emotional response and not one of happiness.

As she said to me, 'Why would I be happy when thinking of the options between chemotherapy and radiotherapy, what would I have to laugh about there?' She had left his office without reaching a decision over treatment and knew she would have to go back for another meeting. She wanted to go to that meeting feeling calm and clear.

Repeat 3 times while tapping the Karate Chop:

Even though he really upset me I deeply and completely love and accept myself

Eyebrow:	*Feeling upset*
Side of Eye:	*Mr X upset*
Under Eye:	*Feeling upset*
Under Nose:	*Mr X upset*
Chin:	*His words*
Collar Bone:	*His upsetting words*

108

Under Arm:	*Feeling upset*
Top of Head:	*This upset*

Repeat 3 times while tapping the Karate Chop:

Even though he thought he didn't understand me I deeply and completely love and accept myself

Eyebrow:	*Feeling hurt and misunderstood*
Side of Eye:	*Feeling hurt and misunderstood*
Under Eye:	*He just didn't get it*
Under Nose:	*He didn't understand me*
Chin:	*This hurt*
Collar Bone:	*Mr X hurt*
Under Arm:	*He just didn't understand me*
Top of Head:	*This hurt*

Having worked through Carol's initial response, it then turned to anger, which we continued to tap through until that cleared. As the anger released Carol said that she could see he was coming from a place of concern for her and his need to make sure she understood the seriousness of the situation and for her to make a quick decision. She felt able to go back and discuss things again from a clear space.

The Shock of the Unexpected

> *'I know God will not give me anything I can't handle.*
> *I just wish that He didn't trust me so much.'*
> *Mother Teresa*

Occasionally people will have had no idea that they have cancer until the diagnosis. They feel perfectly healthy and energised. The only reason they have a diagnosis at all is due to a routine check up of some form, such as a mammogram. To go from apparent total health to a potentially life threatening diagnosis in this way is highly traumatic and the shock needs to be addressed immediately. And it may also create a mistrust of their body. If this is the case for you, you will need to tap to clear this too:

Tapping Section: Tapping for Shock of the Unexpected

Repeat 3 times while tapping the Karate Chop:

Even though I had no idea this was coming I deeply and completely love and accept myself

Eyebrow:	*I had no idea*
Side of Eye:	*I just wasn't expecting this*

Under Eye:	*I had no sign*
Under Nose:	*This shock*
Chin:	*I had no idea*
Collar Bone:	*I just wasn't expecting this*
Under Arm:	*I had no sign*
Top of Head:	*This shock*

Check in with your body, where do you feel the shock. People often say it is as if they have had the wind knocked out of them, they can't breathe. Notice where you feel the shock the most strongly and tap accordingly. For example:

Repeat 3 times while tapping the Karate Chop:

Even though I had this unexpected shock I deeply and completely love and accept myself

Eyebrow:	*This unexpected shock*
Side of Eye:	*This cancer shock*
Under Eye:	*Out of the blue*
Under Nose:	*This unexpected shock*
Chin:	*This unexpected shock*
Collar Bone:	*This cancer shock*
Under Arm:	*Out of the blue*
Top of Head:	*This unexpected shock*

Repeat 3 times while tapping the Karate Chop:

Even though my body has let me down I deeply and completely love and accept myself

Eyebrow:	*My body has let me down*
Side of Eye:	*My body has let me down*
Under Eye:	*My body has let me down*
Under Nose:	*My body has let me down*
Chin:	*My body has let me down*
Collar Bone:	*My body has let me down*
Under Arm:	*My body has let me down*
Top of Head:	*My body has let me down*

Repeat 3 times while tapping the Karate Chop:

Even though I can't trust my body I deeply and completely love and accept myself

Eyebrow:	*I can't trust my body*
Side of Eye:	*I can't trust it*
Under Eye:	*I can't trust my body*
Under Nose:	*I can't trust my body*
Chin:	*I can't trust my body*
Collar Bone:	*I don't know how to trust it*
Under Arm:	*I can't trust my body*
Top of Head:	*I can't trust my body*

Repeat 3 times while tapping the Karate Chop:

Even though I don't know what healthy looks like for me I deeply and completely love and accept myself

Eyebrow:	*I don't know what healthy looks like for me*
Side of Eye:	*I can't tell if I am healthy*
Under Eye:	*I don't know what healthy looks like for me*
Under Nose:	*I can't tell if I am healthy*
Chin:	*I don't know what healthy looks like for me*
Collar Bone:	*I can't tell if I am healthy*
Under Arm:	*I can't trust how I look*
Top of Head:	*I don't know what healthy looks like for me*

Repeat 3 times while tapping the Karate Chop:

Even though I have this shock in my solar plexus I deeply and completely love and accept myself

Eyebrow:	*Shock in my solar plexus*
Side of Eye:	*Cancer shock in my solar plexus*
Under Eye:	*Shock in my solar plexus*
Under Nose:	*Cancer shock in my solar plexus*
Chin:	*Shock in my solar plexus*
Collar Bone:	*Cancer shock in my solar plexus*
Under Arm:	*Shock in my solar plexus*
Top of Head:	*Cancer shock in my solar plexus*

When you can run through your diagnosis movie without experiencing a traumatic response, and it really is as though you are watching a movie, then move to the next chapter where I explore the many different emotions and self judgments that can arise around cancer and dis-ease in general.

CHAPTER 7

EMOTIONS OF CANCER

'Let's not forget that the little emotions are the great captains of our lives and we obey them without realizing it.'
Vincent Van Gogh, 1889

Once the initial shock and trauma of the diagnosis itself has subsided, a second layer of emotion and thinking often presents. This comprises what, to my mind, can best be referred to as the 'yes buts' and 'what ifs' – all the self blame and self torture that many of us live with on a constant basis. It is not a useful focus of your energy at any time, least of all when you need to conserve all your strength for your healing process.

Self-Judgments

The ultimate lesson all of us have to learn is unconditional love, which includes not only others but ourselves as well.'
Dr. Elisabeth Kübler-Ross

Back to you now, what are you saying about yourself? What are you imagining others are saying? Listen to any inner critic, or indeed outer critic, and tap as follows, adapting your words to include your own specific self-judgments or criticisms.

Say it as it is for you, be brutally honest, you need to get these judgments on the table and clear them. They are judgments, and illusions, not truths, and you don't need them. Below are a number of common emotional responses and self-judgments that regularly manifest themselves amongst my client population.

Tapping Section: Tapping for self judgments

Repeat 3 times while tapping the Karate Chop:

Even though I'm weak I deeply and completely love and accept myself

Eyebrow:	*I'm weak*
Side of Eye:	*This cancer weakness*
Under Eye:	*I'm weak*
Under Nose:	*This cancer weakness*
Chin:	*These judgments*
Collar Bone:	*I'm weak*
Under Arm:	*I'm really weak*
Top of Head:	*This weakness*

Repeat 3 times while tapping the Karate Chop:

Even though the cancer is my fault I deeply and completely love and accept myself

Eyebrow:	*It's my fault*
Side of Eye:	*I attracted this to me*
Under Eye:	*It is all my fault*
Under Nose:	*I brought it on myself*
Chin:	*It's my fault*
Collar Bone:	*I attracted this to me*
Under Arm:	*It is all my fault*
Top of Head:	*I brought it on myself*

Repeat 3 times while tapping the Karate Chop:

Even though I am not strong enough I deeply and completely love and accept myself

Eyebrow:	*I'm weak*
Side of Eye:	*I am just not strong enough*
Under Eye:	*I should have been stronger*
Under Nose:	*I'm weak*
Chin:	*It is all my fault*
Collar Bone:	*I am just not strong enough*
Under Arm:	*I should have been stronger*
Top of Head:	*I'm weak*

Continue:

Eyebrow:	*These judgments*
Side of Eye:	*Judging myself*
Under Eye:	*These harsh judgments*
Under Nose:	*Beating myself up*
Chin:	*I wouldn't judge anyone else like this*
Collar Bone:	*But I'm different*
Under Arm:	*These self judgments*
Top of Head:	*I am open to the possibility I can begin to let them go*

When you have reduced the SUDS levels on the judgments themselves, continue as follows:

Repeat 3 times while tapping the Karate Chop:

Even though I must be bad I deeply and completely love and accept myself

Eyebrow:	*I'm bad*
Side of Eye:	*I'm bad*
Under Eye:	*I must be*
Under Nose:	*I know I'm bad*
Chin:	*I am really bad*
Collar Bone:	*I am so bad*
Under Arm:	*I'm bad*
Top of Head:	*I'm bad*

Continue:

Eyebrow:	*I choose to be gentle with myself*
Side of Eye:	*I choose to be kind*
Under Eye:	*I deserve to be kind*
Under Nose:	*I deserve gentleness*
Chin:	*These remaining self judgments*
Under Arm:	*Beating myself up*
Under Arm:	*I choose kindness and gentleness now*
Top of Head:	*And I choose for that to be easy*

Guilt

> *'Guilt is anger directed at ourselves'*
> *Peter McWilliams*

A cancer diagnosis may bring with it a misplaced but real sense of guilt. This can take many shapes and forms: guilt towards family and friends, guilt towards the self, the 'should haves', the 'If only's', the 'oughts':

- *If I had eaten healthily*
- *If I had stopped smoking*
- *If I had taken better care of myself*
- *I should have spotted this earlier*
- *I should have done things differently*

115

When you have reduced the SUDS on the judgments themselves continue and fill in the blanks as follows:

- **If only...**
- **I ought to...**

The list goes on and on.

Guilt in this instance is a useless emotion, the only person it really hurts is you and you have enough going on without adding to it unnecessarily. It is a very important emotion to work through and clear.

Tapping Section: Tapping for guilt

Repeat 3 times while tapping the Karate Chop:

Even though I feel guilty about having cancer I deeply and completely love and accept myself

Eyebrow:	*This cancer guilt*
Side of Eye:	*It's all my fault*
Under Eye:	*I'm guilty*
Under Nose:	*I should have been different*
Chin:	*I should have done things differently*
Collar Bone:	*This guilt*
Under Arm:	*It's all my fault*
Top of Head:	*No it's not*

Check in again with your SUDS Scale and notice what is happening. If there is still any guilt continue to tap on it until it clears, either saying:

Repeat 3 times while tapping the Karate Chop:

Even though I still have some of this guilt I deeply and completely love and accept myself

Eyebrow:	*Remaining guilt*
Side of Eye:	*Remaining guilt*
Under Eye:	*Remaining guilt*
Under Nose:	*Remaining guilt*
Chin:	*Remaining guilt*
Collar Bone:	*Remaining guilt*
Under Arm:	*Remaining guilt*
Top of Head:	*Remaining guilt*

Continuing as follows, if relevant:

Repeat 3 times while tapping the Karate Chop:

Even though I feel guilty about having cancer and how it's affecting the people I love I deeply and completely love and accept myself.

Eyebrow:	*This guilt*
Side of Eye:	*Guilt at hurting those I love*
Under Eye:	*Guilt at letting them down*
Under Nose:	*Guilt at hurting them*
Chin:	*Guilt at needing their support*
Collar Bone:	*This guilt*
Under Arm:	*This guilt at causing this pain*
Top of Head:	*This guilt*

To truly justify feeling guilty you have to prove that you did something to someone or something (including yourself) with the clear intention of causing hurt or harm. That is the role of a jury after all, and the difference between murder and manslaughter. It is all about the intention.

Is this the case here, did you deliberately, and consciously go about creating your cancer? Was that your intention? I imagine not. You may feel that you consciously created a lifestyle which put you at risk, such as smoking or alcohol use or high stress levels, but did you actively, consciously create your cancer? If so, how did you do that? Are you really that talented??

If the answer to the last question is yes, and I would agree with you that you are *exceptionally* talented in many ways, as is each and every one of us, then how can you usefully use your talents to support your healing process?

A cancer diagnosis will inevitably create a disruption to the status quo. Treatment and surgery may lead to a reduction in income, lifestyle changes, unforeseen expenses and more. If you are the main bread winner or your role is as the mainstay, the rock in your world, suddenly those who depend upon you may be asked to take on the stronger role. This can be a difficult adjustment not only for you, but for your partner/ family/ colleagues/ friends. The 'you' they knew, who is always there, may be temporarily absent during this time. And you may feel guilty for putting them into a new unfamiliar place, or maybe for feeling unable to offer them the support they need as you focus on your healing.

Equally, they may feel some misplaced guilt too, perhaps they feel they have somehow contributed to the cancer... Remember, guilt is rarely logical in these instances. Maybe they encouraged a particular way of being or living? I will look at ways in which they can work through these emotions in Chapter 23 when I look at practical ways in which those close to you can use the tapping to support themselves on this journey.

The key thing is to clear this guilt as it **will** interrupt your healing process. Your family, friends and those close to you would not want you to feel this way. Your energy will be far better spent in a more useful healing direction. Let's kick the guilt out of the door now!

Work through the following Set Up Statements and Sequences, taking a SUDS rating on the scale of 0 – 10 for each one, and using persistence to root out any remaining guilt, or blaming thoughts, you may have about the effects of your diagnosis.

Keep testing yourself as you work, noticing how the Set Up Statements sound after a couple of rounds, do they have any intensity or do they sound like any other statement now, just a collection of words with no particular relevance anymore? When you reach that point where what you are saying is factual, such as in the Statement below, but has no charge, move on to the following one.

Repeat 3 times while tapping the Karate Chop:

Even though this cancer will disrupt all our lives I deeply and completely love and accept myself

Eyebrow:	*Disruption guilt*
Side of Eye:	*Disruption guilt*
Under Eye:	*Disrupting everyone's lives*
Under Nose:	*This guilt at changing the status quo*
Chin:	*Disruption guilt*
Collar Bone:	*Disruption guilt*
Under Arm:	*Disrupting every one's lives*
Top of Head:	*This guilt at changing the status quo*

Repeat 3 times while tapping the Karate Chop:

Even though things are going to change for us I deeply and completely love and accept myself

Eyebrow:	*Guilt at creating change*
Side of Eye:	*Guilt at the changes*
Under Eye:	*Guilt at creating these changes*
Under Nose:	*Guilt at the upset*
Chin:	*This change upset*
Collar Bone:	*This guilt at changing their lives*
Under Arm:	*This remaining guilt*
Top of Head:	*This remaining guilt*

Clare's story

*Clare had received her breast cancer diagnosis about a week before she, her husband and their three small children were due to go on holiday as a family. Her immediate response was "I will deal with this when I get back from holiday", but her oncologist was absolutely adamant that she needed to get into hospital there and then to have a lumpectomy immediately followed by chemotherapy. She was feeling incredibly guilty. Her family had been looking forward to their annual summer holiday, they always went to the same place, saw the same people, and it was **the** event of the family calendar. So we tapped on:*

(Please tap along...)

Repeat 3 times while tapping the Karate Chop:

Even though I feel guilty I deeply and completely love and accept myself

Eyebrow:	*This guilt*
Side of Eye:	*This guilt*
Under Eye:	*This guilt*
Under Nose:	*This guilt*
Under Nose:	*This guilt*
Chin:	*This guilt*
Collar Bone:	*This guilt*
Under Arm:	*This guilt*
Top of Head:	*This guilt*

Repeat 3 times while tapping the Karate Chop:

Even though I have ruined their holiday I deeply and completely love and accept myself

Eyebrow:	*This guilt*
Side of Eye:	*I've ruined their holiday*
Under Eye:	*It's all my fault*
Under Nose:	*This holiday guilt*
Chin:	*This guilt*
Collar Bone:	*I've ruined their holiday*
Under Arm:	*It's all my fault*
Top of Head:	*This holiday guilt*

Repeat 3 times while tapping the Karate Chop:

Even though I should just go on holiday I deeply and completely love and accept myself

Eyebrow:	*I should just go*
Side of Eye:	*I ought to go anyway*
Under Eye:	*I should just go*
Under Nose:	*I ought to go anyway*
Chin:	*I should just go*
Collar Bone:	*I ought to go anyway*
Under Arm:	*I should just go*
Top of Head:	*I ought to go anyway*

Repeat 3 times while tapping the Karate Chop:

Even though the holiday is more important than my health I deeply and completely love and accept myself

Eyebrow:	*The holiday is more important than my health*
Side of Eye:	*That thought*
Under Eye:	*The holiday is more important than me*
Under Nose:	*That powerful thought*
Chin:	*The holiday is more important than my health*
Collar Bone:	*That thought*
Under Arm:	*The holiday is more important than me*
Top of Head:	*That powerful thought*

Continue:

Eyebrow:	*I am open to the possibility that I have made a mistake*
Side of Eye:	*I am open to the possibility that my health is more important than a holiday*
Under Eye:	*I am open to that possibility*
Under Nose:	*Maybe*
Chin:	*I am open to the possibility that my health is more important than a holiday*
Under Arm:	*I am open to that possibility*
Top of Head:	*Maybe*

Repeat 3 times while tapping the Karate Chop:

Even though I am being a bad mother I deeply and completely love and accept myself

Eyebrow:	*I'm a bad mother*
Side of Eye:	*Feeling like a bad mother*
Under Eye:	*Stopping their fun*
Under Eye:	*I'm a bad mother*
Under Nose:	*I'm a bad mother*
Chin:	*Feeling like a bad mother*
Collar Bone:	*Stopping their fun*
Under Arm:	*I'm a bad mother*
Top of Head:	*I'm a bad mother*

Continue:

Eyebrow:	*No I'm not*
Side of Eye:	*I am a bad mother*
Under Eye:	*No I'm not*
Under Nose:	*I am a bad mother*
Chin:	*I am open to the possibility that a bad mother would put her health at risk*
Collar Bone:	*I am open to the possibility that I can be a good mother*
Under Arm:	*I am open to the possibility that I can have immediate treatment*
Top of Head:	*And be a good mother*

All the different aspects of this came up and we tapped through each thought systematically. Eventually, Clare was able to see that, logically, it would be a 'bad' mother to allow the cancer to spread for the sake of a holiday and that maybe, just maybe, her children would forgive her in years to come for missing one summer holiday but for being around for the next however many years, rather than taking the risk of delaying treatment, which could be life threatening.

Fear of Needing/Asking for Support

'The I in illness is isolation, and the crucial letters in wellness are we.'
Author unknown, as quoted in Mimi Guarneri, The Heart Speaks: A Cardiologist Reveals the Secret Language of Healing

A cancer diagnosis is likely to be a shock for your loved ones too, and whilst it is natural to worry about them and how they will cope and to want to support them, all of which is entirely reasonable, at this point this is about you, and your healing.

It is *ALL* about you! It has to be, for you and for them. Humans are very resourceful and you are doing your spouse/ family/ friends a disservice by doubting their abilities to cope. They may find it hard, which is why I have devoted a chapter in this book to them, but in the majority of cases they will step up to the proverbial plate, and support you willingly and naturally. Often, especially when it is the stronger member of the group with the diagnosis, it offers the more dependent parties the opportunity to grow and strengthen too.

Charles' story

Charles, an accountant, was very anxious about his wife's ability to cope with his pancreatic cancer diagnosis. He had protected her from all the tests, describing her as fragile and a worrier. Finally, he had to be honest with her as he needed a spell in hospital. To his surprise, this apparent wallflower blossomed before his eyes into a strong, resourceful woman, able to support him in many unexpected ways, even learning to drive and passing her test in order to take him on his appointments!

Their marriage, and the traditional roles they had taken on, changed dramatically during that time. Charles' wife found her voice and Charles discovered that she was interesting and entertaining to be with. Their love reached new depths – all as the result of a cancer diagnosis!

Tapping Section: Tapping for needing support

Repeat 3 times while tapping the Karate Chop:

Even though they won't cope with me being ill I deeply and completely love and accept myself

Eyebrow:	*They won't cope*
Side of Eye:	*I have to hold it all together*
Under Eye:	*I can't ask for support*
Under Nose:	*I don't ever take support*
Chin:	*They won't cope*
Collar Bone:	*I have to hold it all together*
Under Arm:	*I can't ask for support*
Top of Head:	*I don't ever take support*

There are those amongst us for whom asking for support or needing anyone else is an intolerable concept. Pride prevents us from going there. It is not our role in the world. Maybe people come to you for support. Are you the carer? The one who is there for everyone else? Ask yourself how you feel when you consider needing support from others, even being physically or financially dependent on them for a while. How does that thought make you feel? Do you get a physical response to it? Where? What does it feel like? What sort of people, in your mind, need support?

If you are the sort of person who never asks for support you may feel embarrassed at the prospect of doing so. Perhaps you feel vulnerable and exposed in some way. Are you expecting to be judged for this? Or teased? If so, by whom? When has that happened before? What does it remind you of? Use EFT to clear the emotional intensity of any specific memories that arise, taking care to zoom into the piece with the highest charge each time.

The chances are that if you are experiencing intense resistance to the thought of asking for help or support you have other negative experiences contributing to it.

Repeat 3 times while tapping the Karate Chop:

Even though I feel guilty at putting X through this I deeply and completely love and accept myself

Eyebrow:	*This guilt*
Side of Eye:	*Guilt at putting X through this*
Under Eye:	*Guilt at his/her/their pain*
Under Nose:	*Guilt at being the cause*
Chin:	*This guilt*
Collar Bone:	*Putting X through this*
Under Arm:	*Pain guilt*
Top of Head:	*This guilt*

Repeat 3 times while tapping the Karate Chop:

Even though I don't know how to ask for support I deeply and completely love and accept myself

Eyebrow:	*I can't do it*
Side of Eye:	*It's too difficult*
Under Eye:	*I don't know how to*
Under Nose:	*I can't go there*
Chin:	*It feels too humiliating*
Collar Bone:	*I just can't do it*
Under Arm:	*I don't know where to begin*
Top of Head:	*It is too hard*

Continue:

Eyebrow:	*I can't do it*
Side of Eye:	*It is too hard*

Under Eye:	*I can't do it*
Under Nose:	*Yes I can*
Chin:	*No I can't*
Collar Bone:	*Yes I can*
Under Arm:	*I am open to the possibility that I can't ask for support now*
Top of Head:	*I am open to that possibility*

Are you open to that possibility? If no, continue tapping as above, if yes, continue as follows:

Repeat 3 times while tapping the Karate Chop:

Even though I don't know how to accept support I choose to enjoy allowing support into my life

Eyebrow:	*Remaining 'It's too difficult' emotions*
Side of Eye:	*Remaining 'I don't know how to' emotions*
Under Eye:	*Remaining 'It's too hard for me' emotions*
Under Nose:	*Remaining 'I don't know how to' feelings*
Chin:	*Remaining 'It's too difficult' emotions*
Collar Bone:	*Remaining 'I don't know how to' emotions*
Under Arm:	*Remaining 'It's too hard for me' emotions*
Top of Head:	*Remaining 'I don't know how to' feelings*

Continue:

Eyebrow:	*I choose for it to be surprisingly easy*
Side of Eye:	*I choose to enjoy accepting support*
Under Eye:	*I choose to allow support easily now*
Under Nose:	*I choose for it to be surprisingly easy*
Chin:	*I choose for it to be surprisingly easy*
Collar Bone:	*I choose to enjoy accepting support*
Under Arm:	*I choose to allow support easily now*
Top of Head:	*I choose for it to be surprisingly easy*

Continue:

Eyebrow:	*Remaining 'It's too difficult' emotions*
Side of Eye:	*I choose for it to be surprisingly easy*
Under Eye:	*Remaining 'I don't know how to' emotions*
Under Nose:	*I choose to enjoy accepting support*
Chin:	*Remaining 'It's too hard for me' emotions*
Collar Bone:	*I choose to allow support easily now*
Under Arm:	*Remaining 'I don't know how to feelings'*
Top of Head:	*I choose for it to be surprisingly easy for me*

Are you anxious about what people might say or think? Does it feel embarrassing? Can you really read their minds? How do you know? Are they judging you, or, in fact, is it you judging them?

Repeat 3 times while tapping the Karate Chop:

Even though I feel embarrassed to ask for support I deeply and completely love and accept myself

Eyebrow:	*This embarrassment*
Side of Eye:	*This embarrassment*
Under Eye:	*Embarrassment at that thought*
Under Nose:	*This embarrassment*
Chin:	*Feeling embarrassed*
Collar Bone:	*Feeling embarrassed at asking for support*
Under Arm:	*This embarrassment*
Top of Head:	*This embarrassment*

Repeat 3 times while tapping the Karate Chop:

Even though they will think I am X I deeply and completely love and accept myself

Eyebrow:	*Their judgment*
Side of Eye:	*Their words*
Under Eye:	*I know what they'll say*
Under Nose:	*Fear of their judgment*
Chin:	*Fear of being judged*
Collar Bone:	*I know what they'll think*
Under Arm:	*I know what they'll say*
Top of Head:	*This fear of being judged*

Louise's story
Louise, a psychotherapist who strongly identifies with the role of the carer and supporter, said the following when asked some of those questions:

'I am the one who is there for everyone else, people depend on me, I can't let them down. I just have to be here for them'.

In that one sentence, she gave me enough information for months of therapy, but in a nutshell what she was saying was, on the surface, that she was too important to take time off, or to let go of this role, yet underneath that she had very low self worth. She had created a world for herself where she developed being needed (not healthy in any context, but especially not in therapy) and she was so attached to that identity of the carer that she was prepared to ignore a potentially life threatening diagnosis so as not to let her client base down. When challenged as to how helpful it would be to them were she to die from lack of treatment she was able to laugh at herself and see how dangerous her behaviour was to her. Apart from the neatly concealed arrogance (I have her permission to use that word) about her vital role in her clients' lives, along with the very genuine belief that they would not survive without her, she was putting herself at very serious risk.

How do you see yourself? Are you indispensible to your family/ work/ volunteer organizations? Do you think everything will collapse if you take time out? Is it OK to take time for yourself?

Repeat 3 times while tapping the Karate Chop:

Even though I'm letting them down I deeply and completely love and accept myself

Eyebrow:	*Fear of letting them down*
Side of Eye:	*I can't let them down*
Under Eye:	*They are more important than me*
Under Nose:	*They won't manage without me*
Chin:	*Fear of letting them down*
Collar Bone:	*I can't let them down*
Under Arm:	*They are more important than me*
Top of Head:	*They won't manage without me*

Repeat 3 times while tapping the Karate Chop:

Even though I'm indispensible I deeply and completely love and accept myself

Eyebrow:	*Feeling indispensible*
Side of Eye:	*They need me*
Under Eye:	*I can't not be there for them*
Under Nose:	*I have to look after them*

Chin:	*I can't take time out*
Collar Bone:	*I have to be there for them*
Under Arm:	*They need me*
Top of Head:	*I can't let them down*

Continue:

Eyebrow:	*I'm open to the possibility that they might want me to heal*
Side of Eye:	*I may be more useful to them healthy*
Under Eye:	*I'm open to the possibility that they will understand*
Under Nose:	*I need to look after me now*
Chin:	*It is OK to look after me now*
Collar Bone:	*I deserve to put me first*
Under Arm:	*I choose to look after me*
Top of Head:	*I choose to focus on my healing in whatever way I need to*

Ask yourself, in your world, what sort of people need support? What judgments are you making?

Repeat 3 times while tapping the Karate Chop:

Even though only weak (or any similar judgment) people need support I deeply and completely love and accept myself

Eyebrow:	*I can't ask for support*
Side of Eye:	*It is not OK to need support*
Under Eye:	*Only weak people need support (or any similar belief)*
Under Nose:	*I can't accept support*
Chin:	*I can't ask for support*
Collar Bone:	*It is not OK to need support*
Under Arm:	*Only weak people need support (or any similar belief)*
Top of Head:	*I can't accept support*

Keep going until that judgment/belief begins to sound ridiculous to you, when it no longer holds any truth for you.

Fear of Loss of Independence

127

'No man is an island, entire of itself; every man is a piece of the continent.'
John Donne

For some people, especially the head of the household or the main breadwinner, the concept of needing anyone or anything can be terrifying. The very real fear of losing your independence can be intense, perhaps you won't be able to get around on your own for a while, perhaps you will have to give up your hard earned freedom. Your very identity is being challenged, how you see yourself and how others see you, and in turn relate to you. What does being dependent mean to you?

Geoff's story

For Geoff the most frightening part of his cancer diagnosis was the possibility of needing to depend on others for a while. He was really scared of relying on anyone other than himself, he wanted to get through his treatment on his own, and would not even let his partner come with him to consultant appointments. He needed to feel in control the entire time, he insisted on driving himself to and from hospital, despite considerable pain. He said he didn't want to have to rely on anyone ever. Whilst in essence this was OK, it was causing ructions at home as his partner wanted to be involved in his treatment plan.

When we began to explore this terror of dependency it became clear that every time Geoff had ever allowed himself to rely on anyone it had ended in disaster for him. He had lost a successful business when he took on a new partner in an attempt to expand, he had been betrayed and let down in romantic relationships. He felt vulnerable and at risk whenever he let his guard down and relied on anyone for anything important. He was totally self -reliant and always had been. So I asked him about his childhood, babies have to rely on others to survive, when had he learnt that he always had to be in control?

Geoff had had an alcoholic mother who was both violent and unpredictable. He had spent years being starved and abused before he was taken into care. He spent 4 years in care, moving from home to home. It felt as though every time he settled or began to feel safe he was uprooted and placed somewhere else, sometimes in a new area altogether and he would have to start again. There was no constancy in Geoff's world apart from himself. Unsurprisingly, he needed to be in control of his environment at all times, and was terrified of the vulnerability of true emotional or physical intimacy. No one got really close to him, and he never depended on or needed anyone.

Tapping Section: Tapping for losing independence

Repeat 3 times while tapping the Karate Chop:

Even though I am terrified of becoming dependent on X I deeply and completely love and accept myself

Eyebrow:	*Fear of being dependent on X*
Side of Eye:	*Fear of losing control*
Under Eye:	*Fear of being dependent on others*
Under Nose:	*This fear*
Chin:	*This strong fear*

Collar Bone:	*Fear of being dependent*
Under Arm:	*Fear of losing control*
Top of Head:	*This fear*

Using the Movie Technique we then worked through about 7 mini movies that were supporting Geoff's fears, the majority of which were around his childhood experiences. When we had cleared the intensity on these I tested our work by asking him how he felt about being dependent on others now. He felt much better, but there will still some charge there so we continued:

Repeat 3 times while tapping the Karate Chop:

Even though it's still not safe to rely on others I deeply and completely love and accept myself

Eyebrow:	*Remaining 'It isn't safe' emotions*
Side of Eye:	*Remaining fears*
Under Eye:	*Remaining 'Everyone lets me down' emotions*
Under Nose:	*Remaining 'It isn't safe to depend on others' emotions*
Chin:	*Remaining fear of being vulnerable*
Collar Bone:	*Remaining 'It isn't safe' emotions*
Under Arm:	*Remaining fear of being vulnerable*
Top of Head:	*Remaining 'Everyone lets me down' emotions*

I checked in with Geoff again and he said he could see the benefits of sharing the burden of his treatment but was still not sure he could actually do it. So we continued:

Eyebrow:	*I can't do it*
Side of Eye:	*I can't accept support*
Under Eye:	*Maybe*
Under Nose:	*What if I can?*
Chin:	*What if it is OK?*
Collar Bone:	*No, I can't do it*
Under Arm:	*Maybe*
Top of Head:	*What if it really is OK?*

Continue:

Eyebrow:	*I am open to the possibility that I can accept support now*

Side of Eye:	*I am open to the possibility that I can do it*
Under Eye:	*I am open to the possibility that it's safe to be supported*
Under Nose:	*I deserve to be supported through this*
Chin:	*What if it could be fun?*
Collar Bone:	*No, that is not possible*
Under Arm:	*Yes it is*
Top of Head:	*I really am open to that possibility*

Checking in with Geoff again he was smiling and said he might be prepared to give it a try, but only in very small steps. He realised that as an adult he could choose what help or support he could allow into his life safely now and maybe this was a good moment to begin trusting again. This was a huge step for him, and it is likely that he would meet further fears as he began making these changes. However, knowing how to tap with them was very reassuring to him... He knew he could depend on himself to work with any fears or anxieties that emerged after the session... ultimately he was still in charge!

So, back to you...

When you honestly feel OK about taking support, and all those old judgments vanished, continue as follows:

Eyebrow:	*I choose to effortlessly accept being supported on this journey*
Side of Eye:	*I choose to enjoy loving support easily*
Under Eye:	*I choose to allow loving support into my life now*
Under Nose:	*It is safe for me*
Chin:	*I choose to effortless enjoy being supported on this journey*
Collar Bone:	*I choose to enjoy loving support easily*
Under Arm:	*I choose to allow loving support into my life now*
Top of Head:	*It is safe for me*

Continue:

Eyebrow:	*This remaining resistance*
Side of Eye:	*I choose gratitude instead of this*
Under Eye:	*This remaining resistance*

Under Nose:	*I choose gratitude instead of this*
Chin:	*This remaining resistance*
Collar Bone:	*I choose gratitude instead of this*
Under Arm:	*This remaining resistance*
Top of Head:	*I choose gratitude instead of this*

Responsibility

> *'It's a question of discipline,' the little prince told me later on. 'When you've finished washing and dressing each morning, you must tend your planet.'*
> Antoine de Saint-Exupéry, The Little Prince

This section is about taking responsibility for your own healing and working through any conscious or unconscious blocks, physical or emotional, which may be preventing you experiencing optimum health, whatever those two words mean to you. Clearly something is in conflict in your world to present as this dis-ease, and that needs your attention. Your only responsibility now is to find and resolve that conflict and gain a sense of inner peace. But taking responsibility is not the same as feeling guilty, one is pro active, the other limiting at best. Taking personal responsibility for your healing may be the most empowering and exciting thing you ever do.

What do I mean by taking responsibility? The very word responsibility may bring up negativity for some of you. It may take you back to school, or perhaps some other memory or memories. It is a word that is bandied about randomly, usually when you have done something wrong, or somebody wants something from you that you do not want to give them. Who do you think of when you hear that word? Does taking responsibility sound like hard work to you?

If you have a negative response to the word, tap on it as follows shortly. You are looking towards a positive, empowered response to it. Accepting responsibility for your own healing path, whichever direction you may choose, puts you in a new and exciting place where there are possibilities and options. Rescinding responsibility to others to heal you is de-energising and disempowering.

This is your dis-ease, and no one, not the doctors, not the therapists, certainly not me, has the ability to heal you. We can offer you the best treatments and tools to support your journey, which will certainly help, but the true healing comes from inside... Remember, in-curable means curable from within. When you step into your power in this way, the journey may become rewarding, even an adventure.

Read through the following tapping protocols and choose the ones that are appropriate for you. It may be that you uncover some specific memories of times when you have been given responsibility and it hasn't been a positive experience, or of other people who have been given responsibility over you and have abused that role somehow.

When you hear the word 'responsibility' who pops into your head. How does that person make you feel? What does he/she mean to you?

If any such memories appear during your tapping, make a note of them, and return to them using the Movie Technique. However irrelevant they may seem to you, trust that they have been offered by your unconscious mind for a purpose.

Repeat 3 times while tapping the Karate Chop:

Even though I hate (or other emotion) that word I deeply and completely love and accept myself

Eyebrow:	*That word*
Side of Eye:	*And everything it means to me*
Under Eye:	*The feelings it gives me*
Under Nose:	*The negativity I am giving it*
Chin:	*And everything it means to me*
Collar Bone:	*The feelings it gives me*
Under Arm:	*The negativity I am giving it*
Top of Head:	*That word*

Josie's story

Josie, who has uterine cancer, told me that as a child she and her siblings were all given 'responsibilities' around the house, they each had their own specific housework roles, and this was set in stone. She remembered how she had longed to have her own 'responsibility' like her elder siblings, and how she was so excited when, on her seventh birthday, one of her 'gifts' was to take responsibility for sorting out the clean laundry and delivering each family member their own clothes. She came from a large family and this task was required almost daily.

One day, she unpegged the laundry from the washing line as usual and was walking back to the house when she lost her balance on the grass and the pile of washing fell into a flower bed. She remembered this event with total terror, even now, thirty or so years later. She had picked up all the washing, but a few things had got mud on them, including her elder sister's new designer jeans. When she got back to the house she compared it to walking into a kangaroo court, where she had been found guilty, tried and convicted in absentia. She remembered the utter humiliation of having her 'responsibility' removed from her, and being told she was obviously too small to be helpful.

Now to the adult reading this it may sound trivial, to still remember such a minor incident. Perhaps you are feeling compassion for the little 7 year old, perhaps you feel sad she had to go through that. But perhaps you are also thinking what does this have to do with anything. I will tell you.

The outcome of this experience was twofold:

1. Josie developed a fear of responsibility and a very entrenched belief that she was incapable of being responsible. This had resulted in holding her back from promotion at work as she couldn't bear the thought of doing anything too important. She KNEW she would fail.

2. She was extremely overweight. She had made a decision at that point that it was not safe to be little, and her unconscious mind had taken that

132

instruction on board literally. No matter how hard she tried, she could not reduce her weight.

Her life was extremely limiting. She was living it according to the beliefs of a small child, it was not safe to take responsibility, or to be 'small'. Interestingly, her cancer prevented her from having her own children and the responsibility that entails.

Is taking responsibility safe for you? If not, why not?

Having worked through this specific event, and the myriad of beliefs that had been formed at that time, over a period of weeks Josie gradually began to lose the excess weight. At the same time, she took charge of both her healing process and her life.

Now she weighs the perfect weight for her, she is free of cancer, and she is living a healthy happy life with a new partner. All seemingly from clearing this one specific event... It makes you think, does it not?

So, back to you, what is your honest reaction to that word, and where did you learn that?

Dread is a word commonly associated with responsibility. When have you felt like that before?

Tapping Section: Tapping for taking responsibility

Repeat 3 times while tapping the Karate Chop:

Even though taking responsibility fills me with dread (or other emotion) I deeply and completely love and accept myself anyway

Eyebrow:	*Responsibility*
Side of Eye:	*This dread*
Under Eye:	*Responsibility*
Under Nose:	*I can't do it*
Chin:	*This huge responsibility*
Collar Bone:	*It feels overwhelming*
Under Arm:	*Responsibility*
Top of Head:	*This sense of dread*

Repeat 3 times while tapping the Karate Chop:

Even though I am terrified by the thought of taking responsibility I deeply and completely love and accept myself anyway

Eyebrow:	*This terror*
Side of Eye:	*This terror of taking responsibility*
Under Eye:	*I can't do it*

Under Nose:	*It is too much*
Chin:	*What if I fail?*
Collar Bone:	*What if I succeed?*
Under Arm:	*No, I just can't do it*
Top of Head:	*This terror of taking responsibility*

The concept of taking responsibility for your healing may well feel overwhelming right now, and that is OK and understandable. You may also feel like you are on your own with this responsibility. Dealing with a serious disease can often feel lonely and solitary.

This is one of the many reasons why the Breast Cancer Haven, and other similar organisations are so valuable. In these safe and calm oases, which are available in various forms throughout the world, you get a chance to meet other people in similar situations. The power of the group is very important to any human being, we are not born to be alone, and most of us need to connect with others to thrive. We need to belong. Cancer support groups provide this.

Caroline Myss speaks of the concept of 'woundology' and this is a very important point. Woundology is when a group forms with a particular problem in common; in this case cancer. The natural temptation of many people, unconsciously, is to have the most dramatic story, or to talk about the negatives. This is human nature. How many horrific birthing stories have you heard? How many beautiful ones? The majority of births are wonderful, bonding, miraculous events yet we, as human beings, naturally seem to give the power to the negative.

I would highly recommend meeting other people experiencing the same journey as you, but take care to pay good attention to the stories you hear, and to tap away any negative ones immediately to clear their potential impact. People don't do this mischievously or to intentionally create harm, but it is important to release any emotional response at once. Perhaps you could teach them how to tap too!

Back to the 'burden of responsibility' – ever heard that expression before? Is it a truth for you? If so, challenge it now.

Repeat 3 times while tapping the Karate Chop:

Even though it is all down to me and that feels X I deeply and completely love and accept myself

Eyebrow:	*It is all down to me*
Side of Eye:	*I have to heal myself*
Under Eye:	*It is all down to me*
Under Nose:	*This terrifying burden*
Chin:	*I want someone else to do it*
Collar Bone:	*I don't want to be responsible*
Under Arm:	*This heavy burden*

134

Top of Head:	*Responsibility*

It may be that the very concept of taking responsibility is too much to handle. And that would also be very understandable, you have a lot to deal with when diagnosed with cancer. However, you will deal with it far more easily from a more powerful place, so keep tapping as follows:

Repeat 3 times while tapping the Karate Chop:

Even though I don't want to be responsible I deeply and completely love and accept myself

Eyebrow:	*I don't want this responsibility*
Side of Eye:	*I have enough to deal with*
Under Eye:	*It is too big*
Under Nose:	*Too difficult*
Chin:	*I can't do it*
Collar Bone:	*I don't want this responsibility*
Under Arm:	*I can't handle it*
Top of Head:	*It is all too much*

Perhaps it is as simple as just not wanting to take on that responsibility. Tap on whatever you feel, and say it as it is. By clearing your response to the concept of responsibility you will put yourself in a place where you have a choice whether to take it or not. Right now you do not have that freedom and you deserve to have it.

My colleague, Carol Look, gets people to tap on 'refusing' to do whatever it is they ultimately want and it is very effective. Try it out on yourself as follows, it often brings humour into the situation and humour is incredibly liberating.

Repeat 3 times while tapping the Karate Chop:

Even though I don't want to be responsible I deeply and completely love and accept myself

Eyebrow:	*I don't want this responsibility*
Side of Eye:	*I have enough to deal with*
Under Eye:	*It is too big*
Under Nose:	*Too difficult*
Chin:	*I can't do it*
Collar Bone:	*I don't want this responsibility*
Under Arm:	*I can't handle it*
Top of Head:	*It is all too much*

Repeat 3 times while tapping the Karate Chop:

Even though I refuse to take responsibility for this I deeply and completely love and accept myself

Eyebrow:	*I refuse to take this responsibility*
Side of Eye:	*I won't do it*
Under Eye:	*You can't make me*
Under Nose:	*I refuse to do it*
Chin:	*I am not going to do it*
Collar Bone:	*You can't make me*
Under Arm:	*I refuse*
Top of Head:	*I just won't*

Are you laughing yet? Give it some volume, stamp your foot, shout! How old are you?

Tiredness/Exhaustion

> *'Laughter and tears are both responses to frustration and exhaustion.*
> *I myself prefer to laugh, since there is less cleaning up to do afterward.'*
> *Kurt Vonnegut*

You may be feeling too tired to take on anything more, and once again, this is understandable, you are dealing with a major shock and all your energy has gone into keeping you functioning. Anything extra can seem impossible. However, as you continue tapping you will find that you develop a more healthy tiredness, your sleeping patterns improve and you will become more energised during the day, even during treatments such as chemotherapy.

And that process is beginning now. You have already begun to release the shock and trauma of diagnosis from your body, and will continue to do this more specifically in the next chapter. The message here is please keep tapping, it will help you strengthen and feel better, even if you feel you are too exhausted right now.

If you have read this far you are doing amazingly, although you may not realise quite how amazing you are, yet!

Again, using the SUDS scale of 0 – 10, just how tired are you? Are you more tired than you could have imagined? Are you physically tired alongside the emotional exhaustion?

Tapping Section: Tapping for tiredness /exhaustion

Repeat 3 times while tapping the Karate Chop:

Even though I am too tired to take this on I deeply and completely love and accept myself anyway

136

Eyebrow:	*I'm too tired*
Side of Eye:	*I can't do it*
Under Eye:	*It feels too much*
Under Nose:	*I am so exhausted*
Chin:	*I'm too tired*
Collar Bone:	*I can't do it*
Under Arm:	*It feels too much*
Top of Head:	*I am so exhausted*

Now check in with your body and your mind and see what has happened. Has the tiredness reduced? Maybe the quality has changed? Tiredness manifests in many different ways. Is it an aching tiredness, a heavy tiredness, a sickening tiredness? Adapt your tapping protocol accordingly and continue tapping until you reach a place where the tiredness, whilst possibly still there, feels healthy and then allow yourself to lie down and enjoy a well deserved rest, no matter what time of day it is.

Rebalancing your energy system is tiring work, allow yourself the chance to rest and congratulate yourself on the work you have done so far. Listen to your body and what it is telling you, and then follow its instructions. If you want to lie down, lie down. If you feel like a long hot bath, have one. Your body knows what it needs, now is the time to really listen to it.

Self Blame

> *'The weak can never forgive. Forgiveness is the attribute of the strong.'*
> *Mahatma Gandhi*

All too often clients will make statements of blame:

- **It is my fault**
- **I deserve this**
- **I am a bad person**
- **It must be my lifestyle**

And many other shoulds and oughts

- **I shouldn't have drunk alcohol**
- **I should have looked after myself better**
- **I should have stopped smoking**
- **I should have exercised more**

And so on......

Yes, possibly some of those latter statements may be truths, and contributory, but they are not the full picture. Blaming yourself is an attempt at making sense of cancer, an attempt to take some control over it, to reason with it. This is an impossible demand, you cannot make complete sense of a cancer diagnosis, you can second guess, you may even have reasonable contributory factors such as smoking and other lifestyle issues, but even that does not explain why one person will get the disease and another, with similar conditions, will not.

My 16 year daughter, a young adult with an old soul and infinite wisdom said the following to me this week, when I was upset about a friend's diagnosis.

'The devil sneezes and cancer scatters around the world'

I love her words, they seem to sum up very simply the seeming randomness of a cancer diagnosis. They allow us to let go of the 'why me's, the need for answers... often there are none. Where there are practical life style issues to be resolved that will be part of it, but even then, not necessarily the whole picture.

- **What are you saying to yourself?**
- **Are you blaming yourself?**
- **Do you feel the cancer is some form of punishment you have somehow attracted to you?**

Tapping Section: Tapping for self blame

Repeat 3 times while tapping the Karate Chop:

Even though it's all my fault I deeply and completely love and accept myself

Eyebrow:	*It's all my fault*
Side of Eye:	*This blame*
Under Eye:	*It's my fault*
Under Nose:	*This blame*
Chin:	*It's all my fault*
Collar Bone:	*This blame*
Under Arm:	*It's my fault*
Top of Head:	*This blame*

Repeat 3 times while tapping the Karate Chop:

Even though I should have X I deeply and completely love and accept myself

Eyebrow:	*I should have X*
Side of Eye:	*I should have X*
Under Eye:	*It's all my fault*
Under Nose:	*I should have X*

Chin:	*I should have X*
Collar Bone:	*I should have X*
Under Arm:	*It's all my fault*
Top of Head:	*I should have X*

OR:

Repeat 3 times while tapping the Karate Chop:

Even though I should not have X I deeply and completely love and accept myself

Eyebrow:	*I shouldn't have X*
Side of Eye:	*I shouldn't have X*
Under Eye:	*It's all my fault*
Under Nose:	*I shouldn't have X*
Chin:	*I shouldn't have X*
Collar Bone:	*I shouldn't have X*
Under Arm:	*It's all my fault*
Top of Head:	*I shouldn't have X*

> *'You should listen to your heart, and not the voices in your head.'*
> *Marge Simpson*

Paula's story

Paula had stomach cancer. She had had surgery and chemotherapy and was waiting to find out the results from the treatment. Whilst she was happy to have completed those hurdles she was unable to let go of her self judgments about having cancer in the first place. She had this voice inside her head continually nagging at her, telling her it as all her fault, she was bad, she deserved to be sick, and more. We started work just there doing a few rounds on:

Repeat 3 times while tapping the Karate Chop:

Even though I have this voice I deeply and completely love and accept myself

Eyebrow:	*This voice*
Side of Eye:	*This voice*
Under Eye:	*This familiar voice*
Under Nose:	*This voice*
Chin:	*Everything it says*
Collar Bone:	*This voice inside me*

| Under Arm: | This voice |
| Top of Head: | This voice |

Repeat 3 times while tapping the Karate Chop:

Even though I can't stop this nagging voice I deeply and completely love and accept myself

Eyebrow:	This nagging voice
Side of Eye:	I can't stop it
Under Eye:	It won't go
Under Nose:	This nagging voice
Chin:	Getting to me
Collar Bone:	I can't stop it
Under Arm:	Maybe
Top of Head:	What if I can

Then I asked Paula whose voice it was, and she said 'It's my grandmother, I never did anything right for her and she went on and on at me'. Her grandmother had lived with her family when she was a child but had died many years ago. So we continued tapping:

Repeat 3 times while tapping the Karate Chop:

Even though I am still listening to Nan, and she is not even here anymore, I deeply and completely love and accept myself

Eyebrow:	Nan
Side of Eye:	Listening to Nan
Under Eye:	Nan's nagging
Under Nose:	Nan's voice
Chin:	Nan
Collar Bone:	Listening to Nan
Under Arm:	Nan's nagging
Top of Head:	Nan's voice

Continue:

Eyebrow:	Her voice
Side of Eye:	Still getting to me
Under Eye:	Her voice

Under Nose:	Still nagging
Chin:	I am open to the possibility I can let Nan go now
Collar Bone:	I am open to the possibility that it is safe to let her go now
Under Arm:	I am open to the possibility she would want me to let her go now
Top of Head:	I choose to let Nan go now

Repeat 3 times while tapping the Karate Chop:

Even though I am not sure I can let this voice go I deeply and completely love and accept myself and I love and accept Nan too

Eyebrow:	Not sure I can let her go
Side of Eye:	Not sure I can let her go
Under Eye:	Maybe I can
Under Nose:	Not sure
Chin:	I am open to the possibility I can love and accept Nan
Collar Bone:	Maybe
Under Arm:	I am open to the possibility she wouldn't want me to be feeling like this
Top of Head:	I love and accept myself, and I choose to let Nan go now

Then I asked Paula to tune into the voice again and see what happened. She looked surprised and started to cry very softly. I tapped on her fingers silently until she felt able to speak. She said the volume and tone of the voice had changed, as had the content, and she had a very clear image now of her grandmother talking to her. I asked what she was saying and she said she was asking for forgiveness and saying she had never meant to hurt Paula, that she had been old and ill and tired, but that she had always loved her very much. She said how sad she was that Paula was going through such a difficult time and that she was there for her.

I asked Paula how, by hearing this, had those old thoughts of self blame and I am bad changed? What had happened to them? She said she had spent her whole life thinking she wasn't good enough, and whilst it felt strange, maybe she could begin to allow the thought that she had made a mistake and that actually she was OK exactly as she was, and always had been.

Perfection

'Ring the bells that still can ring
Forget your perfect offering.

There is a crack in everything,
That's how the light gets in.'
Leonard Cohen

Having to be perfect is a very common backdrop to many people's lives. But what is perfection? Is anyone perfect? And if so, do you want to be like them? Striving for perfection is an exhausting and thankless task. If there were such a thing, and you were to achieve it, then there is only one direction to go in from that pedestal of perfection – down! The pressure of trying to be the 'perfect person', be that wife, husband, father, mother, lover, sibling, boss, employee and even patient expends an enormous amount of energy which would be far better spent elsewhere, focussing on your healing.

Whilst most people will not admit that they have this belief – recognising that the belief itself is imperfect, it is worth checking out whether the above resonates with you and working to release it.

Very often, the need to be perfect develops from early childhood. Usually parents or teachers install this belief unintentionally. Many a small child has learnt *"If I don't get everything right I'm going to get into trouble'.*

Suzy's story
Suzy had paralyzing problems with perfection. She couldn't understand where her terror of criticism came from but it was running her life. To her, getting anything wrong felt totally life threatening and it made no sense. She said she had had a happy childhood. There were no particular memories that came to mind, nothing that seemed to support this belief which seemed to be controlling her life, so we did a bit of tapping around that.

Please tap along:

Tapping Section: Tapping for fear of criticism

Repeat 3 times while tapping the Karate Chop:

Even though I am terrified of criticism I deeply and completely love and accept myself

Eyebrow:	*Terror of criticism*
Side of Eye:	*Terror of criticism*
Under Eye:	*Terror of criticism*
Under Nose:	*Terror of criticism*
Chin:	*Terror of criticism*
Collar Bone:	*Terror of criticism*
Under Arm:	*Terror of criticism*
Top of Head:	*Terror of criticism*

Repeat 3 times while tapping the Karate Chop:

Even though I've got no idea where this has come from I deeply and completely love and accept myself

Eyebrow:	*I don't understand*
Side of Eye:	*I don't know where this has come from*
Under Eye:	*I don't get it*
Under Nose:	*I just don't understand*
Chin:	*I don't understand*
Collar Bone:	*I don't know where this has come from*
Under Arm:	*I don't get it*
Top of Head:	*I just don't understand*

Repeat 3 times while tapping the Karate Chop:

Even though criticism feels dangerous to me I deeply and completely love and accept myself

Eyebrow:	*Criticism*
Side of Eye:	*Feels so dangerous*
Under Eye:	*Fear of being criticized*
Under Nose:	*Fear of doing something wrong*
Chin:	*Criticism*
Collar Bone:	*Feels so dangerous*
Under Arm:	*Fear of being criticized*
Top of Head:	*Fear of doing something wrong*

Suddenly Suzy got a memory of being a small child, probably about 7 years old, at school in a maths class. She had been asked to stand up and recite her 2 times table. She had been one of the first in the class to learn the table and the teacher had been very proud of her. She had been very excited and had stood up and recited it in front of the class. She got it wrong and everybody laughed. The teacher made her stand up on a chair and keep trying until she got it right. The more she recited it, the more of a muddle she got into and the more mistakes she was making. The teacher was getting more and more angry and her classmates were giggling at her. She felt humiliated and embarrassed.

From that point onwards, Suzy vowed never to make a mistake. She was academically highly successful, she passed everything with flying colours. She worked extremely hard. Now she had a high-flying job in the City. She was married with children who were immaculately dressed and beautifully behaved. But she was not happy, she was exhausted and she couldn't understand why.

Part of her wanted her children to just go out and get muddy, but when they came back in a muddy dirty state, she used to panic. Logically, she knew it was irrational and she really wanted to work on understanding and changing this, especially because now, with a diagnosis of breast cancer, she wasn't going to be in the place where she would have the time or the energy to ensure this kind of perfection; perfection around the house, everything in the right place, everybody doing the right thing. She realized that the immaculate lifestyle she had been keeping on behalf of everyone was not going to be viable when she was undergoing chemotherapy and radiotherapy. She just wouldn't have the time or the energy, and she was already feeling a failure. We began with the 2x table memory, using the Movie Technique:

Repeat 3 times while tapping the Karate Chop:

Even though I have these 2 times table emotions I deeply and completely love and accept myself

Eyebrow:	*2 times table emotions*
Side of Eye:	*2 times table emotions*
Under Eye:	*2 times table emotions*
Under Nose:	*2 times table emotions*
Chin:	*2 times table emotions*
Collar Bone:	*2 times table emotions*
Under Arm:	*2 times table emotions*
Top of Head:	*2 times table emotions*

As we tapped, she could feel the terror in her body. She was physically shaking when she tuned into that little girl standing on the chair having to recite and getting it wrong again and again. She couldn't remember the end of the story, but it didn't matter because her body was doing it for her.

Having cleared this and various other related memories that came up, all of which were school memories, Suzy was able to experience feeling compassion for the younger her, as well as compassion to the adult.

This allowed her to calm down and start to enjoy her life, even during treatment. She became more relaxed with her children, not getting quite so paranoid about what they looked like, how they were behaving, how well they were achieving at school. She reported that her whole family life seemed to have become easier and she was able to enjoy everybody's support around the treatment.

Now, at the end of her treatment and having been given the all clear, Suzy says her lifestyle is completely different. She feels far more relaxed, she has far more time for her family and she enjoys everything that she is doing in a whole new way. She sees the world through new eyes!

Whilst you have done fantastically if you have persevered and tapped your way through this chapter, cancer is an emotional rollercoaster and you may need to return to various protocols many times over in different situations. The next chapter is spent looking specifically at depression and ways in which you can positively affect your mood with the tapping. However, it should be noted that anyone suffering from depression, however mild, should always seek professional medical advice.

CHAPTER 8

DEPRESSION

'Dare to believe in miracles. Look beyond the mud on the windshield, beyond the impossible, and know life is more than anguish and stress. Reach out to someone, when your heart is too heavy to feel the sunlight or to taste the rain. Rid yourself of dark thought and melancholy. Open your mind to fresh air, to the unlimited music in your soul'
Joyce Sequichie Hifler

Is it normal to feel depressed with cancer?

The answer is yes and no, yes it is normal to feel sad and anxious and no, not everybody will feel the true symptoms of depression as listed below.

The symptoms of major depression include the following (The National Cancer Institute, www.cancer.gov):

- **Having a depressed mood for most of the day and on most days.**
- **Loss of pleasure and interest in most activities.**
- **Changes in eating and sleeping habits.**
- **Nervousness or sluggishness.**
- **Tiredness.**
- **Feelings of worthlessness or inappropriate guilt.**
- **Poor concentration.**
- **Constant thoughts of death or suicide.**

If the thought of feelings of sadness and/or anxiety resonates with you then apply the tapping to those emotional states. By tapping on them when they first present, it is often possible to pre-empt a downward slide into true depression.

Tapping Section: Tapping for sadness

Repeat 3 times while tapping the Karate Chop:

Even though I have this sadness I deeply and completely love and accept myself

Eyebrow:	*This sadness*
Side of Eye:	*This sadness*
Under Eye:	*This sadness*
Under Nose:	*This sadness*
Chin:	*This sadness*
Collar Bone:	*This sadness*

146

| Under Arm: | This sadness |
| Top of Head: | This sadness |

Repeat 3 times while tapping the Karate Chop:

Even though I feel really low I deeply and completely love and accept myself

Eyebrow:	Feeling low
Side of Eye:	Feeling really low
Under Eye:	Feeling low
Under Nose:	Feeling so low
Chin:	Feeling low
Collar Bone:	Feeling really low
Under Arm:	Feeling low
Top of Head:	Feeling so low

Repeat 3 times while tapping the Karate Chop:

Even though I feel down I deeply and completely love and accept myself

Eyebrow:	Feeling down
Side of Eye:	Feeling down
Under Eye:	Feeling down
Under Nose:	Feeling down
Chin:	Feeling down
Collar Bone:	Feeling down
Under Arm:	Feeling down
Top of Head:	Feeling down

Repeat 3 times while tapping the Karate Chop:

Even though I feel anxious I deeply and completely love and accept myself

Eyebrow:	Feeling anxious
Side of Eye:	Feeling anxious
Under Eye:	This anxiety
Under Nose:	This anxiety
Chin:	Feeling anxious
Collar Bone:	Feeling anxious

Under Arm:	*This anxiety*
Top of Head:	*This anxiety*

If you think you are suffering from depression in any form, the first step is to **consult your doctor**. With medium/severe depression it can be hard to work with the tapping until the depression lifts at least a little. Sometimes it is appropriate to take a short course of antidepressants to make a beginning and allow a window of opportunity to facilitate treatment. Whilst I am not advocating the use of antidepressants on a long term basis there are times when they can be useful to assist the process.

In the UK, antidepressants have a reputation for being handed out for anything, but there are many instances when they are not only useful but also essential. Dealing with cancer can be one of them. Surely a cancer diagnosis is enough without having to manage depression on top of it? if you think antidepressants might help you, see your doctor and get professional help.

Major depression affects about 25% of all cancer sufferers and can easily be diagnosed and treated. It is important to realise that sadness and grief are normal reactions to the diagnosis, and with EFT that should calm and pass through you relatively quickly. If you find that it doesn't and you are not getting any noticeable change in those feelings, or they are becoming more invasive, go to see your doctor and tell him/her what is going on for you honestly. No one needs depression on top of cancer.

The mass of men lead lives of quiet desperation.
Henry David Thoreau, Walden

The shame of depression
Sadly, for some there is still a stigma attached to the word 'depression', even in the 21st century. Depression is an illness of the mind, in the same way that a cold is an illness of the nose! It is a hormonal/chemical imbalance which, given the appropriate support, can be alleviated. The bottom line being, it is **JUST** an illness, I say JUST, because it often runs the danger of becoming an identity as in 'I am a depressive'. No you are not, you are a normal person, experiencing depression.

For some, depression is still considered something to be pushed under the carpet, not to be mentioned, not to be talked about, something to be ashamed of – absolutely not. It is what it is, and if you are suffering from depression you are suffering for very good reasons. It is not because there is something wrong with you, it is simply a response to your life experiences. If you do feel ashamed or concerned that you have depression but you can't talk about it to anybody tap as follows:

Tapping Section: Tapping for shame of depression

Repeat 3 times while tapping the Karate Chop:

Even though I am ashamed of being depressed I deeply and completely love and accept myself

Eyebrow:	*This depression shame*

Side of Eye:	*This humiliating depression shame*
Under Eye:	*This awful shame*
Under Nose:	*This depression shame*
Chin:	*This depression shame*
Collar Bone:	*This humiliating depression shame*
Under Arm:	*This awful shame*
Top of Head:	*This depression shame*

Repeat 3 times while tapping the Karate Chop:

Even though it is weak to be depressed I deeply and completely love and accept myself

Eyebrow:	*This weakness*
Side of Eye:	*This depression weakness*
Under Eye:	*This depression weakness*
Under Nose:	*I'm weak*
Chin:	*This weakness*
Collar Bone:	*This depression weakness*
Under Arm:	*This depression weakness*
Top of Head:	*I'm weak*

One of the things that can help alleviate depression enormously is being able to speak about your problems, to be able to talk to your family or your close friends, or a therapist, to express how you feel, and to work through things. This can help not just you, as the cancer patient, but also the rest of the family. If possible, it is worth bringing everything out into the open and discussing it. If this brings up any worries, tap as follows:

Repeat 3 times while tapping the Karate Chop:

Even though I can't talk to 'X' about how I feel I deeply and completely love and accept myself

Eyebrow:	*I can't talk to 'X'*
Side of Eye:	*It's not okay*
Under Eye:	*They will judge me*
Under Nose:	*I just can't talk about this*
Chin:	*I can't talk to 'X'*
Collar Bone:	*It's not okay*
Under Arm:	*They will judge me*

149

Top of Head:	*I just can't talk about this*

Repeat 3 times while tapping the Karate Chop:

Even though I want to hide from the world I deeply and completely love and accept myself

Eyebrow:	*Wanting to hide*
Side of Eye:	*I just want to hide in bed*
Under Eye:	*Can't get out of bed*
Under Nose:	*No point*
Chin:	*This pointlessness*
Collar Bone:	*This pointlessness*
Under Arm:	*I just want to hide*
Top of Head:	*I can't get out of bed*

Depression can also be extremely isolating. Have you heard of people who talk about wanting to 'hide under the duvet'? Ever felt that way yourself? Often it can be hard to get out of bed. People suffering from depression rarely want to socialise, yet at the same time as hiding themselves away there can be a pervasive feeling of loneliness and longing for company. If this resonates with you, tap as follows:

Repeat 3 times while tapping the Karate Chop:

Even though I am depressed I deeply and completely love and accept myself

Eyebrow:	*This depression*
Side of Eye:	*This isolating depression*
Under Eye:	*I'm so lonely*
Under Nose:	*This lonely depression*
Chin:	*This depression*
Collar Bone:	*This isolating depression*
Under Arm:	*This loneliness*
Top of Head:	*This depression*

Depression is usually the result of a number of experiences or traumas, which have led to the forming of negative self-beliefs, and will often clear as a result of the work that you do in other areas with the tapping (such as your emotional spring cleaning). Focusing on the depression itself may be useful in as much as it will begin to take the edge off the feelings, but the actual depression is unlikely to lift fully until the specific thoughts/ memories/ events contributing to it are worked through. In EFT terms depression is a global issue, an accumulation of responses to specific events.

However you can work to take the surface layers off it as follows:

Tapping Section: Tapping for despair

Repeat 3 times while tapping the Karate Chop:

Even though I am feeling this despair I deeply and completely love and accept myself

Eyebrow:	*This depression*
Side of Eye:	*Feeling really depressed*
Under Eye:	*This deep depression*
Under Nose:	*What's the point*
Chin:	*This despair*
Collar Bone:	*Deep depression*
Under Arm:	*Feeling really depressed*
Top of Head:	*I can't cope*

Continue:

Eyebrow:	*It's too much*
Side of Eye:	*This depression*
Under Eye:	*Feeling like giving up*
Under Nose:	*What's the point*
Chin:	*I can't go on*
Collar Bone:	*Yes I can*
Under Arm:	*This depression*
Top of Head:	*It's all too much*

Continue:

Eyebrow:	*Feeling low*
Side of Eye:	*Feeling depressed*
Under Eye:	*Feeling low*
Under Nose:	*This depression*
Chin:	*This despair*
Collar Bone:	*I can't cope*
Under Arm:	*Yes I can*
Top of Head:	*Maybe I can*

151

Continue:

Eyebrow:	*This darkness*
Side of Eye:	*I choose to feel light*
Under Eye:	*This tiredness*
Under Nose:	*I choose energy*
Chin:	*This darkness*
Collar Bone:	*I choose light*
Under Arm:	*This exhaustion*
Top of Head:	*I choose energy*

In order to achieve any results when working this globally it is necessary to timetable the tapping into your daily routine and make sure you do a few rounds on this every couple of hours, throughout the day. It can help to set an alarm, or a reminder on your phone to develop this habit.

Returning to Robert Caldini's metaphor of the tabletop. If you take depression to be the tabletop, it is now important to begin finding the specific legs that support it. If you have no prior experience of depression it is very possible that your diagnosis is one of the main legs. In which case, having worked through the different pieces of that memory, and subsequent connected ones, you may well have already done much of the work.

However, if the depression has not lifted there has to be more contributing to it. You will be addressing the specific events that may be supporting the depression when you work through your negative history, so here we will take a look at your thought processes.

- What are your persistent thoughts? Make a list of them as they pop into your mind.

- What do you need to think to bring the depression to the fore?

- What would I need to do to feel like you do?

Tapping Section: Tapping for depressive thoughts

Repeat 3 times while tapping the Karate Chop:

Even though I think that, I deeply and completely love and accept myself

Eyebrow:	*That thought*
Side of Eye:	*That depressing thought*
Under Eye:	*That powerful thought*
Under Nose:	*And everything connected to it*

152

Chin:	*That thought*
Collar Bone:	*That depressing thought*
Under Arm:	*That powerful thought*
Top of Head:	*And everything connected to it*

Here we will harness the power of your thoughts and tap to change those which are less than useful right now.

Repeat 3 times while tapping the Karate Chop:

Even though I have those thoughts I deeply and completely love and accept myself

Eyebrow:	*Those thoughts*
Side of Eye:	*Those negative thoughts*
Under Eye:	*Those thoughts*
Under Nose:	*Dragging me down*
Chin:	*Those thoughts*
Collar Bone:	*Those negative thoughts*
Under Arm:	*Those thoughts*
Top of Head:	*Dragging me down*

When you feel like you have got a reduction in your emotional and physical response to that thought or thought process continue as follows:

Eyebrow:	*That thought/those thoughts*
Side of Eye:	*What if I couldn't think it/them*
Under Eye:	*That thought/those thoughts*
Under Nose:	*What if I could let it/them go*
Chin:	*That thought/those thoughts*
Collar Bone:	*What if I couldn't think it/them*
Under Arm:	*That thought/those thoughts*
Top of Head:	*What if I could let it/them go*

Continue:

Eyebrow:	*What if I had a choice about this*
Side of Eye:	*What if I couldn't think that thought/those thoughts*
Under Eye:	*What if I could let it/them go*
Under Nose:	*What if I just couldn't think it/them anymore*
Chin:	*What if I had a choice about this*

Collar Bone:	*What if I couldn't think that thought/those thoughts*
Under Arm:	*What if I could let it/them go*
Top of Head:	*What if I just couldn't think it/them anymore*

Continue:

Eyebrow:	*That thought/those thoughts*
Side of Eye:	*I choose peace instead of it/them*
Under Eye:	*That old thought/those old thoughts*
Under Nose:	*I choose peace instead of it/them*
Chin:	*That thought/those thoughts*
Collar Bone:	*I choose peace instead of it/them*
Under Arm:	*That old thought/those old thoughts*
Top of Head:	*I choose peace instead of it/them*

Continue:

Eyebrow:	*I deserve peace instead of this*
Side of Eye:	*It is possible to have peace instead of this*
Under Eye:	*I deserve peace instead of this*
Under Nose:	*I choose peace instead of this*
Chin:	*I deserve peace instead of this*
Collar Bone:	*I choose peace*
Under Arm:	*I deserve peace*
Top of Head:	*I choose peace*

Lulu's story

Lulu described herself as walking through thick soup. Every step was an effort - she couldn't move in any direction. It felt as though everything was pushing down on top of her, that she was about to drown in this soup. She believed that nothing she could do would make any difference, nothing seemed to work for her.

Very clearly, Lulu was depressed although she was denying it. Her doctor had been advising a short course of antidepressants which she had refused. But now she found that she was totally unable to pull herself out this dark place. Added to which, she was putting herself under more pressure because she felt her mood was interrupting her healing process; she couldn't focus on it because the depression kept descending on her, and she was feeling increasingly desperate. While she was trying her best to be pro-active, it just wasn't working, she said she felt as if she was just being pushed under the soup, pushed down on her shoulders so we started tapping with that.

154

Tapping Section: Tapping for feeling stuck

Repeat 3 times while tapping the Karate Chop:

Even though I can't move forward I deeply and completely love and accept myself

Eyebrow:	*I can't move forward*
Side of Eye:	*I can't pull myself out of this depression*
Under Eye:	*It is pushing me under*
Under Nose:	*I can't stop it*
Chin:	*I can't move forward*
Collar Bone:	*I can't pull myself out of this depression*
Under Arm:	*It is pushing me under*
Top of Head:	*I can't stop it*

Continue:

Eyebrow:	*Feeling stuck*
Side of Eye:	*I can't move forward*
Under Eye:	*Walking through soup feelings*
Under Nose:	*Being pushed under feelings*
Chin:	*Walking through soup*
Collar Bone:	*Being pushed under*
Under Arm:	*I can't move forward*
Top of Head:	*This stuckness*

We did a few rounds like that and I asked her "Who is pushing you?". She said she didn't know but maybe it was actually her. I asked her if it was okay to have water wings, maybe as a beginning, as we were playing with this metaphor of the soup. This amused her, and she gave herself some green water wings. However, she still didn't feel comfortable; understandably she didn't want to be wading through thick soup! So in her mind she changed the soup to pale pink transparent, free flowing water which felt immediately better. However, it was still hard work as she said she couldn't move through it very fast and it was tiring.

Repeat 3 times while tapping the Karate Chop:

Even though I am wading through pink water now and it feels easier I deeply and completely love and accept myself

Eyebrow:	*Pink water*
Side of Eye:	*Pink water emotions*

Under Eye:	*Pink water and everything contributing to it*
Under Nose:	*Pink water emotions*
Chin:	*Pink water and everything it means to me*
Collar Bone:	*Pink water emotions*
Under Arm:	*Pink water and everything contributing to it*
Top of Head:	*Pink water emotions*

Repeat 3 times while tapping the Karate Chop:

Even though it is still hard work I deeply and completely love and accept myself

Eyebrow:	*This hard work*
Side of Eye:	*It's is too hard*
Under Eye:	*I can't do it*
Under Nose:	*It is too difficult*
Chin:	*This hard work*
Collar Bone:	*Hard work*
Under Arm:	*I can't do it*
Top of Head:	*I'll never do it*

I asked Lulu what she would need to make it easy, to allow it to be easy, was she able to give herself permission to swim now? She was surprised by that question and said:

'How can I give myself permission to swim, I've got cancer, how can I feel cheerful when I have got cancer?'

Both are reasonable questions, but so much has been written about positive mental attitudes and the power of positive thinking that we know it plays an important role in healing.

Repeat 3 times while tapping the Karate Chop:

Even though I can't be cheerful with cancer I deeply and completely love and accept myself

Eyebrow:	*I can't be cheerful*
Side of Eye:	*I have cancer*
Under Eye:	*I can't be cheerful*
Under Nose:	*Why would I be?*
Chin:	*I have cancer*
Collar Bone:	*It is not possible to be cheerful*

| Under Arm: | I can't do it |
| Top of Head: | I have cancer |

Continue:

Eyebrow:	People with cancer
Side of Eye:	Can't be cheerful
Under Eye:	It isn't in the rule book
Under Nose:	I can't do that
Chin:	I can't break the rules
Collar Bone:	Maybe
Under Arm:	Maybe I can
Top of Head:	No, I'm not allowed to be cheerful,

Continue:

Eyebrow:	I have to be sad
Side of Eye:	That's what they say
Under Eye:	That's how it is…maybe
Under Nose:	I am open to the possibility that I might allow myself
Chin:	To be just a little cheerful
Collar Bone:	I know how to be sad if I don't like it
Under Arm:	I am open to that possibility
Top of Head:	What if I can be cheerful with cancer

Half way through the second round, Lulu started to laugh. She said she felt she had a little bit more of a choice now and that perhaps she didn't need to go back into that depression, maybe she could help herself clear it. Even if she might not feel the life and soul of the party, or the happiest person on the block, she felt she was in a place where she could begin to move forward now. She said she felt she could focus on her healing without being stopped by this soup of negativity.

I worked with Lulu every week for about three months and occasionally she would drop back in to the depression, dipping a toe into it, finding herself in soup again rather than the flowing pink water. When this happened however, she managed to turn it around in her own mind every time, quickly and easily. As she did that, she said she could physically feel that lightness beginning to flow through her, it was like the sun coming up in the morning, a fresh day.

I don't know whether changing her mood helped her change her healing approach or whether indeed it contributed to her ultimately going into remission from her cancer, but I can't help but feel that cancer is a tricky enough journey in the first place and if we can help ourselves in any way, finding creative ways to move through depression, then it must be a positive step.

Keith's story
Keith found it hard to get out of bed, he found himself crying a lot, having to take himself off on his own, he didn't feel comfortable within his family, everything felt wrong and on top of this he had a diagnosis of lung cancer.

It was obvious to me that Keith was depressed. He had many of the symptoms mentioned earlier. I knew from taking his history that he was not on antidepressants.

I asked Keith if he felt he was depressed and he quickly said no, but it was unconvincing. I am not saying that he was lying to me, not at all, I think he genuinely believed that he was feeling bad, but that this was not what he called depression. I wondered whether there were some fears around that word. So I gently asked him what the word 'depression' meant to him. He said it was something that 'women' get, men are meant to be the stronger sex and don't give in to depression. We talked a little more about depression and the symptoms as described by The National Institute of Cancer and Keith was gradually able to recognise that he could relate to the majority of them.

It became clear that it was just not ok to have spotted that he had depression, to mention it, he didn't think it was showing to anybody and he certainly wasn't prepared to talk about it. He felt that it was very shameful and a real weakness, he felt embarrassed that he, as he put it 'Had given in to this depression', and whist he was prepared to throw everything at addressing the cancer, the depression was not up for discussion.

Keith's reaction is not unusual. People often feel embarrassed or ashamed like somehow it is their fault, that there is something REALLY wrong with them. It can seem as if, to some people, a cancer diagnosis is acceptable, but depression is absolutely unmentionable, like some heinous crime or assault on their character. Unfortunately I see this a lot, I have had clients who have had to hide their antidepressants from their partners. I have had clients who just will NOT admit that there is anything wrong.

One of my strongest desires is to break through this barrier or stigma around depression, people don't GET depression on purpose, anymore than they get a cold on purpose as I have said before.

Returning to Keith, I suggested because our sessions were obviously 100% confidential that perhaps it wouldn't do any harm to maybe just do a little bit of work around his depression, just to see if there was any way he might be able to feel just a bit better and he agreed so we tapped on various rounds as follows:

Tapping Section: Tapping for male depression shame

Repeat 3 times while tapping the Karate Chop:

Even though I feel so ashamed I deeply and completely love and accept myself

Eyebrow:	*This shame*
Side of Eye:	*This shame*

Under Eye:	*Depression shame*
Under Nose:	*Depression shame*
Chin:	*This shame*
Collar Bone:	*My shame*
Under Arm:	*Depression shame*
Top of Head:	*Depression shame*

Repeat 3 times while tapping the Karate Chop:

Even though only women get depressed I deeply and completely love and accept myself

Eyebrow:	*Only women get depressed*
Side of Eye:	*Men don't get depressed*
Under Eye:	*This depression*
Under Nose:	*My shameful depression*
Chin:	*Men don't get depressed*
Collar Bone:	*I'm depressed*
Under Arm:	*This shame*
Top of Head:	*My shame*

Repeat 3 times while tapping the Karate Chop:

Even though I'm weak I deeply and completely love and accept myself

Eyebrow:	*I'm weak*
Side of Eye:	*This judgment*
Under Eye:	*This weakness*
Under Nose:	*Depression weakness*
Chin:	*Depression weakness*
Collar Bone:	*I'm so weak*
Under Arm:	*Maybe, maybe not*
Top of Head:	*This depression weakness*

We continued for several rounds, until gradually Keith was able to accept that maybe there was more to it than this; maybe it is as it is, and he had good reasons for feeling low at that particular time; maybe it was normal in some people to feel that way.

Even beginning to consider that it might be a normal response, and that it might be possible to change it, Keith's judgements around the depression began to lift and we were able to begin to work with it more directly, discovering the various table legs that were supporting it and beginning to collapse them. It only took a couple of sessions for him to feel noticeably better.

I think that the stigma around being depressed, and all the judgments Keith was putting on himself, were the glue to holding the depression in place. The shame and stress of the depressive feelings were the most challenging part of our work, once they had reduced it was easy for Keith to move through the specific thoughts and events that underpinned the table top.

Whilst Keith was still not happy about his diagnosis, understandably, he certainly became more energized and his mood definitely changed for the positive. As a result, he was able to get outside and do a little bit of exercise, which in turn helped with his breathing capacity and his lungs.

It is very important to note that after the first session Keith did agree to see his doctor about his mood. Between them they decided to wait until he had done a little more work on it with the tapping, just one week, before deciding on the antidepressants. Keith went back a week later, and regularly thereafter, but never needed to take the medication. However, that had to be a decision between Keith and his doctor. If you do feel depressed at any point, whether you're tapping or otherwise, I urge you to go and see your doctor immediately.

'Little by little, one travels far.'
J R R Tolkien

Sandra's story
Sandra had a long history of depression. Before she was diagnosed with cervical cancer, she had, as she put it, yo-yoed in and out of depression for many years. Her father had it, and his mother before him, so her belief was that this was just one of those things she was probably disposed to it. That may be true, however there is a difference between being predisposed to something and actually having it. Having a genetic predisposition to something does not mean that you HAVE to suffer from it.

I wanted to know how Sandra maintained the depression as her periods of depression had often lasted many years. What was the thinking that seemed to be supporting it?

Although now there was a more obvious reason for it, I wondered in the past what had happened? What was the construct of her depression? By construct, I meant what was the internal unconscious mechanism which facilitated the depression, which allowed it to continue. What did she have to do to keep it going? What thoughts did she have to think? What would I have to do or think to be depressed her way? In essence, I was asking her to teach me how to 'do' her depression. By breaking the global concept of depression into smaller pieces, it very quickly became clear that there was a stream of thinking which repeated itself again and again, thoughts like:

- *It's all pointless*
- *There is no point having fun because it is not going to last*
- *How can I be happy?*
- *I'm feeling really unhappy*
- *Life is awful for me*
- *I'll never get over this*
- *Nothing works*
- *Everything is black*

160

- *I can't be bothered*
- *It is just the way it is*
- *I can't change it*

We took each of those phrases, I asked her various questions around each statement and we tapped on them, which led us to the specific memories where she had made the decision behind each of those thoughts. For example:

I will never get over this

When did you decide that?	*When I was 17*
What was happening in your life?	*I was diagnosed with depression*
Is it true that you will never get over it?	*It feels true*
How do you know?	*The doctor tells me*
How would you know if you did get over this?	*I would feel happy and light*

Sandra's belief had come partly from her family history and partly from the doctor who, when he first diagnosed her with depression when she was 17, had told her that she could expect to feel like this, on and off for the rest of her life. What a thing to say to a teenage girl! At that point Sandra had decided it wasn't worth making an effort to enjoy life because whatever fun she had was always going to be taken away by the next bout of depression, hence the "What is the point".

We tapped on that specific memory of the doctor, and then through her many beliefs around depression and her specific negative thoughts for three sessions, until they just didn't seem to resonate anymore. She couldn't get their power back, they were words, yes, they meant the same thing, but her response to them changed. They were no longer personal to her; she didn't own them anymore.

She went through a stage of feeling a little bit unsettled because she hadn't been in this new place of possibility about life since her early to mid-teens. She was a stranger to positives, to seeing and experiencing the good in the world. Gradually she started doing things that she didn't think she would ever do, including taking up salsa dancing classes! She started meeting people; she started laughing again! It was as if a different person was emerging and it was very beautiful to observe. She also began writing down her positive thoughts so she could return back to them, hold onto them, hold them in her heart.

Many doctors and therapists believe that once you are diagnosed with depression it is something that will be with you for life; you will dip in and out of it just as Sandra was saying.

Is that true? I don't know. It may seem true, but how much does the thought bring about the reality? If you spend your life telling yourself that you have got depression and that there is no choice, that you are going to have it for the rest of your days, what do you think is likely to happen? There are many, many examples of depression lifting permanently, using the tapping, although it is sometimes necessary to take the antidepressants to get a foot in the door in order to work with this. Depression is both a complex and serious issue and the support of both your doctor and a therapist are both advisory, and in some cases essential.

In the following chapter we are going to begin to explore your personal history in the years preceding your diagnosis with a view to clearing anything that is still triggering an excessive emotional response in the present day. This is the beginning of your Personal Peace Procedure, and is targeted specifically at the period leading up to your illness.

CHAPTER 9

WHAT HAPPENED BEFORE THE CANCER?

'The ocean is made of drops'
Mother Teresa

You are entering into an important journey as you begin to explore the emotional and physical components of your life which are showing up as cancer in the present day. Be gentle on yourself and take your time.

Ultimately with tapping, the most effective way of achieving long term results is to '**get specific**'. By this, we mean working through all the specific memories in your life which are creating an imbalance in your energy system today. Those things, however slight, that when you think about them now still make you feel cross / guilty / sad/ angry, etc. All those events / experiences which are still showing up in your life today in some form, whether through negative beliefs or habits / behaviours you would like to change.

We store these experiences in our minds as mini movies, very specifically, but we are accustomed to thinking in broader more global terms, such as anxiety, and fear, that we have already looked at. In order to clear these general states we need to work with the individual experiences that have led us to them.

Tapping is a very gentle way of doing this, whereby we do not have to 'revisit' traumatic events in detail until it is comfortable for us to do so. And even then, it is only necessary as a way of testing the results of our work. By giving each mini movie a title (as per the instructions below) you are guiding your unconscious mind into the thought field that you are working in without the need to access the specific emotions. In the same way that if I asked you whether you had seen the movie, Gone with the Wind, you would answer yes or no quickly, without needing to run the whole movie. Working through your emotional history in this way leads not only to emotional health and well being, but renewed strength of mind and spirit.

'When the Japanese mend broken objects, they aggrandize the damage by filling the cracks with gold. They believe that when something's suffered damage and has a history it becomes more beautiful.'
Barbara Bloom

Research is beginning to indicate that there may be a correlation between sudden shock and a cancer diagnosis. Now, you might say 'well everyone gets sudden shocks' and yes, that is certainly true and clearly having a shock is the not the only reason for having a cancer diagnosis. Not everybody who has a sudden shock or a trauma will get cancer, the same way that not everybody who gets cancer will have a trauma or a sudden shock in the five years leading up to it, but there is enough evidence out there to make it worth looking at, just in case this happens to be you.

Cellular memory

You may have heard the term 'cellular memory'. The theory behind cellular memory is that each and every cell in our body has its own memory bank and stores information about our life experiences. Most of this information is benign and plays no negative role in our everyday living. However, traumatic events also get encoded in our cellular memory and inform the way our body reacts to occurrences in the present day. For example, you may have been in a war zone at some point and heard explosions and gunfire. And whilst you know consciously that you are safe now because you are physically away from the war zone, every time a car exhaust blows or a balloon pops you jump. This is your body reacting to a stored trauma in your cellular memory.

Scientists have yet to prove the existence of cellular memory, although some work has been done around organ donation. They have discovered that neuropeptides exist in all the body's tissues, not just the brain as previously thought. Neuropeptides are biochemicals which carry messages to and from the brain and the body's organs, and this seems to suggest that the organs themselves store memory in the same way the brain does.

One extraordinary example of cellular memory was found in an 8 year old girl who received the heart of a 10 year old girl. The recipient started having vivid nightmares about an attacker and a girl being murdered. Unbeknownst to her, the girl whose heart she had just received was murdered and she was able to describe what happened and the murderer so accurately that police were able to arrest and convict the killer.

What we do know is that the body does remember, and that the body doesn't lie. We can trust our bodily responses - like jumping when a balloon pops as I mentioned before - as the result of learned experiences encoded in memory. From a tapping perspective, we seem to be able to release the ongoing responses to trauma from the cellular memory by tuning in to both the physiological and emotional responses to a remembered negative event. The body and unconscious mind literally speak to us. I will explore this further in Chapter 18, where I look at working with traumatic history.

What happened in the last five years?

Now we need to look at what happened before you got cancer, focussing on the five years leading up to your diagnosis.

- What was happening in your life?
- Did you have any sudden shocks or trauma?

If your answer to that immediately was 'yes I had a shock', write it down, we are going to work with it in exactly the same way that we worked with the diagnosis earlier, using the Movie Technique. When you start working with that event you will probably get an emotional response. Notice where you feel that response physically, put a hand over that part of your body, close your eyes and ask yourself:

- What does this remind you of?
- When did you first feel this?

Allow time for your unconscious mind to sift through the internal filing system that is your memory bank, and bring up any appropriate memories, if they are there.

If a memory (or memories) comes to mind, write it / them down, give it / them a quick title (a word or a name, just something that reminds you of that particular time) and then, using The Movie Technique, begin to work through them. You may find a theme evolving or you may find the memories are coming to you seemingly randomly, it doesn't matter, work with whatever presents itself.

As you do this, pay particular attention to any physical feelings as well. Notice where you feel the emotions in your body when you bring these memories to mind, keep testing, keep going back to that place, bringing back the memories, seeing what has happened.

- Do you still have that fear in your stomach?
- Do you still have that anxiety in your breathing?
- What is going on for you?

Keep going. Like a dog with a bone, you have to be really thorough, making sure you get what, in tapping terms, are called 'aspects'. Aspects are every piece of the jigsaw that contributes to the emotional charge around each specific memory.

For example, going back to the chapter on the diagnosis, there may be several aspects showing up:

- Shock of the diagnosis
- Fear of the cancer
- Fear of the treatment
- Anger
- Sadness
- Anxiety
- Sound of the words
- Tone of voice

...to name a few. It is vital to listen to both your emotions and your physical responses as you clear a memory.

This might take you five minutes, half an hour or several attempts over a few days. It doesn't matter. Persistence is key. It is important that you totally clear this energetic thread.

Sometimes you may have no sense of any resonance of that shock. You may just remember the recent shock or trauma but be devoid of emotion. Perhaps you feel you 'ought' to feel something but don't. Tell yourself the story whilst tapping, if you get an emotional response then tap on that and where it leads, if not, then you are emotionally clear on that memory.

If the thought of going back to the story and looking at it brings up any anxiety, STOP there. You will need to find a practitioner who can work through this with you and keep you safe during the process. Do not try and be brave.

Liz's story
Liz had had a car crash about four years previously and whilst she was now able to get back into a car and drive she had been experiencing severe panic attacks

ever since. She came to see me because of a cancer diagnosis, looking for tools to manage her emotional state. As you will see, there were many different aspects of the car crash that needed to be addressed with tapping before the panic attacks subsided and the trauma of the memory was released.

We began by working with the trauma of the diagnosis itself, using the Movie Technique. And then we turned our attention to Liz's recent history, and whether she had experienced any sudden shocks or traumas which, when she brought them to mind now, still 'got' her in some way, either physically or emotionally.

This was when she mentioned the car crash. She thought she had dealt with it well and felt little emotion when talking about it now. However, I decided to tap with it anyway, to double check the shock had been completely released from her cellular memory and energy field.

We began by using the Movie Technique again, giving the memory the title 'The Accident'. Liz gave it a SUDS rating of 7.

Tapping Section: Tapping for trauma preceding cancer

Repeat 3 times while tapping the Karate Chop:

Even though I have this accident movie I deeply and completely love and accept myself

Eyebrow:	*Accident movie*
Side of Eye:	*Accident movie*
Under Eye:	*Accident emotions*
Under Nose:	*Accident emotions*
Chin:	*Accident movie*
Collar Bone:	*Accident movie*
Under Arm:	*Accident emotions*
Top of Head:	*Accident emotions*

After a couple of rounds I checked in with her, asking her to think of the movie now, was it still a 7 intensity? She said it felt like a 2 or 3.

At this point, I asked her whether she would feel comfortable to run the movie in her head, with strict instructions to stop at any point that she felt any discomfort. Below are just some of the aspects that arose:

Repeat 3 times while tapping the Karate Chop:

Even though the car hit me and I was helpless, I deeply and completely love and accept myself

Eyebrow:	*Feeling helpless*
Side of Eye:	*I couldn't stop it*

Under Eye:	*Feeling helpless*
Under Nose:	*I couldn't stop it*
Chin:	*The car hit me*
Collar Bone:	*I couldn't escape*
Under Arm:	*This helplessness*
Top of Head:	*This helplessness*

Repeat 3 times while tapping the Karate Chop:

Even though I feel terrified I deeply and completely love and accept myself

Eyebrow:	*This terrifying memory*
Side of Eye:	*Accident terror*
Under Eye:	*Helplessness terror*
Under Nose:	*Accident terror*
Chin:	*It was terrifying*
Collar Bone:	*Accident terror*
Under Arm:	*Accident terror*
Top of Head:	*Accident terror*

We continued to work through all the different pieces of the movie that still held a charge for her now, as follows:

- *Waiting at the roundabout*
- *Beginning to pull out*
- *Cars beside her*
- *Cars coming towards her*
- *Car lights coming towards her*

I asked her what the person who crashed into her was like, he had apparently been very badly injured, and he had been drunk. We tapped on the alcohol, and Liz's sadness at his being hurt.

We tapped on what happened after the accident, and the immediate aftermath; the police arriving, the ambulance arriving, people taking statements from her, and her confusion and panic at feeling under pressure.

We had several sessions together and whilst the panic attacks definitely subsided she was still experiencing very reduced symptoms, and these seemed to happen randomly: sitting on the bus, going to the cinema, at work, in restaurants.

Liz worked in a university administration department and during her working day she met and interacted with many people. She had begun to feel anxious at work despite being in the job for a long time and being confident and well respected.

We started looking at what was happening at work, specifically when she last got the panic response. We worked through the minutiae of her working day, breaking it into tiny specific pieces, or mini movies.

As we worked through the many different layers that emerged through the tapping Liz had an important insight. She said that it was to do with people having their faces too close to her, with no respect for her personal space. Her boss at work had a habit of speaking to her with his face right up close to her, especially when something was going wrong in the office. Liz always felt suffocated.

Her next memory was of one of the ambulance team doing the same thing. Whilst rationally, she knew he was trying to get her to come round to regain consciousness, when she opened her eyes he was there right up in front of her, his eyes staring at her and she heard him talking to her, very loudly and very fast, and she couldn't understand him. She hadn't remembered this very specific piece of the trauma before.

We tapped on both these memories and the various aspects such as the breath on her face, the urgency of the voices, eyes too close etc until she was able to vividly imagine both events and feel completely calm.

We then tested these results further by looking at the other times she had mentioned, such as the cinema and in restaurants, but she was totally calm throughout.

By tapping through all these different aspects, or pieces, of a very traumatic jigsaw, Liz has had no further panic attacks and she was able to focus on her healing. She was able to go to hospitals and allow doctors to closely examine her and remain calm throughout, and she managed her journey with cancer with strength and resourcefulness.

Having cleared the impact of your immediate history we are now going to begin to explore your beliefs around your cancer. What is possible for you? What thoughts and beliefs are limiting you? Beliefs are our most powerful enemy, but, healthily aligned, they are also our strongest friend. We could not ask for a better ally in our healing that a positive belief system.

CHAPTER 10

BELIEFS

'Things are only impossible until they're not.'
Jean-Luc Picard, Star Trek: The Next Generation

In this chapter, we will to begin to unearth any belief system that may be getting in the way of your healing process. Beliefs are probably the most powerful mechanism in our lives. People die for their beliefs, they fight for them, religions are based on them, and governments are elected because of them. Do not underestimate the power of belief systems in your healing process. Our beliefs become our truths, the writing on our walls by which we lead our lives. They are the blueprint for the way we all live our lives.

Our beliefs come from many different directions, we may have religious beliefs, cultural beliefs, family beliefs etc. and most of them will be useful and necessary in order to function in the world.

Your beliefs about cancer
However, here we need to discover what these beliefs are in the area of cancer and serious disease, and tap to change those which are not helpful to your healing. It is possible to change your mind and your life, and in order to begin making those changes, you need to get blocking beliefs out on the table.

I am not going to try and convince you to change your beliefs, I am not going to try and persuade you - none of that will work and we will only get into conflict. Your beliefs are the rules by which you live your life at the moment, it is not for me to change them, it is for me to ask you whether they are useful, whether they are true, really true. Because beliefs are illusions, they are not truths, they are not real they are just conclusions we reach as a result of specific events.

'Society leads us to believe that we must always seek cures outside ourselves, dismissing 'mind over matter' as nonsense, but such a belief negates the body's natural healing process. Believing that we need to be cured often stops the body from making its own effortless recovery.'
David Hamilton, PhD

Some of our most stuck beliefs are beliefs that we set up and took on in childhood as a response to a particular way of being, a particular way of being treated, or a particular experience. Then, as we go through life, we can become magnets, attracting other similar experiences that would seem to validate these beliefs and make them feel more and more real, more and more true for us.

In fact, many of us are running our lives according to the belief systems we established when we were very young, the three or four year old us is often running the show. If you think of that consciously I wonder how it feels to be handing your healing over to the skills of a small child.

So have a think, what are your beliefs around cancer and around YOUR cancer and your journey with it,

- Do you believe it is possible for you to heal?
- Do you have to have side effects from the treatment?
- Does it have to be awful?
- Do you have to feel ill?

Notice people around you, what are their beliefs, they may be sharing them generously with you.

- Do they believe you are going to die?
- Do you believe you are going to die?
- Do you believe your life is never going to be the same?
- Do you believe that you will have cancer forever?

What are you saying to yourself? What thoughts and beliefs are running around in your mind? I offer it to you that they are JUST beliefs, not truths.

My colleague Steve Wells calls belief systems B.S. I will leave it to you to fill in the gaps, but he is right. We create our own beliefs, we make decisions about the world around us and we stick with them. It is important to examine your beliefs around health, your health, around cancer, your cancer and then around your family history too, asking yourself questions like the above and then tapping on what comes up for you.

> *'Aerodynamically the bumblebee shouldn't be able to fly, but the bumblebee doesn't know that so it goes on flying anyway.'*
> *Mary Kay Ash*

So how do you begin to find any blocking beliefs relating to your cancer?

Firstly, check your family history. Look for any unresolved grief, and specific memories of any family members who have had cancer. Cancer that is not due to an obvious inherited pattern is called "sporadic cancer." It is believed that most—perhaps 90%—of all cancers are sporadic (http://www.facingourrisk.org/hereditary_cancer/hereditary_cancer_and_genetics.html). The malignancies in a significant number of cancer patients are derived from environmentally-induced epigenetic alterations and not defective genes (Bruce Lipton, The Biology of Belief). In other words, it is the effect of the environment (our internal world as well as the world we live in) on the genes that creates the cancer cells, not the genes themselves.

- Who in your family has had cancer?
- Is it the same cancer as yours?
- What happened to them?
- How does that affect how you feel about your prognosis?
- Do you feel the outcome is inevitable?
- Is it possible for you to heal?
- If you heal and they didn't would that be okay?

- What would that mean?
- What do you believe your prognosis is?
- Is it possible for you to have a long healthy life?

Check your answers to these questions and see whether you have any negative responses. You may be surprised! Ask yourself on a scale of 0 to 10 how much you believe the response, with 10 being I completely 100% believe it and 0 being you don't buy into that belief at all.

Then begin tapping, starting with the highest scoring statements. For example:

Tapping Section: Tapping for beliefs about cancer

Repeat 3 times while tapping the Karate Chop:

Even though it's not possible for me to heal I deeply and completely love and accept myself

Eyebrow:	*It's not possible for me to heal*
Side of Eye:	*I can't heal*
Under Eye:	*It isn't possible*
Under Nose:	*I can't do it*
Chin:	*No one does it*
Collar Bone:	*I can't heal*
Under Arm:	*It isn't possible*
Top of Head:	*I can't heal*

Why sometimes I've believed as many as six impossible things before breakfast'
Lewis Carroll, Alice in Wonderland

Becky's story
Becky's Mum had died of breast cancer 20 years earlier and Becky believed that her breast cancer diagnosis was genetic. Becky was doing everything she could to heal herself. She was taking everything the medical profession had to offer, cutting edge approaches, including participating in drug trials. She had researched all the treatment options and felt empowered and in charge of her healing plan, supporting the medical model with complementary therapies such as acupuncture, tapping, nutrition etc. But for whatever reason she still was not out of the woods, she still wasn't healing completely.

I wondered why, and what it was that was getting in the way of her healing process. Was there anything that we could do to change that? I knew that Becky's mum had died of breast cancer and that Becky had an identical diagnosis and I wondered if that was playing into it in some way. Becky was open to that possibility, although it wasn't in her conscious thinking. We both felt it was important to check it out. So we tapped as follows. Remember to tap along too:

Repeat 3 times while tapping the Karate Chop:

Even though Mum died of this so I'm going to too I deeply and completely love and accept myself

Eyebrow:	*This cancer*
Side of Eye:	*Mum died*
Under Eye:	*I'm going to die*
Under Nose:	*Mum died*
Chin:	*I'm going to*
Collar Bone:	*This cancer*
Under Arm:	*Mum died*
Top of Head:	*I'm going to too*

Repeat 3 times while tapping the Karate Chop:

Even though Mum died of this and that means ___ I deeply and completely love and accept myself

Eyebrow:	*Mum didn't heal*
Side of Eye:	*I can't do it*
Under Eye:	*Mum couldn't do it*
Under Nose:	*So I won't be able to*
Chin:	*These mum emotions*
Collar Bone:	*She died*
Under Arm:	*I can't heal*
Top of Head:	*These mum emotions*

This brought a flood of tears and sadness, sadness that her Mum had had to die, sadness that she had gone through this journey and sadness that Becky was having to follow in her footsteps, as she put it. I asked her what would have happened if she didn't follow in her footsteps if she had a different outcome to her Mum, would that be ok? What would that mean to her? She thought for a moment and said, 'I can't ... I can't do differently from Mum, I can't be better than Mum, I can't show her up as somehow being inadequate in her healing process because she died, I have to do the same as her.'

What Becky was doing was protecting her Mum's memory, she had idealised her. To Becky, her Mum was this lady who was wonderful, loved, and brilliant at everything and Becky had preserved her memory in this way. Here she was now having an opportunity where possibly she might achieve something that her Mum didn't and it was NOT ok, absolutely not, she couldn't risk doing something better than her Mum, taking back her power from her Mum. Becky was shocked and surprised by these thoughts, and rationally recognised that they were untrue, yet her unconscious mind seemed to be communicating a deeper belief to her.

At this point we needed to go to the memory or series of memories around her mum's illness, and death, when Becky's belief took root, using the Movie Technique or Tearless Trauma to reduce the high intensity. There were many aspects around these memories, thoughts, beliefs and emotional responses such as sadness and pain.

When the charge on each piece of the memories had cleared and Becky could talk about them freely I asked her the following questions:

- *Would Mum want you to heal?*
- *Would it be OK to heal if Mum died of this?*

The answer to both questions was yes, accessing an even deeper rooted belief about Mum loving and caring for Becky, and which was much stronger than the 'I can't heal because Mum didn't' belief that was running before. So we continued to tap, inserting a Choice, as follows. Please tap along:

Repeat 3 times while tapping the Karate Chop:

Even though Mum died and it is really sad, I am open to the possibility that medicine has moved on since then and that maybe it is ok for me to live.

Eyebrow:	*Mum dying sadness*
Side of Eye:	*I honour and respect mum*
Under Eye:	*And I choose to be different*
Under Nose:	*I'm open to the possibility that I can heal from this now*
Chin:	*It is possible for me to heal*
Collar Bone:	*It is possible for me to have a long healthy life*
Under Arm:	*I choose to have a long healthy life*
Top of Head:	*I choose to heal now*

Repeat 3 times while tapping the Karate Chop:

Even though Mum died and I am still alive I am open to the possibility that that is the way she would want it

Eyebrow:	*She died*
Side of Eye:	*I love and respect mum*
Under Eye:	*And I choose to heal*
Under Nose:	*It's possible for me to heal from this cancer*
Chin:	*Mum would have wanted me to heal*
Collar Bone:	*I believe it's possible for me to heal*
Under Arm:	*I choose to focus on my healing process now*
Top of Head:	*I choose to heal for me and my mum, wherever she is*

173

It is important to dig out any inherited beliefs too. Kerry, below, is an excellent example of someone who had taken on beliefs passed down by her mother. Whilst she was not particularly concerned about them, and had accepted them as how it was in her family, she was worried about the effect of her thoughts on her own daughters. Intuitively, she already recognised the power of her beliefs, and she was determined not to engage her daughters in her thinking. This was the reason she wanted to work with me. As you will see, she got a shift in her belief systems, which in turn was reflected in her life style and quality of life, no matter how long she had to live.

Kerry's story

Whilst Kerry was going downhill fast, she was actually in remission from bowel cancer. Her medical team were baffled by her fading like this. There were no more tumours, they had all been removed, they had checked her, they had scanned her, she had the all clear, and they could not understand what was going on.

We talked for a while and Kerry seemed very matter of fact with her situation. She wasn't troubled by the fact that she was going downhill fast, she was slightly bemused that people thought it was a problem and she was completely convinced in her own mind that she was going to die of cancer, that there was no other option, this is how it was going to be - she'd had cancer therefore she was going to die.

I asked her where she had got that belief from because, had she done any research on her particular diagnosis, she would have found studies showing a positive increase in survival rates for cancers such as hers. Kerry had had a colostomy followed by chemotherapy, and tests indicated she was clear of cancer. So why was she fading?

I saw her for probably a month, and she was getting weaker and weaker despite our work together. On the third time I saw her I said, "Look I'm confused, I don't understand what is going on here? As far as the medical profession are concerned you are in remission so what is your body doing? Why is this happening?, Tell me what YOU think about cancer and what is going on?"

She was quite an elderly lady in her early 70's, and new to any form of therapy. She started telling me her understanding or her beliefs around cancer, totally matter of fact, with a total conviction.

- *I will die of cancer*
- *Cancer will kill me*
- *Cancer kills people*

Emma: Yes it can do but you are in remission. What does that say to you?

Kerry: It's only a matter of time and it will come back and I'm okay with that.

Emma: What makes you so sure it's going to come back?

Kerry: That is how it is with cancer, that is what I have been brought up to believe, that is what it is like in my family

Emma: Tell me a bit more about that

Kerry started to tell me a story about her mother's sister who had developed cancer at about the same age as Kerry is at now, she wasn't sure what cancer it was so I didn't know if we were talking about the same diagnosis.

Emma: What do you remember about that time?

Kerry: I remember the doom and gloom in the house, this complete acceptance that she was going to die.

Emma: Why do you think they accepted it in that way?

Kerry: Well cancer is a death sentence, I can remember my mother saying it. I remember saying to my mother, well she might get better and my mother going 'Kerry, cancer is a death sentence'.

I asked her if she would be ok with us tapping around that and she looked at me as though I was mad but conceded, humoured me, so we started to work on that:

Repeat 3 times while tapping the Karate Chop:

Even though cancer is a death sentence I deeply and completely love and accept myself

Eyebrow:	*Cancer is a death sentence*
Side of Eye:	*Death sentence emotions*
Under Eye:	*Cancer death sentence*
Under Nose:	*Death sentence emotions*
Chin:	*Cancer*
Collar Bone:	*That death sentence*
Under Arm:	*Cancer*
Top of Head:	*Death sentence emotions*

Repeat 3 times while tapping the Karate Chop:

Even though Mum said that I deeply and completely love and accept myself

Eyebrow:	*Mum's words*
Side of Eye:	*Cancer is a death sentence*
Under Eye:	*Those powerful words*
Under Nose:	*My death sentence*
Chin:	*Mum's words*
Collar Bone:	*My belief*
Under Arm:	*Cancer is a death sentence*

Top of Head: *Mum's words*

After a few rounds of that I asked if this was true, was cancer a death sentence? Kerry said' Well no, not for other people but in my family it is'. So we worked on that aspect:

Repeat 3 times while tapping the Karate Chop:

Even though cancer is a death sentence in MY family I deeply and completely love and accept myself.

Eyebrow:	*This belief*
Side of Eye:	*Death sentence belief*
Under Eye:	*Our belief*
Under Nose:	*My family belief*
Chin:	*What if we made a mistake*
Collar Bone:	*What if it isn't true*
Under Arm:	*This belief*
Top of Head:	*Family death sentence belief*

When I started questioning this a little bit more Kerry suddenly said:

'If I heal, I will be the first one in my family to do so and I won't belong. I will be different and I don't want to be different. I want to be part of my family, I want to be loved and be one of them.'

We continued:

Repeat 3 times while tapping the Karate Chop:

Even though I have to die to be accepted by my family I deeply and completely love and accept myself.

Eyebrow:	*Dying to be accepted*
Side of Eye:	*I have to die*
Under Eye:	*I need acceptance*
Under Nose:	*Dying to be accepted*
Chin:	*I have to die*
Collar Bone:	*Maybe*
Under Arm:	*Maybe not*
Top of Head:	*Dying to be accepted*

Repeat 3 times while tapping the Karate Chop:

Even though my family die of cancer so I have to, maybe, I deeply and completely love and accept myself.

Eyebrow:	*I have to die*
Side of Eye:	*To fit in*
Under Eye:	*To be accepted*
Under Nose:	*I have to die*
Chin:	*I am open to the possibility*
Collar Bone:	*That this belief is no longer useful*
Under Arm:	*I am open to the possibility*
Top of Head:	*That I can live, and be accepted*

Continue:

Eyebrow:	*I am open to the possibility that I can heal and be accepted*
Side of Eye:	*I am open to that possibility*
Under Eye:	*I choose to change this family belief now*
Under Nose:	*I choose to break this pattern*
Chin:	*I am open to the possibility that it is safe to heal*
Collar Bone:	*I am open to the possibility that they will accept me anyway*
Under Arm:	*I choose to change this old belief now*
Top of Head:	*I choose to break this pattern*

Then I asked Kerry how she was feeling? She looked very different – her face had colour and her features seemed more relaxed, she was also breathing more deeply. All signs that there were some internal shifts taking place.

Emma: How true is that belief that cancer is a death sentence?

Kerry: Well it's not true for everyone.

Emma: How about 'Cancer is a death sentence in my family?

Kerry: That has been true but perhaps it feels different now

Emma: Do you want your children to through life thinking that if they get cancer it will kill them?

Kerry: No I don't at all, No I want them to think Hey Mum beat it so I can.

Emma: What needs to happen for them to believe that?

177

Kerry: (Laughing) I guess I have to show them!

I only saw Kerry for one more session after that. When she turned up it might have been a different lady. Having been emotionless before, she was now full of laughter, she was giggly, she was fun, she had a wicked sense of humour and she had clearly decided that she was going to live, she was embracing life to the full and it was wonderful to see. I tested that old belief and it was clear that it no longer resonated with her. She also told me that her daughters were delighted by the change in her, and that despite the history neither of them had ever believed that a cancer diagnosis would be inevitable for them.

Presuppositions can become beliefs - Jim's story:
When Jim went back to the doctors following a course of chemotherapy, with cancer that had spread to many of his major organs, he was told by his doctor "If you are very lucky you won't need chemotherapy again until July". July, being in three months time.

What message do you think that Jim took from that statement? In NLP (Neuro-Linguistic Programming) terms we call that a presupposition. That statement presupposes that Jim will need more chemotherapy, which in itself presupposes that the tumours will begin to grow again. These thoughts and the assumed inevitability pushed Jim into a place of deep depression and he gave up at that point.

Luckily for him, his family realised that this was happening and they took him to this doctor and he was put on a course of anti depressants whilst he worked through that consultant's words. But, regardless of that, come July, to the day, Jim was back having more chemotherapy, such is the power of language on the body. It wasn't necessarily Jim's belief but he had no stronger belief with which to counteract it so he took it on board.

As ever with the tapping, we are always looking for the specific memories/ experiences which have created these beliefs in the first place. Perhaps it is a family member dying of cancer, or a friend. Maybe it was a film, documentary, book, an article on the internet. Perhaps it was someone's response to your diagnosis, their words or tone. Whatever supports these beliefs, it is important to work with them as above, always taking care to zoom in on the specific piece with the highest emotional crescendo and then working from that point.

Be vigilant and thorough in your self work. Beliefs can be very sneaky, they will seem like truths, and often slip past you unnoticed. Look out for them!

Look at your childhood. Who did you admire? What were your values?

Rosie's story
Rosie was in her early thirties, a working mother with her own thriving business, and with two small children. She had recently received a diagnosis of breast cancer. We worked for many sessions, but it was during an informal chat between rounds that she said the following:

'Do you remember that Blondie song, Die Young Stay Pretty? Well that was my anthem when I was growing up'

To me, that was one of the most important turning points in her healing process, we needed to clear that from her energy system. She had identified with that 'heroine' to such an extent as a teenager that her thoughts did indeed seem to be creating her reality. Whilst on the one hand this seemed a little mad, and I did hesitate to bring it to her attention, on the other hand it felt too important to ignore so I braved it and we tapped as follows:

Tapping Section: Tapping for presuppositions about cancer

Repeat 3 times while tapping the Karate Chop:

Even though that was my anthem then I deeply and completely love and accept myself

Eyebrow:	*That song and what it means to me*
Side of Eye:	*Die Young Stay Pretty*
Under Eye:	*My anthem*
Under Nose:	*My song*
Chin:	*Everything it means to me now, and then*
Collar Bone:	*Die Young Stay Pretty*
Under Arm:	*My anthem*
Top of Head:	*My song*

Continue:

Eyebrow:	*I am open to the possibility*
Side of Eye:	*That my song is no longer appropriate*
Under Eye:	*I am open to the possibility that I can let*
Under Nose:	*My connection to those words go now*
Chin:	*Die Young Stay Pretty*
Collar Bone:	*Those words*
Under Arm:	*Stuck in my energy field*
Top of Head:	*I choose to release them now*

Continue:

Eyebrow:	*I love and accept that teenage me*
Side of Eye:	*And I choose to let the power of that anthem go*
Under Eye:	*It was great for the teenager*
Under Nose:	*But it is no longer appropriate for the adult*
Chin:	*I choose to release my connection to those words*
Collar Bone:	*I thank Blondie for her music*

Under Arm:	And I choose to release those words from my energy field now
Top of Head:	I choose to release that old anthem

Whilst I have no idea whether Rosie's unconscious mind had taken those words as an instruction, I feel very strongly that her attachment to that song may well have been being played out in reality. She was young, and she was (and still is!) very beautiful. I feel enormous gratitude to her as this piece of work showed me the possibility that beliefs may be held at a deeply unconscious level, and to watch out for them, however subtly they may show up.

Who are/were your heroes /heroines? Rosie recently told me that her heroes when she was growing up were:

- Marilyn Munro
- James Dean
- Elvis

She still had all her posters at home!

What do they all have in common? They all died young and beautiful…. The unconscious mind is very literal, I feel sure that a part of her dis-ease process was due to it obeying those instructions.

Today she is still young and beautiful, but in vibrant health! And the posters are gone!

'Healing may not be so much about getting better, as about letting go of everything that isn't you - all of the expectations, all of the beliefs - and becoming who you are.'
Rachel Naomi Remen

Listen to yourself! What are you saying to yourself? Be thorough and meticulous in your work, challenge your beliefs, however irrelevant they may seem to you.

Bob's story
A young man, Bob, with testicular cancer was just talking to me, chatting about what he had been through. He had a very good prognosis, he wasn't concerned about that at all, but was curious as to why he had developed the disease. He had been healthy all his life, and ran 5 miles every day. It made no sense to him.

Amongst other intake questions, I asked him whether, as a child, he had had any sense of the future, what did he think the future would hold for him? His precise words were: "I always knew that I would die at 25', I repeated "What, you always knew you would die at 25?" and he said "Yes it was inevitable".

How old was Bob right now, he was 23. I asked him "Do you still believe that?" and he said "Well I am trying not to but I have this nagging doubt. It seemed completely inevitable when I was little, I simply couldn't imagine living longer than 25 – it seemed so ancient! It seemed like that at was a really long life, now I am recognizing that it is just the beginning'.

Repeat 3 times while tapping the Karate Chop:

Even though I believed I am going to die when I'm 25 I deeply and completely love and accept myself.

Eyebrow:	*I know I'm going to die at 25*
Side of Eye:	*I have always known I would die at 25*
Under Eye:	*I just know I will die at 25*
Under Nose:	*I always knew I was going to die at 25*
Chin:	*I know I'm going to die at 25*
Collar Bone:	*I have always known I would die at 25*
Under Arm:	*I just know I will die at 25*
Top of Head:	*I always knew I was going to die at 25*

Repeat 3 times while tapping the Karate Chop:

Even though I decided that when I was very little I deeply and completely love and accept myself.

Eyebrow:	*Even though I decided when I was little*
Side of Eye:	*That was what I decided*
Under Eye:	*That was the plan*
Under Nose:	*I had it all sorted*
Chin:	*Even though I decided when I was little*
Collar Bone:	*I decided that*
Under Arm:	*I'm going to die at 25*
Top of Head:	*Maybe... maybe not*

Repeat 3 times while tapping the Karate Chop:

Even though I decided then that I would die at 25. I am open to the possibility that the younger me made a mistake.

Eyebrow:	*That decision*
Side of Eye:	*What if I made a mistake*
Under Eye:	*That decision*
Under Nose:	*What if it was a mistake*
Chin:	*What if that younger me got it wrong*
Collar Bone:	*I love and accept the younger me*

Under Arm:	*But I choose to let his decision go*
Top of Head:	*I choose to release that mistaken thinking now*

Continue:

Eyebrow:	*I'm open to the possibility that I don't need to live my life...*
Side of Eye:	*According to the decisions of a small child*
Under Eye:	*What if the little me made a mistake*
Under Nose:	*I love and forgive him*
Chin:	*He was just doing the best he could*
Collar Bone:	*This child's belief*
Under Arm:	*I love and accept that younger me and*
Top of Head:	*I choose to let this belief go*

> *'It is not the mountain we conquer but ourselves.'*
> Sir Edmund Hillary

One final thought on the subject of beliefs:

Take the identical twins whose mother died of genetically diagnosed breast cancer. One twin develops the disease, at the same time the other is healthy. Why? They had the same upbringing, they continue to live in the same environment, they have identical cellular structure, they even have similar personalities, so what allows one to be healthy and the other sick?

I am not going to pretend to have the answers, but I wonder when you ask yourself that question, what your response is?

My intuition tells me that belief structures play an enormous part in this, and I would offer that maybe one twin always thought this would happen, whereas the other didn't give the same thought the time of day.

Tall poppies have to be cut down – Anna's story
Anna was as close to a genius as I have ever met, and a pioneer in the medical field. She was a highly intelligent woman with a beautiful manner and spirit. She shone academically and her work was highly regarded internationally. And she also had metastatic breast cancer.

Whilst taking a traditional medical approach to her healing, Anna was supporting herself with a variety of complementary therapies including EFT. She worked hard at her healing, with immense courage and humour, yet as I write she has now sadly died.

During our many conversations, and sessions, Anna brought up the possibility of being in a position, once healed, to truly evidence the power of a fully integrated

182

*healing approach. As soon as she voiced that thought she became quite anxious and said 'Oh no, I can't do that, **tall poppies have to be cut down'**.*

That seemed to come from nowhere, and her voice sounded like a small child. On further investigation she told me that the school that she had gone to at a young age didn't appreciate intelligence, they didn't appreciate the creativity that comes with intelligence, the ability to think outside the box. They considered this to be naughty, bad and disruptive and they tried to stifle it and the young Anna. One of the key phrases that was often used 'Tall poppies have to be cut down'.

I quote this because it is interesting that whist she knew that this was not true – and had valid experiences to prove it - a bit of her was still obeying that old rule, still couldn't let go of that fact that tall poppies have to be cut down – creativity means destruction, it's not safe to be different.

We worked hard to change that deep belief system, and Anna seemed very much to let it go, in fact she was able to laugh at it and forgive the teachers who had taught her that belief. She fully reclaimed that young part of her who was still doubtful about voicing her more 'wacky' ideas in public, and was able to focus on a new future, although sadly that was not to be in this lifetime.

Beliefs play a powerful and important part in every area of our lives. The world is motivated by beliefs, they are responsible for wars, religions, governments, lifestyles etc. Do not underestimate their power.

In the following chapters we will begin to look at applying the tapping to the practicalities that come with a cancer diagnosis: going into hospital, pain management and supporting whatever medical treatment you may elect to undergo.

CHAPTER 11

GOING INTO HOSPITAL

'Courage is not the absence of fear, but rather the judgement that something else is more important than fear'
Ambrose Redmoon

Many people have some fear or anxiety around hospitals, which has been exacerbated recently with the arrival of MRSA and other superbugs in the UK. Whilst few of us would probably volunteer ourselves for a hospital stay sometimes it is inevitable, and the best place we can be.

The following tapping protocols are a good starting place if you feel frightened or anxious about hospitals in general. Whilst I am offering a number of potential aspects here, there are likely to be others more specific to you which may be more appropriate. In this case, alter your words accordingly.

Tapping Section: Tapping for fear of hospitals

Repeat 3 times while tapping the Karate Chop:

Even though I am frightened of hospitals I deeply and completely love and accept myself

Eyebrow:	*Fear of hospitals*
Side of Eye:	*Fear of hospitals*
Under Eye:	*Fear of hospitals*
Under Nose:	*Fear of hospitals*
Chin:	*Fear of hospitals*
Collar Bone:	*Fear of hospitals*
Under Arm:	*Fear of hospitals*
Top of Head:	*Fear of hospitals*

Do a few rounds and then check in with yourself. How intense do you feel now? Has it changed? Gone? If there is any residual fear continue with a few rounds as follows:

Repeat 3 times while tapping the Karate Chop:

Even though I still have this fear of hospitals I deeply and completely love and accept myself

Eyebrow:	*Remaining fear of hospitals*
Side of Eye:	*Remaining fear of hospitals*

Under Eye:	*Remaining fear of hospitals*
Under Nose:	*Remaining fear of hospitals*
Chin:	*Remaining fear of hospitals*
Collar Bone:	*Remaining fear of hospitals*
Under Arm:	*Remaining fear of hospitals*
Top of Head:	*Remaining fear of hospitals*

Repeat 3 times while tapping the Karate Chop:

Even though I have this fear in my stomach/chest/etc I deeply and completely love and accept myself

Eyebrow:	*Hospital fear in my stomach*
Side of Eye:	*Hospital fear in my stomach*
Under Eye:	*Hospital fear in my stomach*
Under Nose:	*Hospital fear in my stomach*
Chin:	*Hospital fear in my stomach*
Collar Bone:	*Hospital fear in my stomach*
Under Arm:	*Hospital fear in my stomach*
Top of Head:	*Hospital fear in my stomach*

Check in again and if you still have some fear ask yourself where you feel that fear in your body and then continue as follows:

Repeat 3 times while tapping the Karate Chop:

Even though I have this remaining hospital fear in my stomach I deeply and completely love and accept myself

Eyebrow:	*Remaining hospital fear in my stomach*
Side of Eye:	*Remaining hospital fear in my stomach*
Under Eye:	*Remaining hospital fear in my stomach*
Under Nose:	*Remaining hospital fear in my stomach*
Chin:	*Remaining hospital fear in my stomach*
Collar Bone:	*Remaining hospital fear in my stomach*
Under Arm:	*Remaining hospital fear in my stomach*
Top of Head:	*Remaining hospital fear in my stomach*

Check in with yourself again. If the fear is still there you will need to begin to get more specific as to precisely what the fear is of, finding the different aspects.

Below is a list of possibilities, by no means exhaustive:

- **Fear of doctors/nurses**
- **Fear of treatments**
- **Fear of being kept in**
- **Fear of the machinery: MRI/CT scanners, radiotherapy etc**
- **Fear of MRSA/superbugs**
- **Specific hospital smells/disinfectant etc**
- **Seeing sick patients**

Begin by tapping on the specific fear, and ask yourself the following questions:

- **When did you first feel like this?**
- **What was happening?**
- **What do these feelings remind you of?**
- **Where did you learn to feel this fear?**

You may not be able to answer these immediately, and that is fine, but if you do get any answers you will need to tap through any specific memories that emerge, using the Movie Technique.

Once again, be your own detective, the answers may not be obvious.

Tina's story
Tina was experiencing what she described as an 'irrational terror of hospitals'. She had had very limited experience of them, her only visits until her cancer diagnosis had been to see friends who had had babies – in her words 'really happy celebratory times'. Her sudden terror seemed very real yet mystifying to her. We had already explored all the possibilities above to no avail.

Having met this many times before, and especially around hospitals, I asked her the following questions:

Had anyone she knew been in hospital?	*Yes, but they were all OK*
Any family members?	*Not as far as she knew*
Had she heard any bad stories?	*Yes, but took them with a pinch of salt*

As we were still not getting anywhere with her fear I suggested another appointment the following week, asking her to tap on anything that emerged in the meantime. I had a very full diary and the only time I could possibly have seen her the following week was late one evening. That seemed fine, until she said 'Actually no, I can't do that, that is ER night, I can't miss it!'

ER, for those who are unfamiliar with it, is an American television hospital drama set in the emergency room. To me, this seemed a strange choice of viewing for someone who was terrified of hospitals. So I asked her about it and she said it did frighten her but she felt compelled to watch it, it felt like reality to her and she was able to describe the characters and storylines as if she was taking part herself.

I suggested, tentatively, that this might be contributing to her hospital fear as ER shows some very traumatic incidents. She wasn't aware of feeling particularly frightened when watching it, but agreed to tap on herself continually whilst she watched this week's episode. She also had recorded several past episodes so we decided that she would rewatch a few of them too, all the time tapping continuously without any words or specific focus.

As we couldn't make an appointment for the following week our next one was scheduled for after her next hospital appointment. Tina knew she could tap on the lead up to the appointment, and also in the hospital itself, if she needed to, which was how she had managed before.

She rang me before she got to the hospital saying she was feeling absolutely fine, no fear, and was a little worried that she was in denial and that she would fall to bits when she walked through the door. We tapped on these minor anxieties and agreed to speak after the appointment. She rang me later completely over the moon. The calmness had continued throughout the appointment, and she had decided to test it further by having lunch in the hospital canteen. Zero fear!

> *'Patience and perseverance have a magical effect*
> *before which difficulties disappear and obstacles vanish.'*
> *John Quincy Adams*

Sometimes it will seem as though the fears and anxieties bombard you relentlessly. Do not give up! Keep tapping! However tough it feels, you will move through these feelings, the important thing is to persist. Notice any additional thoughts you may be having around the process, maybe it is not moving fast enough for you or similar. Tap as follows:

Repeat 3 times while tapping the Karate Chop:

Even though this is taking too long I deeply and completely love and accept myself

Eyebrow:	*It is taking too long*
Side of Eye:	*It is too slow*
Under Eye:	*I am too slow*
Under Nose:	*I will never clear this*
Chin:	*It is taking too long*
Collar Bone:	*It is too slow*
Under Arm:	*I am too slow*
Top of Head:	*I will never clear this*

Repeat 3 times while tapping the Karate Chop:

Even though I feel impatient I deeply and completely love and accept myself

Eyebrow:	*Impatient*
Side of Eye:	*Feeling impatient*

187

Under Eye:	*Impatient*
Under Nose:	*Feeling impatient*
Chin:	*Impatient*
Collar Bone:	*Feeling impatient*
Under Arm:	*Impatient*
Top of Head:	*Feeling impatient*

Continue to work with any remaining fears or anxieties until you either reach a zero on your SUDS scale, or a very low number such as two or three.

At this point you can begin to introduce some Choices. Make some notes as you consider these questions.

- How would you like to feel about this instead?
- What would be a more useful way for you to be?
- Is that reasonable?

If the answer to the last question is yes, then continue using the Choices method, substituting your words as appropriate.

Repeat 3 times while tapping the Karate Chop:

Even though I still have some of this hospital fear I choose to feel calm and confident

Eyebrow:	*Remaining hospital fear*
Side of Eye:	*Remaining hospital fear*
Under Eye:	*Remaining hospital fear*
Under Nose:	*Remaining hospital fear*
Chin:	*Remaining hospital fear*
Collar Bone:	*Remaining hospital fear*
Under Arm:	*Remaining hospital fear*
Top of Head:	*Remaining hospital fear*

Continue:

Eyebrow:	*Remaining hospital fear*
Side of Eye:	*I choose to feel calm and confident*
Under Eye:	*Remaining hospital fear*
Under Nose:	*I choose to feel calm and confident*
Chin:	*Remaining hospital fear*
Collar Bone:	*I choose to feel calm and confident*

| Under Arm: | Remaining hospital fear |
| Top of Head: | I choose to feel calm and confident |

Continue:

Eyebrow:	I choose to feel calm and confident
Side of Eye:	I choose to feel calm and confident
Under Eye:	I choose to feel calm and confident
Under Nose:	I choose to feel calm and confident
Chin:	I choose to feel calm and confident
Collar Bone:	I choose to feel calm and confident
Under Arm:	I choose to feel calm and confident
Top of Head:	I choose to feel calm and confident

Being in hospital

'The very first requirement in a hospital is that it should do the sick no harm.'
Florence Nightingale

There are many different reasons for being in hospital and you are likely to encounter several of them during your cancer treatment. Some stays will be longer than others, but whatever the duration of your stay you can approach it in the same way with the tapping, using a variation on the Movie Technique, where, instead of replaying an old movie you create a new one wherein you imagine your trip to hospital now.

When you are feeling more comfortable about the idea of the hospital itself, begin to work with the specific treatment you are scheduled to have. We will begin by working with surgery – maybe you are having a mastectomy, a colostomy, maybe a hysterectomy, or perhaps removal of a tumour from another area of your body. Tune in to the particular surgery you are going to have. You may know exactly what that will look like, what the piece of the body that is going to be removed will look like. You may have had scans or X-rays highlighting the diseased cells or organs.

Notice how you feel in your body as you think about the procedure ahead. Choose one or more of the following tapping protocols and tap accordingly. Or adapt the wording to suit your feelings if different from those below. Notice where in your body you feel the specific resonance of the emotion.

Tapping Section: Tapping for fear of surgery

Repeat 3 times while tapping the Karate Chop:

Even though I am frightened of the surgery I deeply and completely love and accept myself

189

Eyebrow:	*Fear of the surgery*
Side of Eye:	*Fear of the surgery*
Under Eye:	*Fear of the surgery*
Under Nose:	*Fear of the surgery*
Chin:	*Fear of the surgery*
Collar Bone:	*Fear of the surgery*
Under Arm:	*Fear of the surgery*
Top of Head:	*Fear of the surgery*

Repeat 3 times while tapping the Karate Chop:

Even though I have this surgery fear in my gut I deeply and completely love and accept myself

Eyebrow:	*Surgery fear in my gut*
Side of Eye:	*Surgery fear in my gut*
Under Eye:	*Surgery fear in my gut*
Under Nose:	*Surgery fear in my gut*
Chin:	*Surgery fear in my gut*
Collar Bone:	*Surgery fear in my gut*
Under Arm:	*Surgery fear in my gut*
Top of Head:	*Surgery fear in my gut*

Repeat 3 times while tapping the Karate Chop:

Even though I am dreading the surgery I deeply and completely love and accept myself

Eyebrow:	*Surgery dread*
Side of Eye:	*Surgery dread*
Under Eye:	*Surgery dread*
Under Nose:	*Surgery dread*
Chin:	*Surgery dread*
Collar Bone:	*Surgery dread*
Under Arm:	*Surgery dread*
Top of Head:	*Surgery dread*

Repeat 3 times while tapping the Karate Chop:

Even though I am anxious about the surgery I deeply and completely love and accept myself

Eyebrow:	*Surgery anxiety*
Side of Eye:	*Surgery anxiety*
Under Eye:	*I don't know what will happen*
Under Nose:	*I don't know how I will feel*
Chin:	*Surgery anxiety*
Collar Bone:	*Surgery anxiety*
Under Arm:	*Feeling really anxious*
Top of Head:	*Surgery anxiety*

Continue tapping around on the above protocols until you have cleared the feeling in your body when you think about the impending surgery. You may need to do several rounds, and you may need to do further investigation by asking yourself our favourite question:

What does this remind me of?
If you get an immediate connection to an earlier memory, use the Movie Technique to work through that memory and clear it.

It maybe that you have no experience of being operated on, no experience of hospitals apart from what you may have seen on television or at the cinema.

Repeat 3 times while tapping the Karate Chop:

Even though I am not sure how it is going to be or how I will feel I deeply and completely love and accept myself

Eyebrow:	*Fear of the unknown*
Side of Eye:	*Fear of what might happen*
Under Eye:	*Fear of how it will be*
Under Nose:	*Fear of how I will feel*
Chin:	*All these surgery fears*
Collar Bone:	*Fear of the unknown*
Under Arm:	*Fear of what might happen*
Top of Head:	*Fear of how I will feel*

When you feel calmer about the prospect of going into hospital I would like you to imagine you are at the cinema and you are going to run a movie of you going into hospital the next time you have to go. See yourself:

- **Arriving at the hospital**
- **Going to the relevant department/ward**

191

- **Sitting in the waiting room**
- **Beginning the treatment**
- **Waiting for the doctor/consultant**
- **Preparing for the ultrasound/MRI/CT scan**
- **Having a blood test**
- **Lying in the hospital bed**
- **Looking around the ward**

As you watch yourself on that movie screen, ask yourself the following questions:

- *How do you look?*
- *How do you feel?*
- *What is happening in your body now as you watch that movie?*

Take one scene at a time and tap through any negative emotional response, always being aware of your body responses, until you are able to run that piece of the movie calmly.

Be on the lookout for the different aspects contributing to this feeling. Perhaps you hear the buzzing or the beeping of the various machines in the wards, maybe it is the sight of the doctors in their white coats. Notice what shows up for you, and how it shows up.

- **Is the image in colour or black and white?**
- **Is it close by or far away?**

When you have done a few rounds of tapping, check in with the image and notice any changes.

- **Has it moved further away or nearer?**
- **Has the colour changed?**
- **Has the clarity changed?**
- **What is happening with it?**
- **Are there any specific emotions that come to you when you look at that image now?**

Continue with this until you are completely clear of anything but a normal response to hospital, such as "I'd rather not be there but it's going to be okay".

If you are going in for surgery, you might want to work through all the different components that occur during the surgical procedure. The following are just a few examples:

- **Being on the ward**
- **The medical team talking you through the procedure**
- **Being given a pre-operative sedative**

- **Feeling a little bit sleepy**
- **Being taken down or up to the operating theatre**
- **Being given the anaesthetic**
- **Going to sleep**
- **Waking up/Coming round**
- **Pain**

Are there any particular bits you found un-nerving or upsetting? If there are, tap on those specific pieces of the movie until you clear your feelings towards them. Below are a few common possibilities:

Tapping Section: Tapping for fear of anesthesia

Repeat 3 times while tapping the Karate Chop:

Even though I am scared of the anaesthetic I deeply and completely love and accept myself

Eyebrow:	*Anaesthetic fear*
Side of Eye:	*Anaesthetic fear*
Under Eye:	*Anaesthetic fear*
Under Nose:	*Anaesthetic fear*
Chin:	*Anaesthetic fear*
Collar Bone:	*Anaesthetic fear*
Under Arm:	*Anaesthetic fear*
Top of Head:	*Anaesthetic fear*

Repeat 3 times while tapping the Karate Chop:

Even though I am really scared of being put under I deeply and completely love and accept myself

Eyebrow:	*Fear of being put under*
Side of Eye:	*Fear of being put to sleep*
Under Eye:	*Fear of being knocked out*
Under Nose:	*Fear of being put under*
Chin:	*Fear of being put to sleep*
Collar Bone:	*Fear of being put under*
Under Arm:	*Fear of being knocked out*
Top of Head:	*Fear of being put to sleep*

Fear of feeling out of control, or being out of control seems to be one of the major anxieties around the anaesthetic itself. It is human nature to want to be in control and the thought of being in a deep sleep whilst surgeons operate on you can feel very uncomfortable for some people.

Repeat 3 times while tapping the Karate Chop:

Even though I am terrified about being out of control I deeply and completely love and accept myself

Eyebrow:	*Terror of not being in control*
Side of Eye:	*Terror of not being in control*
Under Eye:	*Terror of not being in control*
Under Nose:	*Terror of not being in control*
Chin:	*Terror of not being in control*
Collar Bone:	*Terror of not being in control*
Under Arm:	*Terror of not being in control*
Top of Head:	*Terror of not being in control*

When you have reduced the fear to a manageable level create a positive Choice. Below are some suggestions, but remember, use your own words, they are much more powerful than mine.

Repeat 3 times while tapping the Karate Chop:

Even though I am frightened of being out of control I choose to place my trust in the expertise of my surgeon

Eyebrow:	*Fear of being out of control*
Side of Eye:	*Fear of being out of control*
Under Eye:	*Fear of being out of control*
Under Nose:	*Fear of being out of control*
Chin:	*Fear of being out of control*
Collar Bone:	*Fear of being out of control*
Under Arm:	*Fear of being out of control*
Top of Head:	*Fear of being out of control*

Continue:

Eyebrow:	*I choose to trust the expertise of my surgeon*
Side of Eye:	*I choose to trust the expertise of my surgeon*
Under Eye:	*I choose to trust the expertise of my surgeon*

194

Under Nose:	*I choose to trust the expertise of my surgeon*
Chin:	*I choose to trust the expertise of my surgeon*
Collar Bone:	*I choose to trust the expertise of my surgeon*
Under Arm:	*I choose to trust the expertise of my surgeon*
Top of Head:	*I choose to trust the expertise of my surgeon*

Continue:

Eyebrow:	*Fear of being out of control*
Side of Eye:	*I choose to trust the expertise of my surgeon*
Under Eye:	*Fear of being out of control*
Under Nose:	*I choose to trust the expertise of my surgeon*
Chin:	*Fear of being out of control*
Collar Bone:	*I choose to trust the expertise of my surgeon*
Under Arm:	*Fear of being out of control*
Top of Head:	*I choose to trust the expertise of my surgeon*

Repeat 3 times while tapping the Karate Chop:

Even though I am frightened of the anaesthetic I choose to keep myself safe even when asleep

Eyebrow:	*Fear of the anaesthetic*
Side of Eye:	*Fear of the anaesthetic*
Under Eye:	*Fear of the anaesthetic*
Under Nose:	*Fear of the anaesthetic*
Chin:	*Fear of the anaesthetic*
Collar Bone:	*Fear of the anaesthetic*
Under Arm:	*Fear of the anaesthetic*
Top of Head:	*Fear of the anaesthetic*

Continue:

Eyebrow:	*I choose to keep myself safe even when asleep*
Side of Eye:	*I choose to keep myself safe even when asleep*
Under Eye:	*I choose to keep myself safe even when asleep*
Under Nose:	*I choose to keep myself safe even when asleep*
Chin:	*I choose to keep myself safe even when asleep*

Collar Bone:	*I choose to keep myself safe even when asleep*
Under Arm:	*I choose to keep myself safe even when asleep*
Top of Head:	*I choose to keep myself safe even when asleep*

Continue:

Eyebrow:	*Fear of the anaesthetic*
Side of Eye:	*I choose to keep myself safe even when asleep*
Under Eye:	*Fear of the anaesthetic*
Under Nose:	*I choose to keep myself safe even when asleep*
Chin:	*Fear of the anaesthetic*
Collar Bone:	*I choose to keep myself safe even when asleep*
Under Arm:	*Fear of the anaesthetic*
Top of Head:	*I choose to keep myself safe even when asleep*

Tapping Section: Tapping for other surgery related fears

Repeat 3 times while tapping the Karate Chop:

Even though I am frightened it is going to hurt I deeply and completely love and accept myself

Eyebrow:	*Fear of the pain*
Side of Eye:	*Fear of the pain*
Under Eye:	*Fear of it hurting*
Under Nose:	*Fear of the hurt*
Chin:	*Fear of the pain*
Collar Bone:	*Fear of the pain*
Under Arm:	*Fear of it hurting*
Top of Head:	*Fear of the hurt*

Repeat 3 times while tapping the Karate Chop:

Even though I am scared it won't work I deeply and completely love and accept myself

Eyebrow:	*Fear of the surgery not working*
Side of Eye:	*Fear of it not working*
Under Eye:	*What if it doesn't work?*
Under Nose:	*What if it does?*

Chin:	*Fear of the surgery not working*
Collar Bone:	*Fear of it not working*
Under Arm:	*What if it doesn't work?*
Top of Head:	*What if it does?*

Repeat 3 times while tapping the Karate Chop:

Even though I am scared I won't cope with the pain I deeply and completely love and accept myself

Eyebrow:	*Fear of not coping with the pain*
Side of Eye:	*What if it is too much to cope with?*
Under Eye:	*What if I can't cope?*
Under Nose:	*Fear of the pain*
Chin:	*Fear of not coping with the pain*
Collar Bone:	*What if it is too much to cope with?*
Under Arm:	*What if I can't cope?*
Top of Head:	*Fear of the pain*

Repeat 3 times while tapping the Karate Chop:

Even though I'm afraid I won't wake up I deeply and completely love and accept myself

Eyebrow:	*Fear of not waking up*
Under Eye:	*Fear of not coming round*
Under Eye:	*Fear of not waking up*
Under Nose:	*Fear of not coming round*
Chin:	*Fear of not waking up*
Collar Bone:	*Fear of not coming round*
Under Arm:	*Fear of not waking up*
Top of Head:	*Fear of not coming round*

Continue until you can look at that specific image or think that particular thought without any emotional charge, when you are able to watch it as if it is just something you are watching on the television.

At this point, re-run your initial movie, making it bigger and in full technicolour.

Vividly imagine being in that hospital

- **Smell the smells**

- **Hear any sounds: machines, voices etc**
- **Look around you, see who is there, what are they doing?**
- **How are you feeling?**

If anything creates an emotional or physical charge, isolate it and continue to tap. For example:

Repeat 3 times while tapping the Karate Chop:

Even though I feel anxious at that bit I deeply and completely love and accept myself

Eyebrow:	*Anxiety at that bit*
Side of Eye:	*That bit*
Under Eye:	*And everything I feel about it*
Under Nose:	*Anxious about that bit*
Chin:	*Anxiety at that bit*
Collar Bone:	*That bit*
Under Arm:	*And everything I feel about it*
Top of Head:	*Anxious about that bit*

Repeat 3 times while tapping the Karate Chop:

Even though the smell still gets to me I deeply and completely love and accept myself

Eyebrow:	*That smell*
Side of Eye:	*Everything it reminds me of*
Under Eye:	*THAT smell*
Under Nose:	*That smell*
Chin:	*That smell*
Collar Bone:	*And everything it reminds me of*
Under Arm:	*That smell*
Top of Head:	*That smell*

If you get stuck on a particular piece, which seems to refuse to collapse or release ask yourself our favourite question:

What does this remind you of?
You may find yourself being taken back to a different memory, which will then need the tapping applied first.

For example, the smell of the hospital disinfectant might remind you of the disinfectant they used at school, which in turn may relate to a negative memory around school. In this case you would make that specific memory into a mini

198

movie and tap to clear the charge around that. Working to collapse that response would very likely change your current response to the hospital.

Whatever comes to mind in response to that question, acknowledge it and tap with it until you have cleared any emotional intensity. Then, and only then, go back to your original hospital movie and run it again, noticing what changes happen and seeing how you feel. Continue with this until you are completely clear of anything but a normal response to being in hospital, when you are able to accept being there, even though it may not be where you would choose to be.

Now, unless you have a needle phobia, go to Chapters 13 and 14 where we look at pain management and specific treatments. If you have a needle phobia the next chapter is for you.

CHAPTER 12

FEAR OF NEEDLES

'There is perhaps nothing so bad and so dangerous in life as fear.'
Jawaharlal Nehru

A very common issue, particularly for children, is a fear of needles. When receiving hospital treatment - be it blood tests, chemotherapy, anaesthesia, intravenous antibiotics – the list is endless, needles play a key role in administering the medication. I have worked with many people for their fear of needles and /or injections and the most common words I hear are 'Why should I like them!?'

Before we start to work with this, it is important to realise that this is not about your liking needles, or injections. I doubt if anyone could claim to actively enjoy having their blood taken or having injections. The intention is to reduce any fear to a point where you feel comfortable enough with the concept to be able to have the treatment or test from a place of calmness, even if that is a place of calm resignation.

A Note of Caution:
There is a big difference between a fear, or intense dislike, and a phobic response. If you know that your response to the thought of needles/ injections, etc is very strong, or you have experienced a severe phobic response in the past then it is probably not sensible to do this work on your own. You need to take care not to get into the fear itself, and an experienced practitioner will have ways of dissociating you from the emotional response whilst you tap to clear it. If your fear of needles registers above 7 on the SUDS scale, I would suggest your doing a session or two with an advanced practitioner.

Phobia: An unreasonable sort of fear that can cause avoidance and panic.
www.medterms.com

Annie's story
Annie, my 12 year old god daughter, had an intense fear of needles, so much so that she had fainted several times during her routine childhood vaccinations. She needed to have her BCG injection, which comprised of two separate parts, firstly the test, then, providing she had no TB immunity, the vaccine itself. She was terrified but also rational, she recognised that it was important to have the injection, and also she wanted to get over her fear so that she could travel in her gap year (5 years time!). She knew I did 'this tapping thing' and she wanted to give it a go. With her mother there with her, we began very gingerly tiptoeing around the issue, using phrases such as:

Tapping Section: Tapping for the mere thought of needles

Repeat 3 times while tapping the Karate Chop:

Even though I can't think about that thing I deeply and completely love and accept myself

Eyebrow:	I can't think about it
Side of Eye:	I can't go there
Under Eye:	I can't think about it
Under Nose:	It is not safe to go there
Chin:	I can't think about it
Collar Bone:	I can't go there
Under Arm:	I can't think about it
Top of Head:	It is not safe to go there

Repeat 3 times while tapping the Karate Chop:

Even though I can't do it I deeply and completely love and accept myself

Eyebrow:	I can't do it
Side of Eye:	I really can't
Under Eye:	I will never be able to do it
Under Nose:	I can't do it
Chin:	No way
Collar Bone:	I'll never do it
Under Arm:	I can't do it
Top of Head:	I just can't do it

Repeat 3 times while tapping the Karate Chop:

Even though I am terrified of that thought I deeply and completely love and accept myself

Eyebrow:	That thought
Side of Eye:	That injection thought
Under Eye:	That terrifying thought
Under Nose:	Injections
Chin:	That thought
Collar Bone:	That terrifying thought
Under Arm:	Feeling terrified
Top of Head:	That terrifying thought

Repeat 3 times while tapping the Karate Chop:

Even though I will never do it I deeply and completely love and accept myself

Eyebrow:	*I will never do it*
Side of Eye:	*I just will never be able to*
Under Eye:	*I will never do it*
Under Nose:	*It just won't happen*
Chin:	*I will never be able to do it*
Collar Bone:	*I just won't*
Under Arm:	*It will never happen*
Top of Head:	*I will never be able to do it*

She didn't seem to be registering a very high intensity on any of these Set-up Statements so I began to get a little more specific, in Gary Craig's terminology, sneaking up on the problem.

Repeat 3 times while tapping the Karate Chop:

Even though injections make me faint I deeply and completely love and accept myself

Eyebrow:	*That thought*
Side of Eye:	*Injections make me faint*
Under Eye:	*That thought*
Under Nose:	*That truth*
Chin:	*Injections make me faint*
Collar Bone:	*All those times*
Under Arm:	*That truth*
Top of Head:	*Injections make me faint*

Repeat 3 times while tapping the Karate Chop:

Even though I am scared of fainting I deeply and completely love and accept myself

Eyebrow:	*Fear of fainting*
Side of Eye:	*Fear of fainting*
Under Eye:	*Fear of fainting*
Under Nose:	*Fear of fainting*
Chin:	*Fear of fainting*
Collar Bone:	*Fear of fainting*
Under Arm:	*Fear of fainting*
Top of Head:	*Fear of fainting*

Repeat 3 times while tapping the Karate Chop:

Even though I always faint around needles I deeply and completely love and accept myself

Eyebrow:	*I always faint around needles*
Side of Eye:	*That is just how it is for me*
Under Eye:	*It always happens*
Under Nose:	*I always faint*
Chin:	*I can't change it*
Collar Bone:	*Maybe*
Under Arm:	*Maybe I can*
Top of Head:	*No, I always faint around needles*

We then used the Movie Technique to tap through the various times when she had fainted having an injection, both at the doctor's and at school. We reduced each of these movies to zero and she could happily tell the story each time.

At this point, having covered all the aspects I could find, I asked Annie how she would feel were she to close her eyes and vividly imagine having an injection now. She said she felt fine about this so she gave it a go. I continued to tap on her finger points as she did it.

Within a couple of seconds all the colour drained from her face and she keeled over sideways on the sofa. With her mother's permission I just continued talking to her and tapping until gradually the colour returned and she came round (probably not longer than 20 seconds). I knew from her history exactly what to expect should she faint, and the three of us had already discussed what to do should it happen.

When Annie was 'back with us' and feeling normal I asked her what exactly had happened. She said she had been imagining being given an injection as discussed and it was the sight of the needle that made her feel strange first. I asked her again what this reminded her of and this time she said that it was about Liz.

Liz is a good friend of her family and also diabetic. She said she could remember Liz injecting herself when Annie had been a very tiny baby sitting on her mother's lap. As she talked about this she began to get very upset. We quickly began tapping on that memory, and how it made her feel then and now. Her mother could remember it too and was amazed that Annie was able to recall it in such detail as she could only have been about 6 months old. There was nothing intrinsically traumatic about the incident itself, but it had been processed in the baby's unconscious as terrifying.

Having tapped through that memory through the eyes of the 12 year old, and also imagining it through the eyes of the baby Annie, I asked her if she would be OK to vividly imagine having an injection now, but to stop the movie as soon as she felt any signs of fainting. She was able to imagine the entire scenario, and then several other ones in different environments, without feeling remotely faint.

She is now 17 and has just left school. One of the last things she did at school was have the vaccination for cervical cancer. Before having it (three different injections) she said she felt a little anxious as she was Head Girl and it wouldn't be cool to faint! She had tapped on that anxiety herself and the injections had been easy!

If you have a fear of needles and feel confident in working on your own, I suggest the following tapping protocol, starting very globally. Again it is important to rate your fear on a scale of 0 – 10, where 10 is very intense (as above) and 0 is where there is no fear.

Tapping Section: Tapping for fear of needles

Repeat 3 times while tapping the Karate Chop:

Even though I am frightened of needles I deeply and completely love and accept myself

Eyebrow:	*Fear of needles*
Side of Eye:	*Fear of needles*
Under Eye:	*Fear of needles*
Under Nose:	*Fear of needles*
Chin:	*Fear of needles*
Collar Bone:	*Fear of needles*
Under Arm:	*Fear of needles*
Top of Head:	*Fear of needles*

Or

Repeat 3 times while tapping the Karate Chop:

Even though I am frightened of injections I deeply and completely love and accept myself

Eyebrow:	*Fear of injections*
Side of Eye:	*Fear of injections*
Under Eye:	*Fear of injections*
Under Nose:	*Fear of injections*
Chin:	*Fear of injections*
Collar Bone:	*Fear of injections*
Top of Head:	*Fear of injections*
Top of Head:	*Fear of injections*

Repeat 3 times while tapping the Karate Chop:

Even though I am frightened of blood tests I deeply and completely love and accept myself

Eyebrow:	*Fear of blood tests*
Side of Eye:	*Fear of blood tests*
Under Eye:	*Fear of blood tests*
Under Nose:	*Fear of blood tests*
Chin:	*Fear of blood tests*
Collar Bone:	*Fear of blood tests*
Under Arm:	*Fear of blood tests*
Top of Head:	*Fear of blood tests*

After a few rounds check out what is happening when you think of an injection, or a blood test or a needle in your arm (whichever carries the strongest response for you).

If you are still having a fear response, continue:

Repeat 3 times while tapping the Karate Chop:

Even though I still have some of this fear of ___ I deeply and completely love and accept myself

Eyebrow:	*Remaining fear of....*
Side of Eye:	*Remaining fear of....*
Under Eye:	*Remaining fear of....*
Under Nose:	*Remaining fear of....*
Chin:	*Remaining fear of....*
Collar Bone:	*Remaining fear of....*
Under Arm:	*Remaining fear of....*
Top of Head:	*Remaining fear of....*

Check in again and notice what changes have happened now, how you feel now when you think of needles, an injection or a blood test?

If there is any remaining fear, notice where that feeling shows up in your body:

- **Is it butterflies in your stomach?**
- **Is it a fear in your throat?**
- **Is it tightness in your chest?**
- **What is your breathing like?**

Whatever physical manifestation you experience, use it in your next tapping sequence. Remember to take a SUDS level before starting so you can test your results.

Tapping Section: Tapping for physical fear of needles

For example:

Repeat 3 times while tapping the Karate Chop:

Even though I have these butterflies in my stomach I deeply and completely love and accept myself

Eyebrow:	*Butterflies in my stomach*
Side of Eye:	*Injection butterflies in my stomach*
Under Eye:	*Butterflies in my stomach*
Under Nose:	*Butterfly fear in my stomach*
Chin:	*Butterflies in my stomach*
Collar Bone:	*Injection butterflies in my stomach*
Under Arm:	*Butterflies in my stomach*
Top of Head:	*Butterfly fear in my stomach*

Repeat 3 times while tapping the Karate Chop:

Even though I have this needle fear in my throat I deeply and completely love and accept myself

Eyebrow:	*Needle fear in my throat*
Side of Eye:	*Needle fear in my throat*
Under Eye:	*Needle fear in my throat*
Under Nose:	*Needle fear in my throat*
Chin:	*Needle fear in my throat*
Collar Bone:	*Needle fear in my throat*
Under Arm:	*Needle fear in my throat*
Top of Head:	*Needle fear in my throat*

Repeat 3 times while tapping the Karate Chop:

Even though I have this tightness in my chest I deeply and completely love and accept myself

Eyebrow:	*Tightness in my chest*
Side of Eye:	*Fear in my chest*

Under Eye:	*Tightness in my chest*
Under Nose:	*Fear in my chest*
Chin:	*Tightness in my chest*
Collar Bone:	*Fear in my chest*
Under Arm:	*Tightness in my chest*
Top of Head:	*Fear in my chest*

Do 3 – 4 rounds like this and then check your SUDS level. If you still have a high number, 5 or above, ask yourself:

- **What does this feeling remind you of?**
- **When did you first feel like this?**
- **What was happening?**

Notice what comes to mind. Your unconscious mind will offer you the next piece to tap with. It may be that you have had a negative experience around needles before, if so, make that into a mini movie, give it a title and an intensity rating and begin tapping on it.

Repeat 3 times while tapping the Karate Chop:

Even though I have this X movie, I deeply and completely love and accept myself

Eyebrow:	*X movie*
Side of Eye:	*X movie*
Under Eye:	*X movie*
Under Nose:	*X movie*
Chin:	*X movie*
Collar Bone:	*X movie*
Under Arm:	*X movie*
Top of Head:	*X movie*

Repeat 3 times while tapping the Karate Chop:

Even though I have these X movie emotions I deeply and completely love and accept myself

Eyebrow:	*X movie emotions*
Side of Eye:	*X movie emotions*
Under Eye:	*X movie emotions*
Under Nose:	*X movie emotions*
Chin:	*X movie emotions*

Collar Bone:	*X movie emotions*
Under Arm:	*X movie emotions*
Top of Head:	*X movie emotions*

Some people can't bear the thought of a needle piercing their skin. Most people don't relish the thought, but can deal with it. For some it becomes their total focus and the piece of the thought of injections that the fear hangs on. My eldest daughter is one of these. She used to obsess about the moment a needle would pierce her skin. Whilst in many ways it is entirely logical and sensible to dislike that moment, there are times when that thought, and the fear that builds from it, are not useful. Blood tests are an important part of monitoring the effects of cancer treatment, medical or otherwise, and obviously needles are a vital component of many of the treatments for the disease.

Tap on the thought itself, as it is that thought which is creating the internal disturbance and fear response. The thought holds all the power. By balancing the system to the thought itself it is possible to easily neutralise the fear.

Tapping Section: Tapping for needle piercing skin

Repeat 3 times while tapping the Karate Chop:

Even though I can't bear the thought of the needle piercing my skin I deeply and completely love and accept myself

Eyebrow:	*That thought*
Side of Eye:	*That powerful thought*
Under Eye:	*I can't bear that thought*
Under Nose:	*That needle thought*
Chin:	*That thought*
Collar Bone:	*That powerful thought*
Under Arm:	*I can't bear that thought*
Top of Head:	*That needle thought*

Repeat 3 times while tapping the Karate Chop:

Even though I hate the thought of the needle piercing my skin I deeply and completely love and accept myself

Eyebrow:	*That thought*
Side of Eye:	*Needle piercing thought*
Under Eye:	*Needle piercing emotions*
Under Nose:	*That thought and how it makes me feel*
Chin:	*That thought*
Collar Bone:	*Needle piercing thought*

Under Arm:	*Needle piercing emotions*
Top of Head:	*That thought and how it makes me feel*

Once you have reduced any intensity around needles/ injections and such, to a manageable level, and before you go into the actual situation, it is important to ensure you are familiar with David Lake's Continual Tapping, so that while you are having an injection/ blood test/ chemotherapy, etc, you can use the fingers on your free hand to continually tap, keeping your energy system balanced during the procedure and ensuring that you address any new aspects, if and when they appear.

In the following chapter we will explore ways of managing pain as well as looking at a specific technique for releasing anxiety from your breath, using the Constricted Breathing Technique.

CHAPTER 13

PAIN MANAGEMENT

'There are only two ways to live your life. One is as though nothing is a miracle. The other is as though everything is a miracle'
Albert Einstein

In Chinese medicine, they believe that stagnant energy or Chi **creates** pain. Stagnant energy creates blockages, which can show up physically, possibly as cancer. Whilst some pain may be necessary as a precaution to causing further damage, the tapping provides an effective way of managing and reducing excess pain. It will not, however, clear pain that is deemed necessary by the unconscious mind. For example, a broken leg needs to be painful in order for us not to do further damage by walking on it.

'If this is a blessing, it is certainly very well disguised'
Winston Churchill

Physical symptoms as metaphors

Physical symptoms are often a metaphor for our emotional states. Indeed, American Indians believe that our physical and emotional worlds mirror each other. With the tapping, it doesn't matter what you work with the physical symptom or an emotional symptom, they are two sides of the same coin and affect each other accordingly. Clear a negative emotion and you will often find a change in physical symptoms and/ or pain and visa versa.

Many people report feeling completely fine and well and pain-free prior to a cancer diagnosis. Cancer is often discovered during routine checks and people may be unaware that they have a problem. Others may have felt a lump or will have experienced some form of physical discomfort or pain. There are many different presentations of cancer, too varied to itemise here, and as I said before, I am not a doctor so my interpretation of any medical terminology would not be much use. However, I do believe that as every individual is different, every healing approach needs to be specifically tailored according to individual needs.

There are often very obvious causes to pain, perhaps an operation, burns from radiotherapy, side effects of drug treatments, or tumour pain itself. It may seem that this pain has a place and a purpose and that it is not possible to relieve it with tapping.

A curious phenomenon of EFT is that even seemingly constant unremitting pain can be relieved through tapping, often permanently. However, the unconscious mind will not allow total freedom from a pain which has a positive purpose for the body, such as the pain of a broken leg, as previously mentionned. Tapping will gain partial relief, but a degree of pain will remain as a reminder not to walk on the leg, and therefore not do more damage. Your unconscious mind keeps you safe both physically and emotionally and will not release 'necessary' pain in either area. However, open your mind to the possibility of a miracle, they really do happen! I am constantly surprised by the seemingly impossible results gained by tapping, and also by the 'added extras', the other symptoms, emotional or physical that often disappear at the same time.

So allow it to be OK to experience a miracle!

Pain is often exacerbated by our feelings about it. Maybe you are angry about it, or frustrated, or depressed, or perhaps you feel powerless to change it.

How to work with pain and tapping
There are three very simple rules for working with pain and physical symptoms with tapping. The main guidelines come in the way one addresses the particular problem.

1. Describe the specific location of the symptom

Where exactly is the symptom? People tend to generalise pain but with EFT again we need to be very specific. Remember the post code analogy in Chapter 3.

2. Describe the quality of the symptom

Symptoms vary in quality and it is important to get exactly the right words for you. Some suggestions are listed below, but these are by no means exhaustive:

Pain, ache, hurt, ouch, sting, burning, nagging, hot, cold, sore, tender, constant, angry, throbbing, intermittent, pulsating, dull, stabbing.

3. Described the intensity of the symptom again on the scale of 0 to 10

This is the intensity of how it feels right now, not yesterday or how you think it will feel tomorrow. The intensity NOW!

For example

Tapping Section: Tapping for physical pain

Repeat 3 times while tapping the Karate Chop:

Even though I have this dull ache at the bottom of my right shoulder I deeply and completely love and accept myself

Eyebrow:	*Dull ache at the bottom of my right shoulder*
Side of Eye:	*Dull ache just there*
Under Eye:	*Dull ache at the bottom of my right shoulder*
Under Nose:	*This dull ache*
Chin:	*Dull ache at the bottom of my right shoulder*
Collar Bone:	*Dull ache just there*
Under Arm:	*Dull ache at the bottom of my right shoulder*
Top of Head:	*This dull ache*

Repeat 3 times while tapping the Karate Chop:

Even though I have this sharp pain at the base of my spine I deeply and completely love and accept myself

Eyebrow:	*Sharp pain at the base of my spine*
Side of Eye:	*Sharp pain at the base of my spine*
Under Eye:	*Sharp pain just there*
Under Nose:	*Sharp pain at the base of my spine*
Chin:	*Sharp pain just there*
Collar Bone:	*Sharp pain at the base of my spine*
Under Arm:	*Sharp pain*
Top of Head:	*Sharp pain just there*

Repeat 3 times while tapping the Karate Chop:

Even though I have this throbbing lump in my left breast I deeply and completely love and accept myself

Eyebrow:	*Throbbing lump in my left breast*
Side of Eye:	*Throbbing lump in my left breast*
Under Eye:	*Throbbing lump in my left breast*
Under Nose:	*Throbbing lump in my left breast*
Chin:	*Throbbing lump in my left breast*
Collar Bone:	*Throbbing lump in my left breast*
Under Arm:	*Throbbing lump in my left breast*
Top of Head:	*Throbbing lump in my left breast*

Another curious thing about pain is that it can move, that pain that was there on the right side of your shoulder, might suddenly move to the lower back or it may move to your left shoulder or to your elbow, pains do move around the body and We call this *Chasing the Pain* (see Chapter 3) and what that means is, you want to chase the pain around the body, checking in each time with the quality, the intensity and the location, just as we have said before, so supposing it moves from your shoulder to your lower back you would change your wording to suit the new symptom:

Repeat 3 times while tapping the Karate Chop:

Even though I have this sharp pain in my lower back I deeply and completely love and accept myself

Eyebrow:	*This sharp pain in my lower back*
Side of Eye:	*This sharp pain in my lower back*

Under Eye:	*This sharp pain in my lower back*
Under Nose:	*This sharp pain in my lower back*
Chin:	*This sharp pain in my lower back*
Collar Bone:	*This sharp pain in my lower back*
Under Arm:	*This sharp pain in my lower back*
Top of Head:	*This sharp pain in my lower back*

If you find you're making little or no progress, look at how you feel about the symptom. Maybe it is the result of surgery in which case ask yourself how you feel about the surgery, whether there is any residue of anger, fear or resentment when you remember that procedure. If so, tap to clear that and often the physical discomfort will ease. This is an example of how our emotions can obstruct the healing process and you will need to tap to clear the blocks, again always using the scale of 1 to 10 to monitor your progress.

For example:

Tapping Section: Tapping for how you feel about symptoms

Repeat 3 times while tapping the Karate Chop:

Even though I have this operation anger/ fear /resentment etc, I deeply and completely love and accept myself

Eyebrow:	*This operation anger/fear/resentment etc*
Side of Eye:	*These operation feelings*
Under Eye:	*This operation anger*
Under Nose:	*These operation emotions*
Chin:	*This operation anger*
Collar Bone:	*This operation anger*
Under Arm:	*This operation anger*
Top of Head:	*These operation emotions*

Continue:

Eyebrow:	*This remaining anger*
Side of Eye:	*This remaining anger*
Under Eye:	*This remaining anger*
Under Nose:	*This remaining anger*
Chin:	*This remaining anger*
Collar Bone:	*This remaining anger*
Under Arm:	*This remaining anger*

Top of Head: *This remaining anger*

Repeat 3 times while tapping the Karate Chop:

Even though I feel frightened by this pain I deeply and completely love and accept myself

Eyebrow:	*This fear*
Side of Eye:	*This frightening pain*
Under Eye:	*I don't know what it means*
Under Nose:	*This fear inside*
Chin:	*This fear of the pain*
Collar Bone:	*This frightening pain*
Under Arm:	*This deep fear*
Top of Head:	*This pain fear*

Repeat 3 times while tapping the Karate Chop:

Even though I feel fed up with this pain I deeply and completely love and accept myself

Eyebrow:	*I'm fed up with it*
Side of Eye:	*I can't change it*
Under Eye:	*I've had enough of it*
Under Nose:	*It is too much*
Chin:	*I can't cope with it*
Collar Bone:	*I have had enough*
Under Arm:	*Feeling fed up*
Top of Head:	*Feeling fed up*

Take a moment now to check in with yourself and your intensity levels on the above protocols. Remember to check your SUDS (0 – 10 scale). Once you have experienced a noticeable reduction in intensity ask yourself these questions:

- **Is it possible to clear it?**
- **Why is it there, what is it saying?**
- **How do you feel about it?**
- **If that pain had an emotional contributor what would it be?**
- **If that pain had a message what might it be?**

Notice your answers to the above questions. Watch your language. Hear what you are saying to yourself, always looking for any blocking beliefs around healing that may surface. Tap to clear any negative responses, and take a note of the positive ones that begin to emerge.

You may be experiencing some uncomfortable or disabling ongoing physical problems as a result of surgery or other treatment. We will explore working with the treatment itself and the direct side effects in the following chapter. However, some people still suffer from physical problems long after the treatment itself is over, such as lymphedema, joint stiffness, muscular pain, impotence, a constant need to urinate etc.

Very often in our tapping groups Sue and I find people just accept these symptoms as something they have to tolerate and live with, yet equally often we find that by tapping on them we can get relief, sometimes in the long term, other times opening the door to that possibility and creating a programme for the individual to continue to work through.

If this is you and you are tolerating something because you feel, or have been told, there is no other way, please try tapping on it. The least that can happen is nothing will change, but many times long term, seemingly intractable, physical symptoms improve, and even go completely, when tapped on.

Again, the same three rules of tapping with physical issues apply:

1. **Specific location**
2. **Quality**
3. **Intensity**

A separate tapping protocol which is often useful when addressing restricted movement of some form is to begin by measuring the extent of the restriction. For example, how far you can move/ stretch right now, and then tap as follows:

Tapping Section: Tapping for restricted movement

Repeat 3 times while tapping the Karate Chop:

Even though I can only stretch (or move) this far I deeply and completely love and accept myself

Eyebrow:	*I can only stretch this far*
Side of Eye:	*I can only stretch this far*
Under Eye:	*I can only stretch this far*
Under Nose:	*I can only stretch this far*
Chin:	*I can only stretch this far*
Collar Bone:	*I can only stretch this far*
Under Arm:	*I can only stretch this far*
Top of Head:	*I can only stretch this far*

In taking the time to work out exactly how far you can stretch or move in that part of your body you will already be tuning into the problem state and 'I can only stretch this far' will be specific enough to work in most cases.

Remember to ask yourself how you feel about the problem:

- **Do you believe it can change?**
- **What have you been told?**
- **Who by?**
- **How does that make you feel?**
- **Is it possible for this issue to heal fully?**

Tap on any answer that has a charge to it, no matter how mild.

Constricted Breathing

'When the breath wanders the mind also is unsteady. But when the breath is calmed the mind too will be still, and the yogi achieves long life. Therefore, one should learn to control the breath.'
Svatmarama, Hatha Yoga Pradipika

Most of us are aware that anxiety tends to show up in our breathing. Often we hold our breath when we are upset or frightened. It is not unusual to remind a client to breathe during a particularly intense session.

Gary Craig's Constricted Breathing Technique is a wonderful way of working with the accumulated anxieties that we all experience on a daily basis, however trivial, and clearing them from our energy system on an ongoing basis. Using this method you do not need to be aware of what anxieties are there, merely assume that by doing this a couple of times a day you are automatically releasing any residual anxieties from the day (or night) and thus preventing them growing into something more severe such as panic attacks, depression etc.

I highly recommend your doing this technique twice a day, routinely, perhaps when you clean your teeth morning and night. After a week or so you will notice that you are feeling calmer and lighter in your general being.

Tapping Section: Tapping for constricted breathing

Take a couple of deep breaths to stretch out the lungs.

Then take the fullest breath possible for you right now and rate it on a scale of 0 – 10 where 0 is no breath at all and 10 is the fullest breath you can imagine taking.

Repeat 3 times while tapping the Karate Chop:

Even though I have this constricted breathing I deeply and completely love and accept myself

216

Eyebrow:	This constricted breathing
Side of Eye:	This constricted breathing
Under Eye:	Something is blocking my breathing
Under Nose:	Something getting in the way of my fullest breath
Chin:	This constricted breathing
Collar Bone:	This constricted breathing
Under Arm:	This block to my fullest breath
Top of Head:	This constricted breathing

Tap using the following Reminder Phrase, or variations thereof:

Eyebrow:	This remaining constricted breathing
Side of Eye:	This remaining block to my fullest breath
Under Eye:	This remaining something blocking my breath
Under Nose:	This remaining constricted breathing
Chin:	The remaining block to my breathing
Collar Bone:	This remaining constricted breathing
Under Arm:	This remaining block to my fullest breath
Top of Head:	This remaining something blocking my breathing

Reassess your breath. Chances are your breathing will be deeper, or more expansive, or have changed quality in some way. Sometimes a snippet of a memory, or an emotion, may surface. If this is the case, make a note to work with that as it will be important and relevant in some way, even if that is not clear now.

In the next chapter we will look at how to manage your treatment and any possible side effects.

CHAPTER 14

CANCER TREATMENT & MANAGING THE SIDE EFFECTS

'The way I see it, if you want the rainbow, you gotta put up with the rain'
Dolly Parton

Cancer treatment is often frightening and sometimes involves invasive surgery as well as chemotherapy and/or radiation and hormone treatment. It can have unpleasant side effects such as hair loss, nausea, burning sensations, impotence or loss of sexual desire, weight loss, weight gain – to name but a few. Whilst no one would volunteer themselves for these treatments it is easy to lose touch with the intended outcome of health and wellbeing.

The body is thrown into conflict, it is being hurt, burnt, poisoned in the name of healing. Patients often respond to the treatment, understandably, with fear/anger/hatred and other negative emotions. When addressing issues around the various treatments (and I only include a small cross section here, you will need to adapt the wording for your own personal experience) the intention is to release the negative emotions and begin to focus attention on the body's healing capacity, embracing the treatment as a positive step towards healing.

A chemotherapy patient once said to me: 'I am being cured to death'. This has always stuck with me as it seemed to accurately describe what it must feel like to experience chemo. I would add that she is actually very much alive now and has no regrets about the course of treatment she opted for. I like to use forest fire as a metaphor in relation to chemotherapy.

Imagine a forest fire, seeking out and burning away old and diseased wood. Now imagine that fire completing its purpose and naturally burning itself out. Out of the ashes very quickly new fresh green shoots appear, the next generation of healthy, stronger trees. It is amazing how, when carefully nurtured and nourished, these saplings grow into a stronger healthier fresh forest. The land beneath them is the same, their roots are still in place, but drawing on the deeper wisdom of Mother Nature something even more special and lasting is created.

Tapping during treatment
It seems that clients who tap their way through the treatment itself, as well as before and after, have noticeably fewer side effects than those who do not tap.

There are two simple ways of working with EFT during the treatment itself:

1. Dr David Lake's continuous tapping

- **Using the forefinger, tap on the side of the thumb and fingers along the nail bed facing the body**

- **Get a rhythm going and tap continuously**

This is also a technique which is extremely helpful to use during treatment itself, and post surgery when mobility might be restricted and it is not possible to reach even the Short Cut points. You can do it using just one hand, and you don't need to focus on any particular set-up statement or reminder phrase, just tap continually to rebalance your system to do what it needs to do to restore health.

2. Imaginary tapping

- **Vividly imagine the tapping points. Imagine that you can feel the texture and sensation of the tapping on your skin at each point.**

- **Imaginary tapping is particularly useful during MRI scans and other procedures where you are required to keep completely still.**

Tap to clear any immediate fears and anxieties first.

Chemotherapy/Radiotherapy/Hormone Treatment

> *'I don't think of all the misery but of the beauty that still remains.'*
> Anne Frank

So much has been written in the media about chemotherapy and other forms of cancer drug treatment that we all probably have strong opinions about them. We hear about the 'terrible side effects', the nausea, the hair loss, etc. Are you afraid of taking drug treatment? That is reasonable, no one would volunteer for it. We will look into supporting the medical model later on but, as with the anxiety, it is important to get a foothold on the fear in order to regain clarity and perspective and to make the best choices for you.

How do you feel about drug treatment or chemotherapy?

How strong is that feeling, on our SUDS scale?

Tapping Section: Tapping for feelings about treatment

Repeat 3 times while tapping the Karate Chop:

Even though I am scared of taking the drugs I deeply and completely love and accept myself

Eyebrow:	*This fear of the drugs*
Side of Eye:	*This fear*
Under Eye:	*This fear of the drugs*
Under Nose:	*This fear*
Chin:	*This fear of the drugs*
Collar Bone:	*This fear*
Under Arm:	*This fear of the drugs*
Top of Head:	*This fear*

If, up until this point, you have always been healthy and you take a pride in not using pharmaceutical drugs, the thought of this treatment may create great internal conflict. Whilst it may or may not be the appropriate treatment for you, it is important, again, to address any layers of negativity around it in order to reach a clear decision.

Do you take pride in your health, and your drug free life style? Who would you be if you did take the medical treatment? What sort of person takes medicines, in your mind?

These are important questions. Answer them with honesty. If you are fully identified with your organic healthy lifestyle, if you ARE that lifestyle, it may be especially hard to even consider mainstream medicine. This is not about trying to change your mind, but it is about clear strong decision-making from an unbiased viewpoint, when you have all the facts on the table.

Sarah's story
Sarah, a young breast cancer client, was in turmoil. Following a mastectomy her oncologist was pushing her to have chemotherapy, as a precaution. She came in crying saying 'I have never even given my children paracetamol'. The concept of going so against her belief systems was overwhelming to her, yet she wanted to be able to look at the facts and reach a sensible decision. She couldn't do that from a place of 'I don't do medicine'. We tapped to clear all her beliefs, judgments and negative experiences around medicine and whilst ultimately she made the decision to forgo the chemo, she made that decision from a clear, rational place.

Was that the right or wrong decision? I don't know! It is not my place to pretend to know. But what I do know is that it was the right decision for her. Furthermore I am confident that after tapping, if that decision had been shown to be dangerous to her future health, she might have gone a different way.

Tapping Section: Tapping for feelings about drugs

Repeat 3 times while tapping the Karate Chop:

Even though I don't want to put drugs into my body and I am anxious about it I deeply and completely love and accept myself

Eyebrow:	*I don't want drugs in my body*
Side of Eye:	*I don't like taking drugs*
Under Eye:	*I never take them*
Under Nose:	*I have to do this*
Chin:	*I don't want to*
Collar Bone:	*I hate taking drugs*
Under Arm:	*I don't take*
Top of Head:	*I never take them*

When you work directly with the treatment options you have chosen, later in this book, you will discover ways of enhancing the healing properties of chemotherapy and/or other drugs, as well as radiotherapy.

Eyebrow:	*This drug anxiety*
Side of Eye:	*This drug anxiety*
Under Eye:	*I don't want to take them*
Under Nose:	*I hate them*
Chin:	*This drug anxiety*
Collar Bone:	*This drug anxiety*
Under Arm:	*I don't want to take them*
Top of Head:	*I hate them*

Some people have an innate mistrust of the medical profession, for whatever reason. Others feel the same about complementary therapies. How are you feeling about this right now? If you feel any negativity in either direction it may hinder your decision making, and also your choices. Whatever treatment or assortment of treatments you decide on, it is important that those decisions are made from a clear empowered place in the present, free of resonances of past negatives experiences.

Tapping Section: Tapping for feelings about doctors

Repeat 3 times while tapping the Karate Chop:

Even though I am frightened to trust the doctors I deeply and completely love and accept myself

Eyebrow:	*This mistrust*
Side of Eye:	*I don't trust them*
Under Eye:	*It is not safe to trust them*
Under Nose:	*This doctor mistrust*
Chin:	*This doctor fear and mistrust*
Collar Bone:	*It is not safe to trust them*
Under Arm:	*This doctor mistrust*
Top of Head:	*This mistrust*

Are all doctors bad/ untrustworthy/ or whatever else you feel? Or is it one specific incident which is supporting this belief?

Most people have some experience of doctors, especially as children.

- **What was your family doctor like?**
- **Was he/she scary?**
- **What stories have you heard about doctors**

- **From friends? In the media?**
- **Have you experienced the medical profession with a family member?**
- **What happened?**
- **How do you feel as you remember that now?**

If you have specific experiences where you 'learned' this, using the Movie Technique tap as follows:

Repeat 3 times while tapping the Karate Chop:

Even though X happened I deeply and completely love and accept myself

Eyebrow:	*These X emotions*
Side of Eye:	*These X emotions*
Under Eye:	*These X emotions*
Under Nose:	*These X emotions*
Chin:	*These X emotions*
Collar Bone:	*These X emotions*
Under Arm:	*These X emotions*
Top of Head:	*These X emotions*

Repeat 3 times while tapping the Karate Chop:

Even though X happened I deeply and completely love and accept myself

Eyebrow:	*This X movie*
Side of Eye:	*This X movie*
Under Eye:	*This X movie*
Under Nose:	*This X movie*
Chin:	*This X movie*
Collar Bone:	*This X movie*
Under Arm:	*This X movie*
Top of Head:	*This X movie*

When you think about what happened now, how do you feel? Rate how you feel on the SUDS scale of 0 – 10?

Continue tapping through the specific emotions connected to that memory until they feel released. Then check back in with the 'doctor mistrust' and notice how you feel now. When it has changed and no longer has a charge to it, tap as follows:

Eyebrow:	*I choose to take charge of my healing process*
Side of Eye:	*I choose to accept whatever help or advice is useful to me*
Under Eye:	*I choose to listen to the experts*
Under Nose:	*I choose to embrace their wisdom*
Chin:	*I appreciate their knowledge*
Collar Bone:	*And I choose to trust that I do know how to heal*
Under Arm:	*I choose to take charge of my healing process now*
Top of Head:	*And I choose to trust in it*

Repeat 3 times while tapping the Karate Chop:

Even though I don't have the expert knowledge I deeply and completely love and accept myself

Eyebrow:	*I am not an expert*
Side of Eye:	*I can't take responsibility for this*
Under Eye:	*I just want someone else to take over*
Under Nose:	*It is too much*
Chin:	*I am not an expert*
Collar Bone:	*I am not a doctor*
Under Arm:	*I can't take charge*
Top of Head:	*I just want them to do it*

Continue:

Eyebrow:	*I am open to the possibility that I can take an active part in my healing process now*
Side of Eye:	*I choose to work alongside the doctors/ therapists/ carers*
Under Eye:	*I choose to heal surprisingly easily*
Under Nose:	*I choose to take that responsibility now*
Chin:	*It is safe for me to take charge*
Collar Bone:	*It is safe to play an active role*
Under Arm:	*I choose to step into my power now*
Top of Head:	*And I choose to be an active member of my own healing team*

It is important to recognise, even at this early stage, that I am using the word 'healing' in a wider sense than purely physical healing. I do not pretend to know what the outcome will be for you, and it is not for me to get in the way of that. That is part of the greater scheme of life. It may not be your destiny to recover physically from this, but whatever happens, I have witnessed the apparent 'impossible' many, many times in my work and would ask you to be open to miracles, in fact to actively encourage them, in whatever shape or form they may be delivered.

However, this does NOT mean abandoning treatment and sitting on a mountainside for a few years - or at least, not yet! Whilst this may be deeply spiritually healing (and I am in no way dismissing any spiritual practice, it is a fundamental part of the healing process), right now it is about taking practical steps to healing. And by that, I mean taking whatever treatments are on offer if, and only if, they fit with your belief system. We will look into ways to work with any such conflicts when we look at supporting the medical model in Chapters 14 and 15.

Consult the experts, and get the information. The medical world has much to offer, and is at the cutting edge of vital research and treatment. Use their valuable wisdom, it is what they are there for. The speed at which cancer treatments have developed over the last 20 years is phenomenal. If it fits with your beliefs, use the amazing skills and processes the medical world have to offer. All I would ask is that you support yourself emotionally alongside your physical healing path. The physical and emotional (including spiritual) are flip sides of the same coin, and both need equal attention for true healing to be facilitated.

Chemotherapy

> *'My veins are filled, once a week with a Neapolitan carpet cleaner*
> *distilled from the Adriatic and I am as bald as an egg.*
> *However I still get around and am mean to cats.'*
> John Cheever, The Letters of John Cheever

Prior to a cancer diagnosis nothing would induce most of us to consider filling our bodies with an overload of chemical toxicity. Yet when faced with this serious disease this becomes a very real option for many people. No wonder people are afraid of chemotherapy.

Let's focus on the word itself 'chemo-therapy'. Yes, chemo means chemical, but are you deleting the 'therapy' from the word? Ultimately, chemotherapy is intended as therapy in the sense of restoration and healing. It just goes about it in a very seemingly un-therapeutic way. Every book we read, every article we download, every magazine or newspaper we read on the subject will emphasise the often extreme negative side effects of chemotherapy treatment; the hair loss, the sickness, the fevers, the exhaustion. No wonder chemotherapy has developed such a culture of fear around it.

What might happen if, having tapped to clear some of the fear and its origins, you were to focus on the therapeutic part of the treatment, on the ultimate intended outcome, on regaining total health? How might that change of focus affect how you approach your treatment?

By tapping to clear the very real fears you may be experiencing, and working towards a place of acceptance of the positive attributes of the treatment and its healing intention you will be able to focus your awareness in a new way. Often, people who tap to change their feelings around receiving chemotherapy experience fewer side effects when they are able to genuinely welcome the drugs into their body.

So, begin with how you are feeling about the chemo right now.

Tapping Section: Tapping for feelings about chemotherapy

Repeat 3 times while tapping the Karate Chop:

Even though I am terrified of chemotherapy I choose for my body to accept the treatment and heal easily now

Eyebrow:	*This chemotherapy fear*
Side of Eye:	*This fear of the treatment*
Under Eye:	*Fear of chemotherapy*
Under Nose:	*Fear of feeling ill*
Chin:	*Fear of the chemo*
Collar Bone:	*Fear of the poisons*
Under Arm:	*Chemotherapy fear*
Top of Head:	*Chemotherapy fear*

Repeat 3 times while tapping the Karate Chop:

Even though I am frightened of losing my hair I deeply and completely love and accept myself

Eyebrow:	*Fear of losing my hair*
Side of Eye:	*Fear of losing my hair*
Under Eye:	*Fear of how I will look*
Under Nose:	*Fear of how people will respond*
Chin:	*Fear of losing my hair*
Collar Bone:	*Fear of looking different*
Under Arm:	*Fear of feeling different*
Top of Head:	*Fear of losing my hair*

Repeat 3 times while tapping the Karate Chop:

Even though part of me really doesn't want to do this treatment I deeply and completely love and accept myself anyway

Eyebrow:	*I don't want to do it*
Side of Eye:	*I am frightened of doing the treatment*
Under Eye:	*Part of me really doesn't want to do it*
Under Nose:	*Part of me knows I will*
Chin:	*This conflict*
Collar Bone:	*This treatment conflict*
Under Arm:	*I don't want to do it*
Top of Head:	*I do want to do it*

Continue:

Eyebrow:	*This treatment conflict*
Side of Eye:	*I choose to let it go*
Under Eye:	*This confusion inside*
Under Nose:	*I choose to accept the treatment and to heal easily*
Chin:	*This remaining conflict*
Collar Bone:	*I choose to release it now*
Under Arm:	*This remaining treatment conflict*
Top of Head:	*I choose to let it go*

Repeat 3 times while tapping the Karate Chop:

Even though I am scared of the side effects I deeply and completely love and accept myself

Eyebrow:	*Those side effects*
Side of Eye:	*Fear of the side effects*
Under Eye:	*Fear of how this will affect my body*
Under Nose:	*Fear of the side effects*
Chin:	*Fear of the nausea/hair loss/exhaustion...*
Collar Bone:	*Fear of not being able to cope*
Under Arm:	*Fear of the side effects*
Top of Head:	*Fear of not coping*

Changing the Focus

'If the only tool you have is a hammer, you tend to see every problem as a nail.'
Abraham Maslow

When you have cleared some of the anxiety around the treatment and are able to think of it without such a negative response, you can create a positive choice.

For example:

Tapping Section: Tapping for accepting chemotherapy

Repeat 3 times while tapping the Karate Chop:

Even though I still have some anxiety about the treatment I choose to allow my body to accept the chemotherapy/ radiotherapy/ surgery etc and to support my healing process easily

Eyebrow:	*This remaining anxiety/fear*
Side of Eye:	*These remaining chemo/radio etc emotions*
Under Eye:	*I choose to release them*
Under Nose:	*I choose for my body to accept the treatment easily now*
Chin:	*I choose for my body to work with the treatment*
Collar Bone:	*I choose to support my healing process*
Under Arm:	*This remaining treatment anxiety/fear*
Top of Head:	*I choose to release it easily now*

Continue:

Eyebrow:	*I choose to support the treatment emotionally and physically*
Side of Eye:	*I choose to allow my body to work with the treatment and to facilitate my healing*
Under Eye:	*I choose to feel calm about the treatment*
Under Nose:	*I choose to accept the chemo/radio etc*
Chin:	*I choose to feel positive about the process*
Collar Bone:	*I choose to surprise myself by how easily I heal now*
Under Arm:	*I choose to surprise myself with my healing process*
Top of Head:	*I choose to support my healing process*

Once this is clear you will then be in a more positive place to receive the necessary treatment.

Next use visualisation skills to help you to accept the treatment. For example, with chemotherapy imagine changing the words to:

- **The silver elixir of life**
- **This healing liquid**
- **This vibrant flow of health**
- **This rejuvenating life force**

It is important to create your own metaphor so use your creative language skills to help you. Close your eyes and ask yourself:

How would you prefer to feel about the chemo/ radiation/wound/scar etc?

Build up the positive feeling/image.

- **How does it look/feel/sound?**

- **Imagine the healing qualities flowing through your body, how does it change how you feel about the treatment?**

- **Vividly imagine what it will be like.**

Once you have cleared your negative feelings about the cancer treatment, and opened yourself to the positives it seems that in many cases the side effects of the treatment noticeably reduce.

Radiotherapy /Radiation

> *'Some days there won't be a song in your heart. Sing anyway.'*
> *Emory Austin*

Radiotherapy (also called radiation treatment) can seem to last a lifetime. For a period of time it can feel like it is taking over your life. Every day is ruled by short hospital visits. The urge to break out, escape, can be overwhelming.

Rachel's story
Rachel would sometimes come to see me immediately after her radiotherapy session. She would often be fraught from delays at the hospital, she would claim to feel like a number and said it was like herding cattle, one person out, the next in. It felt completely impersonal and clinical. All she wanted to do was run away and forget any of it was happening to her. Of course, the rational part of her knew that that wasn't possible, but the urge was so great that on one occasion she had found herself leaving the hospital and driving with no sense of where she was going.

To quote her: 'I just had to get out of the city, away from buildings, I couldn't stand it any longer'. She drove out into the countryside for a couple of hours before she realised what she was doing. At this point, she had stopped, but had become hysterical and unable to drive. That was when she called me. I could not understand a word she was saying, she was so upset, so I just talked her around the points round after round until gradually the tears subsided and she was able to speak to me. Once she was fully calm she was able to retrace her route and head for home, but the experience really scared her. So when we next met, we tapped through the memory of that afternoon, and also her need to escape and the fact that she had felt that she had reached breaking point. Tap along with Rachel as follows if appropriate to you:

Tapping Section: Tapping for breaking point about radiotherapy

Repeat 3 times while tapping the Karate Chop:

Even though I reached breaking point I deeply and completely love and accept myself

Eyebrow:	*Breaking point emotions*
Side of Eye:	*I reached breaking point*
Under Eye:	*Breaking point emotions*
Under Nose:	*I reached breaking point*
Chin:	*Breaking point emotions*
Collar Bone:	*I reached breaking point*
Under Arm:	*Breaking point emotions*
Top of Head:	*I reached breaking point*

Repeat 3 times while tapping the Karate Chop:

Even though I can't cope with any more radiotherapy I deeply and completely love and accept myself

Eyebrow:	*I can't cope with any more*
Side of Eye:	*These radiotherapy emotions*
Under Eye:	*I can't cope with more radiotherapy*
Under Nose:	*Radiotherapy emotions*
Chin:	*I can't cope with any more*
Collar Bone:	*These radiotherapy emotions*
Under Arm:	*I can't cope with more radiotherapy*
Top of Head:	*Radiotherapy emotions*

Gradually, Rachel felt calmer about the final week of radiotherapy and we visualised her future visits to the hospital, tapping on any negative thoughts and feelings as they arose.

She was able to complete her treatment without any further problem.

Tapping and visualising

This combination of tapping and visualisation also seems to be useful in reducing the side effects of radiotherapy.

Visualise bathing the affected area in cool water, or even milk. Really imagine it. If the radiotherapy has been specifically targeted internally, as in brachytherapy, imagine yourself beside the affected area, sponging the coolness around it whilst allowing the radioactive beads to effortlessly do their intended work.

And then tap, again using the Choices method, with words such as:

Tapping Section: Tapping and visualising

Repeat 3 times while tapping the Karate Chop:

Even though my skin is burning I choose for it to be cool and calm

Eyebrow:	*My burning skin just there*
Side of Eye:	*This burning feeling*
Under Eye:	*These burns*
Under Nose:	*These burns*
Chin:	*This burning feeling*
Collar Bone:	*My burning skin*
Under Arm:	*This burning feeling just there*
Top of Head:	*This burning feeling just there*

Continue:

Eyebrow:	*I choose for that area to be cool and calm*
Side of Eye:	*I choose for my skin to be cool and calm*
Under Eye:	*I choose for my skin in that area to be cool and calm*
Under Nose:	*I choose for my skin to be cool and calm*
Chin:	*I choose for that area to be cool and calm*
Collar Bone:	*I choose to bathe that area in cool milk*
Under Arm:	*I choose to bathe my skin in cool milk*
Top of Head:	*I choose for my skin in that area to be cool and calm*

Continue:

Eyebrow:	*This burning feeling*
Side of Eye:	*I choose for my skin to be cool and calm*
Under Eye:	*This burning feeling on my skin*
Under Nose:	*I choose for my skin in that area to be cool and calm*

230

Chin:	This burning feeling
Collar Bone:	I choose to bath my skin in cool milk
Under Arm:	This burning feeling
Top of Head:	I choose for my skin to feel cool and calm

Preparing for Surgery

'See yourself in perfect health, and if you will do it right before you sleep, then there will be many hours where you will be unconscious, where you will not be doing any miscreating to counteract that.'
'Abraham-Hicks, A New Beginning I

When preparing for any form of surgery, from keyhole to tumour removal, visualisation is again very effective, especially when combined with the tapping. When you have cleared your anxieties about the procedure itself, as in the previous chapter, imagine that area of your body beginning to heal, taking it one step at a time.

- **See it immediately post surgery**
- **In a few days time**
- **In a week**
- **In a fortnight**
- **In a month**

Take time to fully engage with each visualisation until you have a clear concept of the healing process and how your body will look afterwards.

Some surgeries are more obviously traumatic in that they may affect your outside appearance, such as a mastectomy, or colonostomy.

Others may have particularly debilitating side effects such as constant desire to urinate, or impotency, which are often ignored such is their seemed lack of importance in the scale of the disease. However, each of these symptoms, and others, can be devastating to the patient, and they do not need to be permanent. Even with conditions where physiological trauma would dictate it impossible to get any improvement positive changes have been recorded using energy therapies such as EFT and acupuncture.

If you are having problems visualising a positive healing outcome turn to Chapter 15 and tap through any blocks.

Jackie's story
Jackie did this work for five days prior to going into hospital for a mastectomy. She spent considerable time focussing on visualising her body after the operation. She was very anxious about losing a breast and simply could not imagine how her body would look afterwards. She had decided to have reconstructive surgery at the same time, in order to minimise the trauma, but was still terrified. She could

not get the word 'deformed' out of her head, and she found herself looking at other women's chests and feeling tremendous grief and envy.

We began by tapping with her immediate feelings around the loss of her breast, and, in her eyes, her femininity.

Tapping Section: Tapping for emotions about losing breast

Repeat 3 times while tapping the Karate Chop:

Even though I am devastated at losing my breast I deeply and completely love and accept myself

Eyebrow:	*Devastation*
Side of Eye:	*I'm devastated*
Under Eye:	*Losing my breast*
Under Nose:	*Losing my breast devastation*
Chin:	*Devastation*
Collar Bone:	*I'm devastated*
Under Arm:	*Losing my breast*
Top of Head:	*Losing my breast devastation*

Repeat 3 times while tapping the Karate Chop:

Even though I will never feel like a woman again I deeply and completely love and accept myself

Eyebrow:	*Losing my sexuality*
Side of Eye:	*Losing my femininity*
Under Eye:	*Losing my sexuality*
Under Nose:	*Losing my identity as a woman*
Chin:	*Losing my sexuality*
Collar Bone:	*Losing my femininity*
Under Arm:	*Losing my sexuality*
Top of Head:	*Losing my identity as a woman*

Repeat 3 times while tapping the Karate Chop:

Even though I am terrified of looking deformed I deeply and completely love and accept myself

Eyebrow:	*Terror of looking deformed*
Side of Eye:	*Terror of looking deformed*

232

Under Eye:	*Deformed*
Under Nose:	*That word and everything it means to me*
Chin:	*Terror of looking deformed*
Collar Bone:	*Terror of that word*
Under Arm:	*Terror of looking deformed*
Top of Head:	*Deformity terror*

Repeat 3 times while tapping the Karate Chop:

Even though I am still anxious about looking deformed I love and accept myself anyway

Eyebrow:	*Remaining anxiety*
Side of Eye:	*Remaining deformity anxiety*
Under Eye:	*What if I look deformed?*
Under Nose:	*What if I don't?*
Chin:	*I am open to the possibility that my body knows...*
Collar Bone:	*Exactly what to do to allow me to heal and be normal*
Under Arm:	*I am open to that possibility*
Top of Head:	*Maybe*

We continued to tap like this for a few rounds until Jackie felt completely comfortable with that possibility.

She then went home and looked up some images of mastectomies on the internet and began to imagine how she might look, and what scars she might have, tapping for any emotions as they arose. Then she began to visualise her healing process. She did all this in the space of 5 days!

By the time she went into hospital for the operation she was not only familiar with the procedure but she also felt prepared and confident about it.

I saw Jackie again a couple of weeks later, and her wound was healing really well. She had continued to both tap and visualise whilst in hospital and she was amazed that her scarring was exactly the same as she had imagined, in the same place, the same size, and healing in the same way.

I asked her how she felt about it and she said, "I feel quite proud of it, I think it is okay, it's good and it saved my life.' Then she made me laugh by adding 'I don't know how I thought I would feel unfeminine and less of a woman, I have never been bought so many flowers in my life, and my colleagues clubbed together and bought me an array of beautiful silk underwear!'. More seriously, she said that she realised that her femininity and sexuality were not determined by her breasts, but were an intrinsic part of her that no surgery could remove, part of her inner beauty.

What a wonderful and courageous woman!

Side Effects

'The most important thing in illness is never to lose heart.'
Nikolai Lenin

In the event that you still experience side effects, tap on them specifically as follows. If you are feeling too ill to physically tap then vividly imagine the tapping whilst repeating the words in your head. I find it useful to imagine the tapping by rote at these times, repeating the name of each point and the problem systematically, for example: Eyebrow point: this nausea, Side of Eye: this nausea etc.

Tapping Section: Tapping for treatment side effects

Repeat 3 times while tapping the Karate Chop:

Even though I feel sick I deeply and completely love and accept myself

Eyebrow:	*Feeling sick*
Side of Eye:	*Feeling so sick*
Under Eye:	*Feeling sick*
Under Nose:	*Feeling so sick*
Chin:	*Feeling sick*
Collar Bone:	*Feeling so sick*
Under Arm:	*Feeling sick*
Top of Head:	*Feeling so sick*

Repeat 3 times while tapping the Karate Chop:

Even though I feel so nauseous I deeply and completely love and accept myself

Eyebrow:	*This nausea*
Side of Eye:	*This nausea*
Under Eye:	*This nausea*
Under Nose:	*This nausea*
Chin:	*This nausea*
Collar Bone:	*This nausea*
Under Arm:	*This nausea*
Top of Head:	*This nausea*

Repeat 3 times while tapping the Karate Chop:

Even though I feel so ill I deeply and completely love and accept myself

Eyebrow:	*Feeling so ill*
Side of Eye:	*Feeling so terrible*
Under Eye:	*Feeling so ill*
Under Nose:	*Feeling so terrible*
Chin:	*Feeling so ill*
Collar Bone:	*Feeling so terrible*
Under Arm:	*Feeling so ill*
Top of Head:	*Feeling so terrible*

Repeat 3 times while tapping the Karate Chop:

Even though I am totally exhausted I deeply and completely love and accept myself

Eyebrow:	*This exhaustion*
Side of Eye:	*Totally exhausted*
Under Eye:	*So exhausted*
Under Nose:	*This exhaustion*
Chin:	*Totally exhausted*
Collar Bone:	*So exhausted*
Under Arm:	*This exhaustion*
Top of Head:	*Completely exhausted*

Repeat 3 times while tapping the Karate Chop:

Even though my palms/ hands/ feet are burning I deeply and completely love and accept myself

Eyebrow:	*This burning*
Side of Eye:	*Burning in my palms/ hands/ feet*
Under Eye:	*Burning feelings*
Under Nose:	*This burning*
Chin:	*This burning*
Collar Bone:	*Burning in my palms/ hands/ feet*
Under Arm:	*Burning feelings*

Top of Head:	This burning

Repeat 3 times while tapping the Karate Chop:

Even though I have lymphodoema in (top of arm/wrist etc)   I deeply and completely love and accept myself

Eyebrow:	Lymphodoema
Side of Eye:	Lymphodoema emotions
Under Eye:	Lymphodoema
Under Nose:	Lymphodoema emotions
Chin:	Lymphodoema
Collar Bone:	Lymphodoema emotions
Under Arm:	Lymphodoema
Top of Head:	Lymphodoema emotions

Repeat 3 times while tapping the Karate Chop:

Even though I have this swelling I deeply and completely love and accept myself

Eyebrow:	This swelling
Side of Eye:	This swelling
Under Eye:	This swelling
Under Nose:	This swelling
Chin:	This swelling
Collar Bone:	This swelling
Under Arm:	This swelling
Top of Head:	This swelling

Repeat 3 times while tapping the Karate Chop:

Even though I am really stiff just there I deeply and completely love and accept myself

Eyebrow:	This stiffness
Side of Eye:	This stiffness
Under Eye:	Stiffness just there
Under Nose:	Stiffness just there
Chin:	This stiffness
Collar Bone:	This stiffness

| Under Arm: | Stiffness just there |
| Top of Head: | Stiffness just there |

Repeat 3 times while tapping the Karate Chop:

Even though my skin is burning I deeply and completely love and accept myself

Eyebrow:	This burning
Side of Eye:	Burning just there
Under Eye:	This burning
Under Nose:	Burning soreness
Chin:	This hot soreness
Collar Bone:	This burning pain
Under Arm:	Burning soreness
Top of Head:	Hot soreness

Body Image and Sexuality

'Science and psychology have isolated the one prime cause for success or failure in life. It is the hidden self-image you have of yourself.'
Bob Proctor, author and speaker

With many cancers there is the prospect of surgery, and with that comes the issue of body image. You may feel deformed or depressed, or experience loss of femininity, masculinity, libido, impotence and loss of sexual identity. Hair loss may occur as a result of chemotherapy. It is an area that it is important to not just acknowledge but to work through. If you have had any sort of surgery or scarring as a result of the cancer, or if you have developed a belief about your body as a result of the diagnosis and treatment, put it on the table and work with it. A loss of any part of the body, as can happen with certain cancers, such as a mastectomy, is extremely traumatic and may affect how you identify yourself in the world.

- **What are you saying to yourself?**
- **What are you thinking?**
- **What are you feeling?**
- **What are you seeing?**

Then tap as follows, using the words that work for you.

Tapping Section: Tapping for body image and disgust

Repeat 3 times while tapping the Karate Chop:

Even though my body is disgusting I deeply and completely love and accept myself

Eyebrow:	*This disgust*
Side of Eye:	*My body is disgusting*
Under Eye:	*I am disgusting*
Under Nose:	*I am disgusting*
Chin:	*This disgust*
Collar Bone:	*My body is disgusting*
Under Arm:	*I am disgusting*
Top of Head:	*I am disgusting*

Repeat 3 times while tapping the Karate Chop:

Even though I have these hideous scars and I can't bear to look at them I deeply and completely love and accept myself

Eyebrow:	*My scars*
Side of Eye:	*My hideous scars*
Under Eye:	*I can't bear to look at them*
Under Nose:	*I don't want to look at them*
Chin:	*My scars*
Collar Bone:	*My hideous scars*
Under Arm:	*I can't bear to look at them*
Top of Head:	*I don't want to look at them*

Repeat 3 times while tapping the Karate Chop:

Even though no one is ever going to find me attractive now I deeply and completely love and accept myself

Eyebrow:	*No one will ever want me now*
Side of Eye:	*I'm so unattractive*
Under Eye:	*How could anybody want me now?*
Under Nose:	*No one will ever want me now*
Chin:	*No one will ever want me now*
Collar Bone:	*I'm so unattractive*
Under Arm:	*How could anybody want me now?*
Top of Head:	*No one will ever want me now*

Repeat 3 times while tapping the Karate Chop:

Even though I feel hideous I deeply and completely love and accept myself

Eyebrow:	*Feeling hideous*
Side of Eye:	*Feeling hideous*
Under Eye:	*Feeling hideous*
Under Nose:	*Feeling hideous*
Chin:	*Feeling hideous*
Collar Bone:	*Feeling hideous*
Under Arm:	*Feeling hideous*
Top of Head:	*Feeling hideous*

Repeat 3 times while tapping the Karate Chop:

Even though I have lost my femininity I deeply and completely love and accept myself

Eyebrow:	*Losing my femininity*
Side of Eye:	*I've lost my femininity*
Under Eye:	*Losing my femininity*
Under Nose:	*I've lost my femininity*
Chin:	*Losing my femininity*
Collar Bone:	*I've lost my femininity*
Under Arm:	*Losing my femininity*
Top of Head:	*I've lost my femininity*

Repeat 3 times while tapping the Karate Chop:

Even though I feel emasculated I deeply and completely love and accept myself

Eyebrow:	*Feeling emasculated*
Side of Eye:	*Feeling emasculated*
Under Eye:	*Feeling emasculated*
Under Nose:	*Feeling emasculated*
Chin:	*Feeling emasculated*
Collar Bone:	*Feeling emasculated*
Under Arm:	*Feeling emasculated*
Top of Head:	*Feeling emasculated*

Repeat 3 times while tapping the Karate Chop:

Even though no one will ever want me sexually I deeply and completely love and accept myself

Eyebrow:	*Feeling sexually unattractive*
Side of Eye:	*No one will want me now*
Under Eye:	*All these scars*
Under Nose:	*Feeling sexually unattractive*
Chin:	*Feeling sexually unattractive*
Collar Bone:	*No one will want me now*
Under Arm:	*All these scars*
Top of Head:	*Feeling sexually unattractive*

Repeat 3 times while tapping the Karate Chop:

Even though I no longer feel like a woman I deeply and completely love and accept myself

Eyebrow:	*Don't feel like a woman*
Side of Eye:	*Don't feel like a woman*
Under Eye:	*Don't feel like a woman*
Under Nose:	*Don't feel like a woman*
Chin:	*Don't feel like a woman*
Collar Bone:	*Don't feel like a woman*
Under Arm:	*Don't feel like a woman*
Top of Head:	*Don't feel like a woman*

Repeat 3 times while tapping the Karate Chop:

Even though I am impotent I deeply and completely love and accept myself

Eyebrow:	*Impotency emotions*
Side of Eye:	*Impotency emotions*
Under Eye:	*Impotency emotions*
Under Nose:	*Impotency emotions*
Chin:	*Impotency emotions*
Collar Bone:	*Impotency emotions*

| Under Arm: | Impotency emotions |
| Top of Head: | Impotency emotions |

Repeat 3 times while tapping the Karate Chop:

Even though I can't trust my body I deeply and completely love and accept myself

Eyebrow:	My body's let me down
Side of Eye:	I can't trust it
Under Eye:	It's not safe to trust my body
Under Nose:	My body's failed me
Chin:	My body's let me down
Collar Bone:	I can't trust my body
Under Arm:	It's failed me
Top of Head:	My body's failed me

Continue:

Eyebrow:	This anger
Side of Eye:	My body's failed me
Under Eye:	It's let me down
Under Nose:	This deep anger
Chin:	This resentment
Collar Bone:	My body's let me down
Under Arm:	I can't trust my body
Top of Head:	It's let me down

Repeat 3 times while tapping the Karate Chop:

Even though my body has betrayed me I deeply and completely love and accept myself

Eyebrow:	Feeling betrayed
Side of Eye:	Feeling betrayed
Under Eye:	Feeling betrayed
Under Nose:	Feeling betrayed
Chin:	Feeling betrayed
Collar Bone:	Feeling betrayed

241

Under Arm:	*Feeling betrayed*
Top of Head:	*Feeling betrayed*

'No one can make you feel inferior without your consent'
Eleanor Roosevelt

It is also useful to stand naked in front of a mirror so you can see your body and focus in on any specific areas that have your negative attention, but as you do, remember to **TAP** around all the points. The tapping is a really important part of this, as it will address the emotions as they are coming up for you, as you look at your body, as you explore what is going on for you.

Also, with women, the treatment may bring about the onset of early menopause and this in itself can be an extremely emotional time, as well as physically distressing with hot flushes etc.

If this is happening with you, ensure you tap on every aspect noticing how you feel about it.

- **Do you have children?**
- **How do you feel about losing that opportunity?**
- **How has this affected your relationship/marriage?**
- **How has cancer changed your life plans?**

Work very gently through all the emotions, grief and loss connected with this. It is never going to make it OK but it will help to remove the excess emotional charge connected with it and bring you to some form of peaceful resolution.

Tapping Section: Tapping for loss of dreams

Repeat 3 times while tapping the Karate Chop:

Even though I have lost my dream I deeply and completely love and accept myself

Eyebrow:	*Loss of my dream*
Side of Eye:	*Loss of my dream*
Under Eye:	*Loss of my dream*
Under Nose:	*Loss of my dream*
Chin:	*Loss of my dream*
Collar Bone:	*Loss of my dream*
Under Arm:	*Loss of my dream*
Top of Head:	*Loss of my dream*

Repeat 3 times while tapping the Karate Chop:

Even though I'm angry that this has happened I deeply and completely love and accept myself

Eyebrow:	*This anger*
Side of Eye:	*This anger*
Under Eye:	*This anger*
Under Nose:	*This anger*
Chin:	*This anger*
Collar Bone:	*This anger*
Under Arm:	*This anger*
Top of Head:	*This anger*

Repeat 3 times while tapping the Karate Chop:

Even though I am so sad about this I deeply and completely love and accept myself

Eyebrow:	*Sadness*
Side of Eye:	*Sadness*
Under Eye:	*Sadness*
Under Nose:	*Sadness*
Chin:	*Sadness*
Collar Bone:	*Sadness*
Under Arm:	*Sadness*
Top of Head:	*Sadness*

Your body's natural default, or tendency is to heal. Think of a paper cut, those irritating little cuts that are painful when they happen. Notice how quickly they heal, how easy it is to forget about them, and how suddenly they're just gone without your even thinking about them.

Your body **does** know how to heal and if something is interrupting this healing state your job is to find out what it is and restore it to balance. Sometimes, for whatever reason, it is not possible to heal the physical. However, emotional healing is of enormous value and whatever the outcome, even death, to reach that from a place of inner peace and acceptance is a true gift.

> *'Faith is taking the first step even when you don't see the whole staircase.'*
> *Martin Luther King*

The most important thing that I hope you take from this chapter is the way that, by clearing the emotional response to a treatment or surgery, it is possible to reduce the potential side effects. When the body works with a treatment from a place of acceptance, letting go of the internal conflict, then it appears that the treatment is easier and more successful.

In the following chapter we are going to look at further enhancing these positive effects by utilising visualisation skills to support our intended outcome.

CHAPTER 15

THE POWER OF VISUALISATION

'Imagination is more important than knowledge'
Albert Einstein

The unconscious mind does not recognise the difference between imagination and reality, past or future 'memories'. This is why we respond emotionally to frightening films even when we are only sitting in the cinema. This can be used positively to support the healing process. Positive visualisation is extremely powerful but it seems that to affect physical change you need to do it many times over. Repetition is key here.

Dr David Hamilton has many useful visualisations in his book 'How Your Mind can Heal your Body', and recommends doing them in the same way that you might take a medicine, three times a day at specific times. They do not need to take very long once you have begun practicing them, but it seems useful to flood the mind with these images.

If you're not a visual person
Clients sometimes say 'I can't visualise' or 'I am not a visual person'. It really doesn't seem to matter. Thinking about imagining something seems to be equally effective.

Working with visual metaphors can be very helpful in cancer treatment. Use visualisation skills to work with the cancer cells or tumour/s.

Begin by shrinking yourself down to a 'Mini-me' and imagine you can travel around your body shining a gentle torch (flashlight) as you go, checking out what is going on for you right now. Notice what you see. Biological accuracy is not necessary – allow your imagination to do the work for you. You may want to make notes as you do this so that you can return to the visualisation easily in the future.

- **What do your cancer cells look like?**
- **Where are they?**
- **What colour are they?**
- **What shape?**
- **Do they have a texture or a quality?**
- **Do they have a smell associated to them?**
- **Any sounds?**
- **Are silent or noisy?**
- **If they're noisy what are they saying?**
- **How do you feel about them?**

When you check through these questions and have a sense of what your cancer cells look like, think about how you'd like them to look as they prepare to heal, at how you can begin to change them so that they become acceptable and easy to clear and release. The first step in the visualisation process is to change the tumours /cells into something less threatening to look at. The next step will be working to clear them.

Here are some examples of this:

- **Red to pink**
- **Black to white**
- **Solid to fluid**
- **Hot to cool**
- **Jagged to smooth**
- **Rough to even**
- **Noisy to quiet**
- **Agitated to calm**
- **Sour to sweet**

Tapping Section: Tapping for changing your cells

Use a tapping protocol to instruct your body to change the structure of the cells as follows:

Repeat each of these 3 times while tapping the Karate Chop:

Even though my cancer cells are red I choose for them to be pink

Even though my cancer cells are hard I choose for them to be soft

Even though my cancer cells are rough I choose for them to be smooth

Even though my cancer cells are agitated I choose for them to be calm

Then, using Choices, (see Chapter 3), tap as follows:

Eyebrow:	*These red cancer cells*
Side of Eye:	*These red cancer cells*
Under Eye:	*These red cancer cells*
Under Nose:	*These red cancer cells*
Chin:	*These red cancer cells*
Collar Bone:	*These red cancer cells*
Under Arm:	*These red cancer cells*
Top of Head:	*These red cancer cells*

Continue:

Eyebrow:	*These red cancer cells*
Side of Eye:	*I choose for them to be pink*
Under Eye:	*These red cancer cells*
Under Nose:	*I choose for them to be pink*
Chin:	*These red cancer cells*
Collar Bone:	*I choose for them to be pink*
Under Arm:	*These red cancer cells*
Top of Head:	*I choose for them to be pink*
Eyebrow:	*I choose for them to be pink*

Continue:

Side of Eye:	*I choose for them to be pink*
Under Eye:	*I choose for them to be pink*
Under Nose:	*I choose for them to be pink*
Chin:	*I choose for them to be pink*
Collar Bone:	*I choose for them to be pink*
Under Arm:	*I choose for them to be pink*
Top of Head:	*I choose for them to be pink*

Create appropriate choices based on the above examples.

Tap on any resistance to the changes, or problems visualising as below.

Tapping Section: Tapping for problems visualising

Repeat 3 times while tapping the Karate Chop:

Even though I just can't see my cells I deeply and completely love and accept myself anyway

Eyebrow:	*I don't want to see them*
Side of Eye:	*I can't see them*
Under Eye:	*I refuse to look at them*
Under Nose:	*I don't want to see them*
Chin:	*I won't do it*
Collar Bone:	*I can't do it*

| Under Arm: | *I refuse to see them* |
| Top of Head: | *I don't want to look at them* |

Repeat 3 times while tapping the Karate Chop:

Even the I can't visualise, I've never been able to visualise, I'm not a visual person I deeply and completely love and accept myself and I choose to release these blocks now.

Eyebrow:	*I can't visualise*
Side of Eye:	*It's not possible for me to visualise*
Under Eye:	*I can't do it*
Under Nose:	*I am not a visual person*
Chin:	*I've never been able to visualise*
Collar Bone:	*I can't do this*
Under Arm:	*I can't see my cells*
Top of Head:	*This is ridiculous*

Continue:

Eyebrow:	*I'll never do it*
Side of Eye:	*Yes I will*
Under Eye:	*I choose to begin visualising now*
Under Nose:	*I can do it*
Chin:	*I will do it*
Collar Bone:	*It is possible for me to visualise*
Under Arm:	*I choose to see my cancer cells now*
Top of Head:	*And I choose to change their structure easily*

Continue:

Eyebrow:	*I can't see anything*
Side of Eye:	*It's impossible*
Under Eye:	*It's too difficult*
Under Nose:	*It's not possible for me*
Chin:	*It is possible for me*
Collar Bone:	*I can do it*

Under Arm:	*I choose to visualise easily now*
Top of Head:	*I choose to have fun with this*

Continue:

Eyebrow:	*I can't visualise*
Side of Eye:	*I choose to visualise easily now*
Under Eye:	*I can't do it*
Under Nose:	*I can do it*
Chin:	*I can't see anything*
Collar Bone:	*I choose to visualise easily now*
Under Arm:	*It is not possible for me*
Top of Head:	*I choose for it to be easy for me to visualise now*

If you have a number of tumours, begin with the biggest, the one that is giving you the most problem. Shrink yourself down again, back into that 'Mini-me' and check out:

- What does it look like now?
- What needs to happen next for it to completely disappear?

Bring in whatever external help you need to support the 'Mini-me' who is standing by the tumour. Visualise the tumour reducing, little by little, until it goes completely. By allowing it to reduce a little at a time it is less challenging to your conscious mind and belief systems than clearing it all at once. Every time you check in to clear a little more, begin working from the last visit, when it had already began to get smaller.

'Feeling and faith are much more than 'mind over matter.' It is really a case of 'mind creates matter'.'
Dr David Hamilton PhD

Some suggestions shared with me by clients are as follows:

- **Hoover it away layer by layer**
- **Scrub it away**
- **Sand it away**
- **Melt it with a hot flame**
- **Slice thin strips off it**
- **Bring in a team of workers to help**
- **Use a power hose**

249

Lois was in one of the cancer groups that I run and we were doing an exercise on visualisation alongside the tapping. She created a visualisation for her breast tumour which really appealed to me.

'I have been visualising a school of dolphins gently nibbling away at the edges of my tumour and then swimming off with it, a little at a time. As they nibble they turn the tumour to golden sand and then put it on a beach for people to enjoy and children to play sandcastles with. I imagine them just nibbling away very gently until the tumour has completely gone'.

You might find a similar visualisation useful. Or perhaps you need a team of workers to help.

Bea's story
Bea brought in a red team to be in charge of sanding a particular series of tumours away. She had a purple team who had wheelbarrows, filling them up and running them up through her system, through her veins, through her arteries and out of her body, actually through her mouth. Then there was a green team who came in and treated the sites where the tumours had been putting on some cold cream to soothe and help them completely heal. Finally she had a yellow team who she put on guard to make sure that her immune system didn't allow these errant cells back. Her whole system was therefore prepared, and knew what to do and how to recognise a cancer cell.

Both of the above visualisations very much appealed to me. Brent Baum (Holographic Memory Resolution) suggests bringing in a recycling angel to scoop up the tumour or tumours and take them away to be recycled into something positive. I love this idea too!

Whatever visualisation works for you, whatever feels natural and comfortable for you, allow it to become real, build it up and return to it every day, at least three times a day, taking great care to really step into it as a mini me, taking time to really allow yourself this important piece of the healing.

Many people will have a clear idea of what their actual tumour looks like. They may have seen it on scans, or researched on the web, and they will often have the measurements. These images provide a clear way of working with EFT.

Taking the factual information available, you can again use the Choices trio (see Chapter 3) to begin to make changes. As with most of our work with EFT, it is important to be very specific again. Whilst I don't know whether it would work to go for a total reduction in a tumour immediately, my intuition tells me it is likely to be more effective to work on it a little at a time, regularly, to initiate changes that seem acceptable and possible.

Work as follows:

Tapping Section: Tapping for reducing tumour size

Repeat 3 times while tapping the Karate Chop:

Even though my tumour is x cm I choose for it to be x cm now

Eyebrow:	*This x cm tumour*
Side of Eye:	*This tumour*

Under Eye:	*This tumour in.... (location)*
Under Nose:	*This x cm tumour in ... (location)*
Chin:	*This tumour*
Collar Bone:	*My tumour*
Under Arm:	*My tumour*
Top of Head:	*My x cm tumour*

Keep visualising the change occurring!

When Sue Beer and I run our cancer groups we sometimes have people who feel embarrassed or ridiculous, doing this work, saying things like: *I can't visualise a team of people inside my body, that's never going to work.* I would ask you to take a leap of faith and just do it anyway. You have nothing to lose, and you never know, the responses of the external body seem to evidence that something positive happens.

Check for any blocking beliefs around doing this work, it working etc. Tap to clear them:

Repeat 3 times while tapping the Karate Chop:

Even though this can't work I deeply and completely love and accept myself anyway

Eyebrow:	*It won't work*
Side of Eye:	*It feels ridiculous*
Under Eye:	*It can't possibly work*
Under Nose:	*It will never work*
Chin:	*This is a waste of time*
Collar Bone:	*It won't work*
Under Arm:	*It feels silly*
Top of Head:	*It can't possibly work*

Work little by little, visualising as you go. When you feel it is appropriate to change the figures again, repeat the process as above with the new figure, always remembering to visualise as you tap.

Whilst there is no documented evidence as to the results of working this way there is clear proof that the tapping can effect physical changes in other areas. I discovered this through working with a number of clients whose veins were close to collapse during chemotherapy and who were being threatened with having a port put in.

Grace's story
Grace was especially adamant that she did not want to have a port as it would affect other complementary therapies she was having, such as Chinese herbs. For her, the medicinal properties of the herbs were a vital component of her healing. So we set up a Choices tapping protocol as follows, using her words:

Tapping Section: Tapping for strong and robust veins

Repeat 3 times while tapping the Karate Chop:

Even though my veins are weak and feeble I choose for them to be strong and robust

Eyebrow:	*My weak and feeble veins*
Side of Eye:	*Weak and feeble veins*
Under Eye:	*My weak and feeble veins*
Under Nose:	*Weak and feeble veins*
Chin:	*My weak and feeble veins*
Collar Bone:	*Weak and feeble veins*
Under Arm:	*My weak and feeble veins*
Top of Head:	*Weak and feeble veins*

Continue:

Eyebrow:	*I choose for my veins to be strong and robust*
Side of Eye:	*I choose for my veins to be strong and robust*
Under Eye:	*I choose for my veins to be strong and robust*
Under Nose:	*I choose for my veins to be strong and robust*
Chin:	*I choose for my veins to be strong and robust*
Collar Bone:	*I choose for my veins to be strong and robust*
Under Arm:	*I choose for my veins to be strong and robust*
Top of Head:	*I choose for my veins to be strong and robust*

Continue:

Eyebrow:	*My weak and feeble veins*
Side of Eye:	*I choose for my veins to be strong and robust*
Under Eye:	*My weak and feeble veins*
Under Nose:	*I choose for my veins to be strong and robust*
Chin:	*My weak and feeble veins*
Collar Bone:	*I choose for my veins to be strong and robust*
Under Arm:	*My weak and feeble veins*
Top of Head:	*I choose for my veins to be strong and robust*

She worked with this many times during each day, whilst visualising her veins as strong and robust, unusual words to describe veins. When she went to hospital for her next round of chemotherapy the nurse looked at the veins in her arms and said 'Wow, you have got strong and robust veins'! Her veins were fine to take the chemotherapy, and she had a further three treatments and never needed the port.

Nearly five years on she is still fit and healthy and has just published her first book! She continues to tap and visualise regularly.

I cannot pretend to understand exactly how this happens, but my sense is that pure intention plays a strong part, combined with dogged determination and persistence. By tapping on any blocks to visualising the desired outcome, it seems the unconscious mind can put all its attention on the positive.

'Visualise this thing that you want, see it, feel it, believe in it. Make your mental blue print, and begin to build'
Robert Collier

Visualisation in a nutshell:

To create a successful visualisation follow the steps below:

- Be clear about your intended outcome.
- Tap for any blocking beliefs.
- Visualise the intended positive outcome.
- Tap using Choices as above.

During training, successful athletes are taught to vividly imagine kicking the winning goal, or winning the specific race. Their coach will take them through the visualisation in minute detail, again and again and again. When they come to the actual match or race, they have already scored that winning goal, or won the race many, many times in their head and their unconscious mind has programmed their neurology to achieve this desired outcome. Do not underestimate the power of the mind, once harnessed in this way. As Napoleon Hill says in 'Think & Grow Rich', "What the mind can conceive and believe, the mind can achieve'.

I have seen this particular occurrence enough times now in my regular group work to believe that physical change is possible with tapping, that it is not just a coincidence. However, you need to be consistent and focussed. Set an alarm and do a round of tapping on the required physical change, along with the visualisation, every hour. Frequency of repetition seems to be important here.

In the following chapter we will look at applying the combination of tapping and visualising to support and boost the immune system, which plays such a crucial role in healing from cancer.

CHAPTER 16

THE IMMUNE SYSTEM

'Live out of your imagination, not your history'
Stephen Covey

The immune system is a biological system designed to protect the body against disease. It does this by identifying and killing pathogens (germs) and tumour cells. White blood cells (also known as leukocytes) are the immune system cells. Their role is to be constantly on alert for signs of disease, and attack and destroy any threat. A malfunction in the immune system can lead to our health being compromised and our becoming vulnerable to disease. There are some very practical ways to support the immune system naturally, through adequate rest, stress management and a healthy diet.

When the immune system is operating healthily it is designed to recognise and clean up any cancer cells in the body. In fact, it is doing this all the time for us. When cancer is not automatically cleared there is some miscommunication happening within the immune system itself. With the combination of tapping and visualisation it seems we are able to support and strengthen the immune system.

There are many ways in which we compromise our immune systems, stress being one of the better known ones. Other ways include lifestyle choices that create havoc in our internal environment. These can also be addressed with the tapping (see Chapter 19).

Tapas Fleming (creator of Tapas Acupressure Technique, another powerful form of energy psychology) is herself a survivor of breast cancer. She suggests asking both a cancer cell and an immune cell to show themselves to you. Ask if your immune system recognises a cancer cell, and if it doesn't educate it accordingly. She then suggests visualising the white blood cells happily eating the cancer cells. (Healing the Emotional Aspects of Cancer by Tapas Fleming), www.tatlife.com .

Imagining your immune cells
Imagine one of your white blood cells (immune cells). As before, you may want to make notes as you do this so that you can return to the visualisation easily in the future.

- **What shape is it?**
- **What size is it?**
- **Is it still or moving?**
- **How healthy does it look?**
- **How alert?**
- **How motivated?**

Now notice how many you have in your body, and how easily they are moving around your bloodstream.

- **How do you feel about what you are seeing?**
- **What needs to happen in order for your immune system to grow stronger now?**

Vividly imagine your white blood cells and entire immune system strong, healthy and vibrant. When you feel comfortable with this image introduce the white blood cells to the cancer cells and imagine the white blood cells cleaning up the cancer in whatever way feels right for you.

Place one hand over the cancerous area, or, if there are several tumours, over the one that has your attention the most strongly. Close your eyes and get a sense of what those cells look like.

- **What shape are they?**
- **Are they active or passive?**
- **What colour?**
- **Do they have faces? If so, what are their expressions?**

Tap on any blocks to visualising, and when you have a clear picture, imagine introducing those cells to your immune cells. Tap as you tell your immune cells exactly what you want them to do with the cancer cells to clear them from your body.

- **Do you want them to eat them?**
- **Kill them?**
- **Hoover them up?**
- **Wash them away?**
- **Scoop them up in a rubbish bag?**
- **Or any other method that feels right to you.**

Then visualise it happening, again tapping for any feelings that may come up as you watch the cancer cells being successfully cleared from your body.

What feels right for you?
Whatever you choose, remember the only rule is that it feels like the congruent choice for you.

Suzy's story
Suzy felt that her white blood cells were lethargic and 'asleep on the job'. She was a keen runner and had a number of motivational tracks on her iPOD which she played when she felt herself flagging. Her favourite of these was 'It's Raining Men'. She decided to play this to her white blood cells to energise and inspire them and she described them as happily dancing around her body enthusiastically collecting any errant cancer cells and clearing them from her body. After only a week she returned to hospital for her next bout of chemotherapy and found that her white blood cell count improved significantly in comparison to her last blood test three weeks previously!

What song gives you that feel good factor? Imagine sharing that with your white cells and spurring them on to increased strength and renewed vigour and health.

255

We will begin by working with the immediate assumption that at some point your immune cells must have been responding abnormally, or at least below par, or that there is some form of miscommunication happening.

Tapping Section: Tapping for abnormal immune cells

Repeat 3 times while tapping the Karate Chop:

Even though my immune cells are responding abnormally I deeply and completely love and accept myself

Eyebrow:	*My immune cells are responding abnormally*
Side of Eye:	*This abnormal response*
Under Eye:	*My immune cells are responding abnormally*
Under Nose:	*This abnormal response*
Chin:	*My immune cells are responding abnormally*
Collar Bone:	*This abnormal response*
Under Arm:	*My immune cells are responding abnormally*
Top of Head:	*This abnormal response*

Repeat 3 times while tapping the Karate Chop:

Even though my immune cells are not recognising the cancer cells I deeply and completely love and accept myself

Eyebrow:	*They are not recognising the cancer cells*
Side of Eye:	*This misunderstanding in my immune cells*
Under Eye:	*They are not recognising the cancer cells*
Under Nose:	*This miscommunication in my immune cells*
Chin:	*This misguided immune cell response*
Collar Bone:	*They are not recognising the cancer cells*
Under Arm:	*This miscommunication in my immune cells*
Top of Head:	*This misguided immune cell response*

Repeat 3 times while tapping the Karate Chop:

Even though my immune cells are getting the wrong messages I deeply and completely love and accept myself

Eyebrow:	*This misunderstanding in my immune cells*
Side of Eye:	*They are getting the wrong messages*

Under Eye:	*They are getting the wrong messages*
Under Nose:	*This misunderstanding in my immune cells*
Chin:	*This misguided immune cell response*
Collar Bone:	*This miscommunication in my immune cells*
Under Arm:	*They are getting the wrong messages*
Top of Head:	*This misguided immune cell response*

Continue:

Eyebrow:	*This immune system mistake*
Side of Eye:	*This immune system error*
Under Eye:	*This immune system mistake*
Under Nose:	*This immune system error*
Chin:	*This immune system mistake*
Collar Bone:	*This immune system error*
Under Arm:	*This immune system mistake*
Top of Head:	*This immune system error*

Then create a Choice, again using your own words. For example:

Repeat 3 times while tapping the Karate Chop:

Even though I have this miscommunication in my immune system I choose for my immune cells/white blood cells to recognise and clear any cancer cells from my body now

Eyebrow:	*This miscommunication in my immune cells*
Side of Eye:	*This miscommunication in my immune cells*
Under Eye:	*They are getting the wrong messages*
Under Nose:	*They are not recognising the cancer cells*
Chin:	*This miscommunication in my immune cells*
Collar Bone:	*This miscommunication in my immune cells*
Under Arm:	*This misguided immune cell response*
Top of Head:	*This misguided immune cell response*

Continue:

Eyebrow:	*I choose for my immune cells to recognise cancer cells*

257

Side of Eye:	*I choose for my immune cells to clear the cancer cells now*
Under Eye:	*I choose for my immune cells to detect and clear any cancer cells now*
Under Nose:	*I choose for my immune cells to eat any remaining cancer cells now*
Chin:	*I choose for my immune cells to recognise cancer cells*
Collar Bone:	*I choose for my immune cells to eat the cancer cells now*
Under Arm:	*I choose for my immune cells to detect and clear any cancer cells now*
Top of Head:	*I choose for my immune cells to eat any remaining cancer cells now*

Continue:

Eyebrow:	*This miscommunication in my immune cells*
Side of Eye:	*I choose for my immune cells to detect and clear any cancer cells now*
Under Eye:	*This misunderstanding in my immune cells*
Under Nose:	*I choose for them to learn to identify and clear cancer cells easily*
Chin:	*This misguided immune cell response*
Collar Bone:	*I choose for my immune cells to detect and clear any cancer cells now*
Under Arm:	*This misguided immune cell response*
Top of Head:	*I choose for my immune cells to recognise and clear cancer cells from my body*

When you have down a few rounds (maybe two or three) on each protocol return to your original visualisation and notice what has changed. Ask yourself the following questions:

- **What does your immune system looks now?**
- **How do you feel about it?**

258

- **Is anything else preventing it from functioning healthily?**
- **What does that block look like?**
- **What could you do to clear it?**

Pick an image that resonates with you. Some ideas might be a map, a network of rivers, a tree … Biological accuracy is not important here.

Allow your imagination to run riot. If the block looks like a pile of mud, for instance, allow yourself to imagine hosing it away. Bring in the cleaners, a scrubbing brush, whatever feels appropriate to you to clear that block. Don't worry about how silly it sounds, just go there anyway.

Tapping Section: Tapping for block to immune system

Repeat 3 times while tapping the Karate Chop:

Even though I have this block to my immune system I deeply and completely love and accept myself

Eyebrow:	*This block*
Side of Eye:	*This block to my immune system*
Under Eye:	*This block*
Under Nose:	*This block to my immune system*
Chin:	*This block*
Collar Bone:	*This block to my immune system*
Under Arm:	*This block to my immune system*
Top of Head:	*This block*

Repeat 3 times while tapping the Karate Chop:

Even though something is blocking my immune system working healthily I deeply and completely love and accept myself

Eyebrow:	*Something in the way of my immune system*
Side of Eye:	*Something blocking its flow*
Under Eye:	*This ___ getting in the way of my healthy immune system*
Under Nose:	*This ___ blocking its flow*
Chin:	*Something is in the way*
Collar Bone:	*Something is blocking my healthy immune system*
Under Arm:	*This block*
Top of Head:	*This block*

259

Repeat 3 times while tapping the Karate Chop:

Even though my immune system is weak I deeply and completely love and accept myself

Eyebrow:	*My immune system is weak*
Side of Eye:	*My immune system is weak*
Under Eye:	*My immune system is weak*
Under Nose:	*My immune system is weak*
Chin:	*My immune system is weak*
Collar Bone:	*My immune system is weak*
Under Arm:	*My immune system is weak*
Top of Head:	*My immune system is weak*

Then add your choice to support and strengthen the immune system:

Eyebrow:	*I choose to clear this block easily*
Side of Eye:	*I choose to allow my immune cells to flow healthily*
Under Eye:	*I choose to support my immune system*
Under Nose:	*I choose a healthy immune system*
Chin:	*I choose to clear any blocks to a healthy immune system*
Collar Bone:	*I choose for my immune cells to strengthen easily*
Under Arm:	*I choose a strong healthy immune system now*
Top of Head:	*I choose a strong healthy immune system now*

Chris's story
Chris visualised his immune system as the London underground map, with many different lines all interconnecting, and different colours. He envisioned a different colour team of cleaners for each area, with himself as the foreman. He travelled on a mini train through all the different tunnels, bringing the relevant teams in to clean any dirt or grime from the walls and the tracks, including graffiti. He then coated all the walls with a non-stick coating which prevented any further dirt or detritus building up again. He visited his network of tunnels (his blood system) every day several times to check everything was running smoothly and remained intact. He likened himself to the Fat Controller in Thomas the Tank Engine!

See yourself in perfect health, and if you will do it right before you sleep, then there will be many hours where you will be unconscious, where you will not be doing any miscreating to counteract that.
Abraham-Hicks, A New Beginning I

The power of visualisation cannot be underestimated. It really does seem that what our mind conceives our body achieves. It is worth setting a certain amount of time aside daily to enhance your visualisation skills. Remember, everyone can do it, it is just that not everyone realises it. You visualise every day, many, many times, all we are doing here is bring that skill into conscious awareness and using it strategically.

In the following chapter we will be looking at the topic of insomnia, a condition that can bring with it extreme anxiety. I will offer you a number of options to work through in order to gain a deep restorative night's sleep.

CHAPTER 17

INSOMNIA

'Have courage for the great sorrows of life and patience for the small ones; and when you have laboriously accomplished your daily task, go to sleep in peace.'
Victor Hugo

There are many reasons for sleeplessness or difficulty in staying asleep and this is particularly relevant with a cancer diagnosis. Some cancer medications, such as steroids can over-stimulate the brain and make it hard for you to sleep.

There are also some very obvious emotional causes for sleeplessness, such as anxiety, fear and depression. If you've already begun to use the tapping while reading this book, you may already be sleeping more easily. However, some of you may still find that at night your mind wakes up, things whirr around and you have a problem settling, or staying asleep. This can be intensely frustrating, as well as debilitating and exhausting.

On a practical note, it can help to establish a bedtime ritual, possibly a hot bath with low lighting and candles or oils, a hot drink, even a short meditation or hypnosis recording. Your mind and body need to be trained into recognising when it is time to go to sleep and having a ritual allows the process of unwinding to begin, and begins to program the unconscious mind towards sleep.

There are a number of ways to support optimum sleep with tapping, one of the most useful of which is imaginary tapping. It makes sense to practice this during daytime so that your unconscious mind gets accustomed to the process and it becomes easy and natural at night. So to begin with, practice this exercise sitting in a comfortable chair.

Imaginary Tapping
Whilst some people find it comforting, I tend not to suggest tapping on yourself whilst you are trying to go to sleep for the simple reason that the physical activity of tapping may well wake you up even more. What I would suggest doing instead is imagine the tapping.

- **Lie in bed/sit in your chair**
- **Close your eyes**
- **Imagine tapping around the points on the shortcut version as follows:**
    - § **Eyebrow**
    - § **Side of your eye**
    - § **Under your eye**
    - § **Under your nose**
    - § **Chin**
    - § **Collar Bone**

§ **Under one arm**

§ **Top of your head**

If your mind is whirring and thoughts are coming into your head, don't try and close them out, as they will just become more persistent. Instead accept the thoughts and, as if you were tapping on a normal daytime routine, just tap continually around the points, naming each one in your head as you move your attention to it, ie eyebrow point, side of the eye etc. You will notice the thoughts beginning to fade as your system relaxes. Allow any thoughts to come, but there is no need to repeat them aloud, acknowledging them is enough here.

Holly's story
My client, Holly said to me one day, *'You know I find it really useful, I imagine George Clooney tapping on me at night. His touch is so soothing that I relax into this blissful place where I have his undivided attention and all is well with the world! It is safe to sleep'*

Whilst I would have thought George Clooney at her bedside might have woken her up, in fact she found it very reassuring and calming! She can feel the actual quality of his tapping, the pressure of his fingers on her skin, she can hear him tapping, she hears his voice saying soothing things to her and eventually she goes to sleep very easily now. In fact, after just a few weeks of practicing this, she just has to think of George Clooney and she relaxes!

It may or may not work for you to imagine someone you know, or a film star tapping on you. But if you were to just close your eyes and vividly imagine the sensation of the tapping on each point, you will find that you pick up a certain rhythm and, as the thoughts come and go, you will begin to become quite drowsy. If you want, you could bring in a Choice at this point, you could choose to feel drowsy. Eventually you will just have to think about tapping during the night and you will fall back to sleep easily.

However, if you find that simply imagining the tapping and repeating the points in your head is not enough for you, look through the following protocols and choose the ones that resonate with you. As always, you can change the words to suit your own state, these are merely suggestions. Ideally, tap through these protocols several hours ahead of your bedtime, but if at bedtime you still find you cannot sleep, and you can't imagine the tapping, then revert to physically tapping on the points as you lie in bed.

Tapping Section: Tapping for not sleeping

Repeat 3 times while tapping the Karate Chop:

Even though I can't sleep I deeply and completely love and accept myself

Eyebrow:	*I can't sleep*
Side of Eye:	*Can't sleep*
Under Eye:	*Not sleeping anxiety*
Under Nose:	*I can't sleep*
Chin:	*Not sleeping anxiety*

263

Collar Bone:	I can't sleep
Under Arm:	Not sleeping
Top of Head:	I just can't sleep

Repeat 3 times while tapping the Karate Chop:

Even though I feel wide-awake I deeply and completely love and accept myself.

Eyebrow:	Feeling wide awake
Side of Eye:	Not being able to sleep
Under Eye:	Feeling wide awake
Under Nose:	I can't sleep
Chin:	Feeling wide awake
Collar Bone:	I can't get to sleep
Under Arm:	I'll never get to sleep
Top of Head:	Feeling wide awake

When you have reduced the charge on the above and it no longer rings entirely true for you it is time to introduce a Choice. My colleague, Sue Beer, often introduces the word drowsy, and it appeals to me too. There is something about the word that echoes the state itself. Try saying it out loud... DROWSY... how do you feel when you say that word?

Repeat 3 times while tapping the Karate Chop:

Even though I am having problems sleeping, I choose to feel drowsy anyway.

Eyebrow:	Sleeping problems
Side of Eye:	I can't sleep
Under Eye:	I'll never be able to sleep
Under Nose:	Sleeping problems
Chin:	Sleeping problems
Collar Bone:	I can't sleep
Under Arm:	I'll never be able to sleep
Top of Head:	Sleeping problems

Continue:

| Eyebrow: | I choose to feel drowsy |
| Side of Eye: | I choose to sleep easily now |

Under Eye:	*I choose to feel drowsy*
Under Nose:	*I choose to nod off now*
Chin:	*I choose to feel drowsy*
Collar Bone:	*I choose to sleep easily now*
Under Arm:	*I choose to feel drowsy*
Top of Head:	*I choose to nod off now*

Continue:

Eyebrow:	*Can't sleep*
Side of Eye:	*I choose to feel drowsy now*
Under Eye:	*Can't sleep*
Under Nose:	*I choose to feel drowsy now*
Chin:	*Can't sleep*
Collar Bone:	*I choose to feel drowsy now*
Under Arm:	*Can't sleep*
Top of Head:	*I choose to feel drowsy now*

How do you feel about sleeping?

Lack of sleep is very debilitating, and can be a complex issue where it may be useful to work with a certified practitioner. The middle of the night can be a very lonely time when our imaginations can run riot. It is useful to be aware of this, and to tap accordingly. If you are not getting change by tapping with the above protocols it is time for further self-reflection. Begin by asking yourself the following questions:

- **How do you feel about not being able to get to sleep?**
- **Do you worry about it all day?**
- **What do you believe about it?**
- **Is it safe to sleep?**
- **How long has sleep been as issue for you?**
- **What was going on in your life when this issue started?**
- **If you were to guess at the underlying causes of this, what would that guess be?**

Whenever you find yourself thinking about the next night and feeling anxious about not sleeping take a couple of minutes there and then to tap through the anxiety. Anxiety about not sleeping can become obsessive, and you may be able to think of little else. The anxiety itself can perpetuate the insomnia so it is important to tap every time you get an anxious thought around sleep. By being persistent with this, the anxiety levels will drop and the likelihood of a good night's sleep will become more probable.

Tapping Section: Tapping for feelings about sleeping

Repeat 3 times while tapping the Karate Chop:

Even though I am so frustrated I deeply and completely love and accept myself

Eyebrow:	*This frustration*
Side of Eye:	*This frustration*
Under Eye:	*I will never be able to sleep*
Under Nose:	*I just can't sleep*
Chin:	*This frustration*
Collar Bone:	*I have to sleep*
Under Arm:	*I can't sleep*
Top of Head:	*This frustration*

Repeat 3 times while tapping the Karate Chop:

Even though I know I won't be able to sleep tonight I deeply and completely love and accept myself

Eyebrow:	*This anxiety*
Side of Eye:	*I know I won't be able to sleep tonight*
Under Eye:	*It's going to be the same*
Under Nose:	*It's always the same*
Chin:	*I just can't get to sleep*
Collar Bone:	*This dread of going to bed, I can't sleep*
Under Arm:	*It's just not possible for me to sleep*
Top of Head:	*This sleeping anxiety*

Repeat 3 times while tapping the Karate Chop:

Even though I dread bedtime and it is going to be another sleepless night I deeply and completely love and accept myself

Eyebrow:	*This bedtime dread*
Side of Eye:	*This sleeping dread*
Under Eye:	*I just can't do it*
Under Nose:	*It's going to be another sleepless night*

Chin:	*I know it's going to be another sleepless night*
Collar Bone:	*This dread of tonight*
Under Arm:	*This dread of not being able to sleep*
Top of Head:	*This dread*

Keith's story

Keith was having terrible problems sleeping. He was plagued with anxious thoughts through the night. He said it was as if as soon as his body relaxed his mind took over. There was no peace and he found himself worrying about the night all through the day now. He was reluctant to try tapping as nothing to date had made any difference, so how could EFT work? I didn't want to give Keith loads of homework or complex tapping protocols so I suggested he carry out an experiment and simply tapped each of the points for a couple of rounds every time he found himself worrying about not sleeping that night. He agreed to give it a try, but before starting we needed to address his belief that nothing ever worked for him. Feel free to tap along with him:

Repeat 3 times while tapping the Karate Chop:

Even though nothing ever works for me I deeply and completely love and accept myself

Eyebrow:	*Nothing ever works for me*
Side of Eye:	*This isn't going to work for me*
Under Eye:	*Nothing works for me*
Under Nose:	*I can't sleep*
Chin:	*Nothing ever works for me*
Collar Bone:	*Tapping won't work for me*
Under Arm:	*I can't change this*
Top of Head:	*I can't sleep*

Repeat 3 times while tapping the Karate Chop:

Even though I will never be able to get to sleep I deeply and completely love and accept myself

Eyebrow:	*Tapping is not going to be able to help*
Side of Eye:	*My mind won't let me sleep*
Under Eye:	*I'll never be able to sleep*
Under Nose:	*I can't sleep*
Chin:	*Tonight is going to be just the same.*
Collar Bone:	*My mind won't let me sleep.*

Under Arm:	I never sleep
Top of Head:	Tapping won't help

When Keith was open to a glimmer of possibility about the tapping working he was able to begin working by himself every time he caught himself thinking about the night's sleep, as follows:

Repeat 3 times while tapping the Karate Chop:

Even though I am really anxious about sleeping tonight I deeply and completely love and accept myself

Eyebrow:	This sleeping anxiety
Side of Eye:	I won't be able to sleep tonight
Under Eye:	I am never able to sleep
Under Nose:	It's going to be the same again
Chin:	This anxious thought
Collar Bone:	This sleeping anxiety
Under Arm:	This sleeping anxiety
Top of Head:	This anxious thought

Continue:

Eyebrow:	This remaining anxiety
Side of Eye:	I'm really anxious
Under Eye:	What if I can never sleep properly again?
Under Nose:	What if I can?
Chin:	This sleeping anxiety
Collar Bone:	This remaining sleeping anxiety
Under Arm:	Remaining sleeping anxiety
Top of Head:	I choose to let it go

Continue:

Eyebrow:	I am open to the possibility that I can sleep easily now
Side of Eye:	I am open to the possibility that I can make these changes
Under Eye:	I am open to the possibility that sleep can come easily to me now

268

Under Nose:	*I am open to the possibility that I can sleep through the night*
Chin:	*I choose drowsiness instead of this*
Collar Bone:	*I choose drowsiness and belief instead of this*
Under Arm:	*I choose to know that I can sleep through the night I have done it before and I choose to know it is possible for me*
Top of Head:	*I choose to trust my unconscious mind to allow me to sleep through the night easily now*

When Keith returned the next day he said he had been doing as asked and whilst he still hadn't had a great night's sleep he did notice he felt less anxious about it. So I felt we could begin to introduce a little variety to his tapping now, leading firstly to the possibility of change, and then ultimately to a Choice as follows:

This was a Friday and I didn't hear from Keith over the weekend but was due to see him again the following Tuesday. He came into my office with a huge grin on his face, he had just had his first full night's sleep in months! It is important to recognise that this change wasn't instant, and that Keith had been very persistent with his tapping, but it had only taken 5 days since he began, and he had done 99% of the work on his own.

Another client case follows which may be useful, as it looks into the effect of childhood on our current reality. It is useful to check out what beliefs you may have around the very emotive topic of sleep. Beliefs about yourself, family beliefs etc.

Lizzie's story
Lizzie was feeling very panicky about her insomnia. Not only was it debilitating her during the day and affecting her work but she was also convinced it was affecting her healing process. She believed that without 8 hours deep sleep a night she would not heal from her cancer. To her, sleep was the healer, no sleep = no healing. Obviously the anxiety coming from this belief alone was feeding the insomnia and Lizzie was desperate and very tearful. She was blaming herself for sabotaging her healing process despite the fact that her oncologist was pleased with her results post chemotherapy.

We talked and tapped around this belief and where she had learned this. I agreed that sleep, or at least rest, was an important part of any healing process but where did she decide that it was the key part, without which healing wouldn't occur? She didn't know, she had always believed this as long as she could remember.

So I asked her to look at her childhood, what happened when she was ill? Had she suffered from the usual childhood illnesses, mumps, measles, chicken pox etc? Yes, she had had her share. How did her mother respond to them? Lizzie said that her mother had always said, no matter what the nature of the illness, that 'a good night's sleep will make everything better' and 'You need to get your sleep to keep healthy'.

For Lizzie this was an AHA! moment, as she realised that she had taken on her mother's words literally. She said that her mother was still saying it now to Lizzie's children! When I asked her whether her mother had meant her to take on this belief so literally, Lizzie said that she thought her mother probably just wanted to get the kids to bed so she could have some peace herself!

Once Lizzie had tapped through the various aspects above she was able to feel more relaxed about sleeping, and as a result began to sleep more deeply and for longer during the night.

Tapping Section: Tapping for healing and sleeping

Repeat 3 times while tapping the Karate Chop:

Even though I have this healing anxiety I deeply and completely love and accept myself

Eyebrow:	*This healing anxiety*
Side of Eye:	*What if I can't sleep*
Under Eye:	*What if that affects my healing process*
Under Nose:	*I choose to know that I can sleep easily*
Chin:	*I choose to remember times when I have slept easily*
Collar Bone:	*And I choose to remind my unconscious mind*
Under Arm:	*I choose to remember times when I have slept easily*
Top of Head:	*I choose to know that I can sleep easily14*

Repeat 3 times while tapping the Karate Chop:

Even though I have this healing anxiety I deeply and completely love and accept myself

Eyebrow:	*This healing anxiety*
Side of Eye:	*What if I can't sleep*
Under Eye:	*What if that affects my healing process*
Under Nose:	*I choose to know that I can sleep easily*
Chin:	*I choose to remember times when I have slept easily*
Collar Bone:	*And I choose to remind my unconscious mind*
Under Arm:	*I choose to remember times when I have slept easily*
Top of Head:	*I choose to know that I can sleep easily*

Repeat 3 times while tapping the Karate Chop:

Even though I won't heal if I can't sleep I deeply and completely love and accept myself

Side of Eye:	*I won't heal if I can't sleep*
Side of Eye:	*I'll never get better if I can't sleep*
Under Eye:	*I have to sleep in order to heal*
Under Nose:	*I can't sleep so I can't heal*
Chin:	*Maybe*
Collar Bone:	*Maybe I can*
Under Arm:	*I have to sleep to heal*
Top of Head:	*Maybe, maybe not*

'A good laugh and a long sleep are the best cures in the doctor's book.'
Irish Proverb

We will now look at Bridget's story which is interesting in as much as the changes Bridget makes are achieved purely through the use of metaphor. Listen to your language, how are you describing that sleepless part of you? Do you too have a demon like Bridget?

Bridget's story
Bridget was having terrible problems sleeping. Every night she would go to bed and drop off to sleep easily, exhausted by her day; and every night at about three or four in the morning she would find herself wide awake with anxious thoughts going round and round in her head - anxieties about her treatment, anxieties about her future, anxieties about her financial position. She described this like having a black demon inside her head who, every time she began to get some form of rest or relaxation, would wake up and nag at her lest she were forget her situation. When I asked her a little bit more about this demon she said " I think he actually wants to help me, he is trying to remind me that I can't afford to take any time off, I can't afford to stop working on this". So we tapped:

Tapping Section: Tapping for waking with anxiety

Repeat 3 times while tapping the Karate Chop:

Even though I have this demon waking me up I deeply and completely love and accept myself

Eyebrow:	*This demon in my head*
Side of Eye:	*Waking me up*
Under Eye:	*Keeping me alert*
Chin:	*This demon*
Collar Bone:	*My demon*

271

Under Arm:	*Trying to help*
Under Arm:	*Waking me up*
Top of Head:	*This demon and everything I feel about it*

Repeat 3 times while tapping the Karate Chop:

Even though I don't want this demon waking me up I deeply and completely love and accept myself

Eyebrow:	*I don't want it*
Side of Eye:	*I don't like it*
Under Eye:	*I wish it would go away*
Under Nose:	*This exhausting demon*
Chin:	*I don't want it*
Collar Bone:	*I really don't want it*
Under Arm:	*This exhausting demon in my head*
Top of Head:	*I don't like it*

Repeat 3 times while tapping the Karate Chop:

Even though I am exhausted I deeply and completely love and accept myself

Eyebrow:	*This exhaustion*
Side of Eye:	*This exhaustion*
Under Eye:	*Not sleeping exhaustion*
Under Nose:	*Not sleeping exhaustion*
Chin:	*This exhaustion*
Collar Bone:	*Feeling so exhausted*
Under Arm:	*This exhaustion*
Top of Head:	*Feeling so exhausted*

Repeat 3 times while tapping the Karate Chop:

Even though the demon won't let me sleep I am open to the possibility that it is doing the best it knows how for me

Eyebrow:	*This demon*
Side of Eye:	*Stopping me sleeping*
Under Eye:	*On my case*

Under Nose:	*This demon*
Chin:	*I don't want it*
Collar Bone:	*This demon*
Under Arm:	*This exhausting demon*
Top of Head:	*This demon*

I asked Bridget to check in with the demon and see what was happening. It had changed from black to a royal blue and it seemed to have calmed down, it wasn't wagging a finger at her anymore.

Interestingly, she described the finger wagging as the same sensation as she could feel internally. She was suffering from stomach cancer, and she often felt twinges in her stomach area which she described as the demon pushing on the lining of her stomach to allow her to keep focussed on the healing there.

She was able to start to accept the demon now, she understood why it was in her body and its positive intention for her. Nevertheless, she felt it was actually interfering with her healing process rather than keeping her on track. She was absolutely exhausted and fed up with these thoughts that kept invading her during the night so I asked her to imagine tapping as if she was the demon with tapping phrases such as:

Repeat 3 times while tapping the Karate Chop:

Even though she doesn't want me there I deeply and completely love and accept myself

Eyebrow:	*Feeling unwanted*
Side of Eye:	*She doesn't want me there*
Under Eye:	*Feeling unwanted*
Under Nose:	*Feeling rejected*
Chin:	*She doesn't want me*
Collar Bone:	*She is angry with me*
Under Arm:	*Feeling rejected*
Top of Head:	*She just doesn't want me there*

Then I asked Bridget what was happening with the demon and she said it looked sad and a bit dejected. She continued to imagine tapping on it:

Repeat 3 times while tapping the Karate Chop:

Even though I feel sad and dejected I deeply and completely love and accept myself

Eyebrow:	*This sadness*
Side of Eye:	*This sadness*

Under Eye:	Feeling dejected
Under Nose:	This sadness, I am just trying to help
Chin:	This sadness
Collar Bone:	Feeling dejected
Under Arm:	This sadness, I am just trying to help
Top of Head:	Feeling dejected

Bridget said it had turned to a more turquoisey blue and seemed to be a lot calmer. It was looking up at her now. I asked her what needed to happen next and she said she wanted to express gratitude, and to let it know that she appreciated what it was doing but it was inappropriate in the middle of the night, that she needed to sleep in order to heal. So whilst she appreciated it, it was making a mistake in keeping her awake in the night.

She continued to tap, imagining herself tapping on the demon itself

Repeat 3 times while tapping the Karate Chop:

Even though I have made a mistake I deeply and completely love and accept myself

Eyebrow:	I've made a mistake
Side of Eye:	My mistake
Under Eye:	This mistake
Under Nose:	This sleeping mistake
Chin:	My mistake
Collar Bone:	This mistake
Under Arm:	This sleeping mistake
Top of Head:	This mistake

Repeat 3 times while tapping the Karate Chop:

Even though I have been stopping Bridget from sleeping I deeply and completely love and accept myself

Eyebrow:	Stopping her sleeping
Side of Eye:	I don't want her to sleep
Under Eye:	I want her to heal
Under Nose:	I want her to get better
Chin:	I am open to the possibility that she needs to sleep now
Collar Bone:	I am open to the possibility that it is safe for her to sleep

Under Arm:	*I choose to help her sleep easily now*
Top of Head:	*I choose to help her heal in a new way*

Then I asked Bridget what the demon was doing now and she said it had curled up and gone to sleep! She felt that she needed to thank it for trying to look after her. As she was talking she said it was transforming within her. It changed into a 'turquoise translucent genie', and was floating around her body, humming, visiting every organ, especially her stomach, and polishing them, checking them out for rogue cells and dissolving them with its touch. She called it her 'internal healer'.

As she was experiencing this, the twinges in her stomach subsided.

We did one more round of tapping, expressing Bridget's gratitude to the genie, and she left feeling happy and empowered.

This round leaves out the Karate Chop point and just focuses on the 8 tapping points of the Short Cut version. We will look into the concept of gratitude and its importance in healing in Chapter 25.

Eyebrow:	*I love and accept my healing genie*
Side of Eye:	*I love and thank my healing genie*
Under Eye:	*I thank my genie and I love and accept it*
Under Nose:	*I love and thank my healing genie*
Chin:	*I love and accept it and I choose to sleep easily now*
Collar Bone:	*I choose to sleep deeply now*
Under Arm:	*And I love and accept my genie for the work it is doing*
Top of Head:	*I choose safe healing sleep now*

Bridget came back for her next session a couple of weeks later and reported that whilst initially she had woken in the night a couple of times, since then she had been sleeping soundly through the night. She was enamoured of her new friend, and had created a healing visualisation for herself around the genie which she returned to several times a day.

We all have had the experience of sleeping through the night at some point in our lives, however distant. So I would like you to do the following exercise:

Exercise
Ask your wise unconscious mind to go to that time when you know that you slept through the night easily in your own bed. As you do that, place your attention on your breathing, notice the rhythm of your breath, the rhythm of your heart, count to five on the in breath, and then five on the out breath, allowing a sense of calmness, just as a beginning. I don't know how quickly that calmness will begin to flow around your body, carried by the tiny bubbles of oxygen in your breath but as you do that, just notice..... And notice where you are when you know how to sleep deeply and how you are feeling, notice the feeling of your sheets under your skin, the pillow under

your head, the covers keeping you just the right temperature for you. And as you do that I would like you to remember, really remember, what it was like just to be able to drift easily off to sleep, allowing the cares and the worries of day just to evaporate, that's right, and as you remember that, ask your wise unconscious mind to remind itself of how easy it is now to sleep all night easily now.

You may like to record yourself reading this so that you can play it back to yourself as you go to bed.

Creating a Safe Space For Sleeping

'The wise man in the storm prays to God, not for safety from danger, but for deliverance from fear.'
Ralph Waldo Emerson

Safety is an important issue when it comes to sleeping. Sometimes the unconscious mind decides it's not safe to switch off, it's not safe to sleep. For whatever reason, your system may feel fully alert at all times. Whilst this can be a symptom of Post Traumatic Stress Disorder (PTSD) it is not always so serious; it can just be a simple miscommunication of the unconscious mind, and often responds very well to tapping.

Work with the following protocols, see what changes you notice, and see what comes up for you. You may get snippets of memories or thoughts of a particular person or place. Whatever emerges, take what is offered, regardless of whether it makes any conscious sense to you, and tap with it.

Tapping Section: Tapping for not being safe to sleep

Repeat 3 times while tapping the Karate Chop:

Even though it's not safe to sleep I deeply and completely love and accept myself

Eyebrow:	*It's not safe to sleep*
Side of Eye:	*I can't switch off*
Under Eye:	*I have to stay alert*
Under Nose:	*It's just not safe to sleep*
Chin:	*It's not safe to sleep*
Collar Bone:	*I can't switch off*
Under Arm:	*I have to stay alert*
Top of Head:	*It's just not safe to sleep*

Continue:

Eyebrow:	*What if I can sleep?*

276

Side of Eye:	*What if it's safe to sleep now?*
Under Eye:	*What if it's easy for me to sleep now?*
Under Nose:	*No it can't be*
Chin:	*But what if it is?*
Collar Bone:	*I choose to be open to the possibility of sleeping easily now*
Under Arm:	*I choose to feel safely held and comfortable*
Top of Head:	*As I drift off to sleep easily now*

Repeat 3 times while tapping the Karate Chop:

Even though it's not safe to switch off I deeply and completely love and accept myself

Eyebrow:	*I can't switch off*
Side of Eye:	*I have to keep alert all the time*
Under Eye:	*I have to keep alert*
Under Nose:	*It is not safe to sleep*
Chin:	*I can't switch off and sleep*
Collar Bone:	*Yes I can*
Under Arm:	*No I can't*
Top of Head:	*Yes I can*

Continue:

Eyebrow:	*I am open to the possibility that it's safe for me to sleep now*
Side of Eye:	*I choose to relax safely*
Under Eye:	*I am open to the possibility that I can sleep easily now*
Under Nose:	*I choose to feel safe falling asleep*
Chin:	*I am open to the possibility that it is safe for me to sleep now*
Collar Bone:	*I choose to relax safely*
Under Arm:	*I am open to the possibility that I can sleep easily now*
Top of Head:	*I choose to feel safe falling asleep*

Jane's story

Jane's insomnia had started when she had been in hospital for surgery for colon cancer, which had resulted in her having a colostomy bag. She found that in the ward she would wake to the slightest sound, a footstep, a whisper. She described herself as a solid sleeper up till that point and was frustrated that the insomnia had continued once she was discharged and at home.

I asked her what she thought it might be doing for her that was positive – a strange question, but a powerful one. Assuming that we are intelligent and that we create specific behaviours for good reasons, what had the insomnia given her in hospital?

She thought for a while and said 'I guess it kept me safe, although I don't understand why I would have felt unsafe'. We tapped on needing to feel safe at night and Jane realised that it was about feeling vulnerable in a room full of people (she was in a ward of 6 others). We tapped on feeling vulnerable and I asked Jane when she had felt that feeling before, what did it remind her of?

She said it was boarding school. She had joined the school a term later than her peers and they already had established friendship groups and she was not welcomed in any of them. Worse than that, some of the older girls in her dormitory had decided to pick on her, and the 'attacks' normally happened at night. She remembered a series of different specific events where she had been subjected to this bullying, and also many nights where she had not dared to go to sleep in case something bad happened to her. Her parents removed her from the school after a term and she had forgotten all about it until now.

We tapped through a number of these specific memories, releasing the charge on each. At the end of the session Jane was exhausted but also relieved. She said she felt much lighter, as if a weight had been lifted. She called the next day to say she had had no trouble going to sleep and had slept all night.

It is worth mentioning that current issues might have obscure origins that would not usually come to mind. Whilst tapping does allow a bridge to the unconscious mind, and therefore an easier way of accessing the unconscious memory bank or memory filing system, it is always useful to ask yourself what that feeling (in Jane's case vulnerability) reminds you of, when have you felt like that before? Very often this will lead directly to a core memory which, once resolved with the tapping, will change the behavioural or emotional response (in this case insomnia). ...

Creating a Safe Space in Your Mind

'May sleep envelop you as a bed sheet floating gently down, tickling your skin and removing every worry. Reminding you to consider only this moment.'
Jeb Dickerson

Another useful exercise is to actively create an environment in your mind in which it feels safe to sleep.

Imagine someone who you really love and trust, imagine them there beside you whilst you are in bed, wrapping their arms around you and holding you very safely, perhaps you can feel their breathing. Allow yourself to feel comfortable, warm and safe and as you do that draw those feelings into your heart putting one hand across your heart chakra just as we did earlier in this book, (Chapter 2) drawing those feelings of safety and comfort and love that are available to you there, nothing disturbs you, nothing matters and you allow yourself just to drift off to an easy sleep safely now.

If you are unable to think of a suitable person then create one. Depending on your beliefs maybe you like to feel God present with you, or you could choose a fictional hero/ heroine such as Superman or a film character. It does not matter who you choose, as long as having that person/ energy with you creates a feeling of safety during the night.

To begin with this may take concentration and effort, and it is important to stick with it until you can really FEEL those arms holding you safe. It will get easier every time until you will no longer need to consciously create that feeling and you will be able to fall asleep easily.

Tapping Section: Tapping choices for sleep problems

Repeat 3 times while tapping the Karate Chop:

Even though I am having problems sleeping I choose to feel held and safe and to sleep easily now

Eyebrow:	*These sleeping problems*
Side of Eye:	*My sleeping problems*
Under Eye:	*I can't get to sleep*
Under Nose:	*My sleeping problems*
Chin:	*I just can't get to sleep*
Collar Bone:	*These sleeping problems*
Under Arm:	*These sleeping problems*
Top of Head:	*I can't sleep*

Repeat 3 times while tapping the Karate Chop:

Even though I just can't sleep I choose to feel safely held and comfortable and to drift off to sleep easily now

Eyebrow:	*I choose to feel held and safe and to sleep easily now*
Side of Eye:	*I choose to feel X's arms around me and sleep easily now*
Under Eye:	*I choose to feel held and safe and to sleep easily now*
Under Nose:	*I choose to feel X's arms around me and sleep easily now*
Chin:	*I choose to feel held and safe and to sleep easily now*

279

Collar Bone:	*I choose to feel X's arms around me and sleep easily now*
Under Arm:	*I choose to feel held and safe and to sleep easily now*
Top of Head:	*I choose to feel X's arms around me and sleep easily now*

Continue:

Eyebrow:	*I just can't sleep*
Side of Eye:	*I choose to feel held and safe and to sleep easily now*
Under Eye:	*These sleeping problems*
Under Nose:	*I choose to feel X's arms around me*
Chin:	*I just can't sleep*
Collar Bone:	*I choose to feel held and safe and to sleep easily now*
Under Arm:	*These sleeping problems*
Top of Head:	*I choose to feel X's arms around me*

If, having worked through the above exercise, sleep remains a problem for you ask yourself the following questions:

- **How long your sleep has been an issue for you?**
- **What was going on in your life when it started?**

It may have nothing to do with the cancer, you may have had a problem like this for a long time. If you have, run a quick scan of your life. When did you very first start having issues around sleep? Now ask yourself:

If I were to guess at the underlying causes, what would that guess be?

It may be that you get a snippet of memory coming up in which case go back to the Movie Technique and use it to clear that piece of memory. Whatever comes into your mind is valid, important and relevant. However extreme it may seem, just follow it, it won't take very long.

Repeat 3 times while tapping the Karate Chop:

Even though I have this X movie I deeply and completely love and accept myself

Eyebrow:	*X movie emotions*
Side of Eye:	*X movie emotions*
Under Eye:	*X movie emotions*

Under Nose:	*X movie emotions*
Chin:	*X movie emotions*
Collar Bone:	*X movie emotions*
Under Arm:	*X movie emotions*
Top of Head:	*X movie emotions*

Continue as per the Movie Technique instructions (Chapter 3) until the memory carries no charge when you bring it to mind now.

Night Time Pain and Discomfort

> *'How long the night seems to one kept awake by pain.'*
> *Bernard Joseph Saurin, Blanche et Guiscard*

Some people wake in the night with physical symptoms like a heart racing or a hot flush. At this point you don't need any words, your unconscious mind will be fully focussed on the physical symptoms, just tap, or imagine tapping, remembering to breathe, for as many rounds as are necessary before the symptoms calm and release.

Tapping Section: Tapping for night pain and discomfort

Repeat 3 times while tapping the Karate Chop:

Even though my heart is racing I deeply and completely love and accept myself

Eyebrow:	*My racing heart*
Side of Eye:	*My racing heart*
Under Eye:	*Beating too fast*
Under Nose:	*My heart*
Chin:	*My racing heart*
Collar Bone:	*My racing heart*
Under Arm:	*Beating too fast*
Top of Head:	*My heart*

Repeat 3 times while tapping the Karate Chop:

Even though I feel panicky I deeply and completely love and accept myself

Eyebrow:	*This panic*
Side of Eye:	*This panic*

Under Eye:	*This sleeping panic in my body*
Under Nose:	*This sleeping panic*
Chin:	*This sleeping panic waking me up*
Collar Bone:	*This panic in my body*
Under Arm:	*This panic in my body*
Top of Head:	*This panic*

Very often, in the quiet and still of the night, pain can seem to be worse and more frightening. I am often asked why pains that seem manageable in the day feel so much stronger at night. Whilst I don't have the answer to this, my guess is that a pain can make itself heard far more successfully in the night when it has your complete attention. I also believe that any pain feels worse when we are tired, physical or emotional.

Remember our 3 rules for working with pain (see Chapter 13):

1. **Location**
2. **Quality**
3. **Intensity**

Repeat 3 times while tapping the Karate Chop:

Even though I have this sharp pain in my chest I deeply and completely love and accept myself

Eyebrow:	*This sharp pain in my chest*
Side of Eye:	*This sharp pain just there*
Under Eye:	*Sharp pain in my chest*
Under Nose:	*Sharp pain just there*
Chin:	*This sharp pain in my chest*
Collar Bone:	*This sharp pain just there*
Under Arm:	*Sharp pain in my chest*
Top of Head:	*Sharp pain just there*

Keep tapping, Chasing the Pain around your body and you will find you gradually relax, allowing the pain will ease and you will be able to drift off to sleep easily.

Night Time Loneliness

> *'When it is dark enough, you can see the stars.'*
> *Ralph Waldo Emerson*

The middle of the night can feel a very solitary time, you may feel like you are the only person awake in the world. You may feel very alone, even when you are not. Things often seem worse in the night, partly because you are tired, and partly because there is little or no distraction. If you feel alone and low, tap as follows:

Tapping Section: Tapping for night time lonliness

Repeat 3 times while tapping the Karate Chop:

Even though I feel so lonely in the small hours I deeply and completely love and accept myself

Eyebrow:	*This loneliness*
Side of Eye:	*This middle of the night loneliness*
Under Eye:	*Feeling all alone*
Under Nose:	*This loneliness*
Chin:	*It's so lonely in the small hours*
Collar Bone:	*Feeling all alone*
Under Arm:	*Feeling all alone*
Top of Head:	*This loneliness*

Everything tends to seem worse in the middle of the night, partly because of the silence that allows your internal voice to seem louder, and partly because your resistance is lower through tiredness so it is easier for the negative thoughts to take root. It is worth acknowledging this with a round of tapping as it allows your unconscious mind to accept that this may happen, and that it is, in fact, normal.

Repeat 3 times while tapping the Karate Chop:

Even though everything seems worse in the middle of the night I deeply and completely love and accept myself

Eyebrow:	*Everything seems worse*
Side of Eye:	*It all seems so bad*
Under Eye:	*Everything seems so huge*
Under Nose:	*Everything feels worse*
Chin:	*These awful feelings*
Collar Bone:	*These middle of the night feelings*
Under Arm:	*These middle of the night anxieties*
Top of Head:	*I choose to begin to release them*

Continue:

283

Eyebrow:	*Things always feels worse in the middle of the night*
Side of Eye:	*These middle of the night anxieties*
Under Eye:	*It is always worse in the night*
Under Nose:	*These middle of the night feelings*
Chin:	*I choose to feel sleepy instead of this.*
Collar Bone:	*These middle of the night anxieties.*
Under Arm:	*I choose to release them.*
Top of Head:	*I choose to let them go.*

You may need to do a number of rounds with this and refer to some of the earlier tapping protocols in this chapter, depending on your individual experience.

Another useful exercise can be to choose a colour that represents peacefulness for you. It can be any colour. Then imagine moving that colour through your body, in whatever direction feels comfortable for you, taking as much time as you need, until every cell in your body is infused with your special colour. As you do this, pay specific attention to any area that is experiencing some form of physical response, noticing how, by absorbing that colour, those responses change.

The more times you repeat this exercise, even during the day, the easier it will become, and shortly your unconscious mind will do the work for you when you just think about sleeping.

A note of caution:
Sleep can be very complex and you may find that you are one of the few people for whom tapping just simply doesn't work in this area. This is not about you or your tapping, it is merely that you haven't found the deeper core issues, that are underlying your sleeplessness and at this point it would be worth referring yourself to an EFT practitioner to help you get through any specific blocks.

In the following chapter we will begin to explore the correlation between trauma and serious disease. We will look at the impact trauma has on our physiology, and how, with tapping, we are able to release the imprint of trauma from our cellular memory. This is one of the most exciting possibilities offered by the Energy Psychologies and opens the door to effective deep healing in a relatively painless way. These techniques are transforming the way therapy approaches trauma work.

CHAPTER 18

TRAUMA

'The past is a foreign country, they do things differently there'
L.P. Hartley

Trauma influences our cognitive schemas (or neural pathways) at a profound level. It rocks our beliefs in both ourselves and our existence, and also our sense of reality as we know it. Before the development of the tapping techniques it has been very difficult, and painful, to release the impact of trauma. Therapists would struggle to keep their clients safe from abreacting (re-experiencing the trauma in real time) and people would avoid bringing traumatic experiences to therapy from a very reasonable fear of having to revisit it.

With the tapping, we have a number of techniques that hold the person safe, and it is often possible to begin working on traumatic events yourself. However, if at any point you feel overwhelmed, even by the thought of going there, it is **imperative** that you work with a skilled practitioner to support your journey. To find a practitioner, please see Chapter 1.

Many forms of trauma
Trauma itself can take many shapes or forms, from failing a school test to universally traumatic experiences such as 9/11 or war. It has been found that the sooner the tapping is applied post trauma, the quicker and easier the results.

When an event happens that challenges our beliefs of the world, and our personal safety, it creates a physiological response as well as an emotional one, and pilot studies indicate that this may be evidenced in the development of diseases such as cancer. As yet there is no scientifically accepted research to support this. However, the possibility of trauma playing an active part in cellular change makes it worth addressing here. The emphasis here is on the ongoing emotional response to the event, not to the 'degree' of intensity of the trauma itself. In other words, do not judge the perceived 'seriousness' of the traumatic incident. Remember that trauma can be anything from failing a school test to war.

The moment before a trauma impacts us we perceive ourselves to be utterly helpless. At this point we dissociate, we momentarily leave our body. The sympathetic nervous system goes into overdrive and our entire physiology is focussed purely on survival. Our blood flow is directed to our muscles, adrenalin pumps through us and we move into fight or flight mode.

Brent Baum (Holographic Memory Resolution) describes this moment as T minus one. In the natural course of events, once the immediate danger has passed, we return to our body and shake to release this freeze response. However, unlike in prehistoric times, in the present day we are often presented with a continual flow of perceived dangerous or stressful events and the opportunity to process these at the time is lost. How many of us would admit to feeling stressed daily?

'Trauma is an experience that permanently changes the structure of the brain, the perception of the mind and the function of the body. Trauma occurs when

285

helplessness leads to the freeze/ disassociation response and the freeze discharge doesn't occur, imprinting the experiences of trauma on the brain.'
Dr Robert Scaer

Dr Robert Scaer is a Trauma Neurologist who is particularly interested in the freeze response and how it effects our ongoing health. He purports that when humans experience the freeze response, they typically hold all this energy in their systems, leading to pain and disease. Scaer goes on to state that if in humans, this discharge does not occur, "the sensorimotor features of that traumatic stress will be imprinted in implicit memory through basic operant conditioning, to be accessed in the future for the purpose of survival." (*The Body Bears The Burden: Trauma, Dissociation, and Disease*, Dr Robert Scaer.)

In other words when something happens which triggers the trauma memory in our unconscious, we find ourselves reacting as if the trauma is happening in the present day. For example, if you have experienced a sexual assault you may well find yourself unable to respond to a loving sexual relationship. It is as if the trauma is indeed stored in your cells and you respond as if that sexual danger is still present. If you are interested in researching Dr Scaer's work further he has some very powerful clips available on YouTube.

After many years working with trauma, both with a little and a capital 'T' I would suggest that with the new Energy Psychologies we have discovered a way of working which effectively facilitates the release of the freeze response from cellular memory. In fact, this often (but not always) happens literally, with the person shaking, or their legs seeming to be running in their chair. I have seen this too many times to believe in it as sheer coincidence now.

A link between trauma and cancer

"The one thing you can't take away from me is the way I choose to respond to what you do to me. The last of one's freedoms is to choose ones attitude in any given circumstance."
Viktor E. Frankl, psychoanalyst, Holocaust survivor

A new study of cancer risk amongst Holocaust survivors by the University of Haifa, Israel, was published in the Journal of the National Cancer Institute, comparing cancer rates amongst Jews who immigrated to Israel from Europe before and after 1945 (post Holocaust).

The study found a 17% increase in risk for all types of cancer amongst the Holocaust survivors. The younger someone was during the Holocaust, the higher the risk for cancer, ie the earlier the traumatic event, the higher the likelihood of contracting the disease. This would indicate that childhood stress may well have an impact on adult susceptibility to cancer and other serious disease.

This research, and Dr Scaer's hypothesis, would seem to go some way to supporting the controversial work of German doctor, Dr. Ryke Geerd Hamer, founder of German New Medicine. Dr Hamer believes that ALL cancer is the result of trauma. His anecdotal research led him to further suggest that every cancer has a specific type of corresponding trauma. If Dr. Hamer's findings are true it will create a whole new perspective in treatment of disease. For further information, see Dr Hamer's website: http://www.newmedicine.ca.

286

Whilst Dr Hamer's work is interesting, it should be noted that there is no scientific research to support his theory, and that it is highly unlikely that any one thing creates a cancer diagnosis.

However, even from a general well being-perspective, it seems important to work to clearing the impact of trauma from our cellular memory, and with EFT with having the perfect tool to do this.

A note of caution: When addressing severe trauma it is highly recommended that you work with an experienced therapist who is skilled in managing trauma release safely and healthily.

Talia's story
Talia used to come for sessions regularly. She had a diagnosis of breast cancer. We were working through her emotional history, using the Personal Peace Procedure. Five years prior to her diagnosis, Talia's mother had died unexpectedly in a car crash, which had obviously been extremely traumatic for Talia. We began working with that specific memory, with the Movie Technique, zooming in to the specific moment when she had received a phone call from her Dad telling her that her mother had been killed. She was only 17 and had been round at a friend's house after school.

Talia felt overwhelmed by grief, guilt and remorse. She and her mother had had an argument just before Talia had left the house that morning, as teenagers and their mothers often do. It was nothing serious, but they had never had the chance to make up and at some level Talia felt responsible for her death, however irrational and illogical she recognised that to be.

She had already been to bereavement counselling and had resolved many of the issues surrounding this, but she still felt stuck with this guilt. We went back to the exact moment when she got the devastating phone call. She could remember it as though it happened yesterday, it was still so very vivid. She described the shock as going through her entire body, from the top of her head to the tops of her toes, as though every cell in her body reverberated with trauma. We started working there.

I would invite you to tap along with the following protocols, even if they seem to have no relevance to your own issues. The unconscious mind has an amazing way of finding connections and applying the tapping to something relevant to you, even if it is out of your conscious awareness. So:

Tapping Section: Tapping for mother's death trauma

Repeat 3 times while tapping the Karate Chop:

Even though every cell was traumatised at that phone call I deeply and completely love and accept myself.

Eyebrow:	*Phone call trauma*
Side of Eye:	*Reverberating through every cell in my body*
Under Eye:	*Phone call trauma*
Under Nose:	*Reverberating through every cell in my body*

287

Chin:	*Phone call trauma*
Collar Bone:	*Reverberating through every cell in my body*
Under Arm:	*Phone call trauma*
Top of Head:	*Reverberating through every cell in my body*

We did a number of rounds on this because Talia was getting some very strong physical responses to those words. She began by being very hot and anxious and then fluctuated into extreme cold. I asked her to put her movie out of the room where she couldn't see it but, whilst that helped a little bit, she could still hear the phone ringing. It one of those old-fashioned ring tones, one of the old dial phones that we used to have in the U.K.

Unfortunately for Talia, that ring tone has come back into popular use now amongst teenagers and suddenly Talia was finding herself hearing it unexpectedly, in shopping centres, or on a train. This was triggering quite a severe shock response and on several occasions she had found herself frozen to the spot and panicked.

We tapped through all the different pieces (aspects) around this. Her father had rung her at her friend's house. He hadn't had time to go to her yet, her other siblings had been at home so we tapped through that, we tapped through his words, we tapped with his voice tone and then we started tapping on her body responses to the memory in the here and now. Whilst there were tears and inevitably much sadness, it didn't seem to be traumatising Talia in quite the same way that it had when we began the work. We did many different rounds, including the following:

Repeat 3 times while tapping the Karate Chop:

Even though I shouldn't have argued I deeply and completely love and accept myself

Eyebrow:	*I shouldn't have argued*
Side of Eye:	*It's all my fault*
Under Eye:	*I shouldn't have upset her*
Under Nose:	*I shouldn't have argued*
Chin:	*I shouldn't have argued*
Collar Bone:	*It's all my fault*
Under Arm:	*I shouldn't have upset her*
Top of Head:	*I shouldn't have argued*

We even managed to bring in a little humour

Repeat 3 times while tapping the Karate Chop:

Even though we had a fight I deeply and completely love and accept myself

Eyebrow:	*We had a fight*
Side of Eye:	*I shouldn't have fought*
Under Eye:	*I shouldn't have had a fight*
Under Nose:	*Teenagers should never fight with their mothers*
Chin:	*No teenagers EVER argue with their mothers!*
Collar Bone:	*I shouldn't have argued*
Under Arm:	*It's all my fault*
Top of Head:	*No teenagers EVER argue with their mothers!*

Continue:

Eyebrow:	*I am open to the possibility that I have made a mistake about this*
Side of Eye:	*What if all teenagers argue with their mothers*
Under Eye:	*What if I made a mistake about this*
Under Nose:	*I am open to the possibility that I was just being a normal teenager*
Chin:	*Maybe*
Collar Bone:	*Maybe not*
Under Arm:	*I am open to the possibility*
Top of Head:	*Maybe I was just being a normal teenager*

Talia began to laugh and said that she could see that her guilt was completely unnecessary and that she was sure that her mother would have understood. We continued with a few more rounds:

Repeat 3 times while tapping the Karate Chop:

Even though we argued and she died I love and accept myself anyway

Eyebrow:	*We argued*
Side of Eye:	*She died*
Under Eye:	*We argued*
Under Nose:	*She died*
Chin:	*It was all my fault*
Collar Bone:	*No it wasn't*

Under Arm:	*I am open to the possibility that it was a tragic accident*
Top of Head:	*I am open to the possibility I can see it in a new light*

Repeat 3 times while tapping the Karate Chop:

Even though we fought and she died I am open to the possibility that she loves and accepts me wherever she is

Eyebrow:	*We fought and she died*
Side of Eye:	*This guilt*
Under Eye:	*We fought and she died*
Under Nose:	*My guilt*
Chin:	*I love and forgive myself*
Collar Bone:	*And I love and forgive Mum*
Under Arm:	*I'm open to the possibility that she loves and accepts me*
Top of Head:	*Wherever she is*

Continue:

Eyebrow:	*I love and accept myself*
Side of Eye:	*And I love and accept Mum*
Under Eye:	*I love and accept myself*
Under Nose:	*And I love and accept Mum*
Chin:	*I love and accept myself*
Collar Bone:	*And I love and accept Mum*
Under Arm:	*I love and accept myself*
Top of Head:	*And I love and accept Mum*

During the last couple of rounds Talia visibly relaxed and her breathing softened. She said that recognising that it was normal teenage behaviour to argue and challenge one's parents allowed her to free herself from her guilt. For her, everything changed with the introduction of the word 'normal'. At this point, her legs began to move, and it looked as though she was running a marathon up and down, up and down. She was laughing, saying 'I can't do anything about it, I don't know what is going on but they won't stop!' Without using any words, I just tapped continuously and gradually they began to slow down at which point I introduced:

Tapping Section: Tapping for freeze response trauma

Repeat 3 times while tapping the Karate Chop:

Even though I have this freeze response in my legs I deeply and completely love and accept myself

Eyebrow:	*This freeze response in my legs*
Side of Eye:	*I just want to get out of here*
Under Eye:	*I wanted to get out of there then*
Under Nose:	*I couldn't*
Chin:	*I couldn't run then*
Collar Bone:	*I was frozen*
Under Arm:	*I choose to release this freeze response from my cellular memory*
Top of Head:	*I choose to discharge this freeze response now*

After a few rounds her legs relaxed and I could see the letting go in her muscles. She said she felt absolutely exhausted but happy. We tested it again by going back to the phone call and rerunning the movie. Whilst it was never going to be a good memory, she could tell the story without emotion and without any of the old feelings of shock showing up in her body.

I continued to work with Talia around her breast cancer for several months and whilst we worked through a string of memories of her mother when she considered she had been a difficult child or she had upset her or she shouldn't have done something, the emotions cleared quickly and she felt completely differently about her history.

An added bonus of the work was that she also felt very differently towards her daughter. She was a single mother of a young daughter and used to be terrified whenever they had any disagreement. Now she was able to recognise that children do test boundaries and that it is a fine and healthy part of her daughter's development.

As an aside, she went into remission with her breast cancer and to the best of my knowledge she remains fit and healthy today.

NOTE: Often legs will begin to shake as the body releases trauma, or they may mimic a running movement. This is the freeze response discharging from the physical body, as mentioned at the beginning of this chapter. It is completely normal but can feel a bit strange. It will pass and the trick is to stay with it and keep tapping as with Talia in the above case study. However, it doesn't happen for every person, or in every situation, and this does not mean that the tapping is not effective.

Stress and the Immune System
It is clearly acknowledged in medical circles that stress affects the immune system. When our immune system is compromised we are more susceptible to dis-ease. So logic would dictate that stress and trauma would have a link with cancer. However, I want to reiterate that this is not the case for every person, or every cancer patient. There are many other factors involved, not least of which

involve life style choices, which we will explore in more depth in the following chapter.

Sarah's story

Sarah also had breast cancer. She was young, in her early thirties, led a healthy lifestyle, regularly worked out in the gym, and to all intents and purposes was in the lowest risk bracket for this diagnosis. Having worked through the immediate intense emotions around the diagnosis, from disbelief, to terror, to sadness, we began to look at her emotional history first over the recent years, with the intention of continuing with her doing her own Personal Peace Process.

Sarah had been let go from her job about four and a half years previously and whilst knowing it was a possibility, and in some ways expecting it, when it actually happened to her it felt devastating.

She took the news very badly, thinking why me, despite knowing it wasn't personal. It triggered a deep fear of being penniless, of being on the streets and losing her home. She had been with the company a long time but they were struggling and had no choice. Others had also been made redundant at the same time and they all seemed to be handling it very well. They had been given good redundancy packages, more than was expected, but Sarah felt totally traumatised by it. She felt abandoned and on her own.

We began by making a mini movie of the redundancy, zooming in on the worst part of it. Was it a conversation? Was it a feeling when she left? What was it? She said it was when she was given the news. Her boss called her in and told her, and he was as upset as she was and in tears. He was clearly devastated by it too but said he had no choice. Sarah felt completely helpless, she had to accept the redundancy, there was nothing she could do about it and it was to take place with immediate effect. She zoomed in on the meeting and gave it the title, 'Bob's Words'. The movie ran for approximately five minutes and, using the Tearless Trauma Technique, she guessed that it would be a ten intensity on the SUDS scale were she to watch it (see Chapter 3).

Tapping Section: Tapping for trauma of losing job

Repeat 3 times while tapping the Karate Chop:

Even though I have this 'Bob's Words' movie I deeply and completely love and accept myself

Eyebrow:	*Bob's words movie*
Side of Eye:	*Bob's words movie*
Under Eye:	*Bob's words movie*
Under Nose:	*Bob's words movie*
Chin:	*Bob's words movie*
Collar Bone:	*Bob's words movie*
Under Arm:	*Bob's words movie*
Top of Head:	*Bob's words movie*

Repeat 3 times while tapping the Karate Chop:

Even though I have these 'Bob's Words' emotions I deeply and completely love and accept myself

Eyebrow:	*Bob's words emotions*
Side of Eye:	*Bob's words emotions*
Under Eye:	*Bob's words emotions*
Under Nose:	*Bob's words emotions*
Chin:	*Bob's words emotions*
Collar Bone:	*Bob's words emotions*
Under Arm:	*Bob's words emotions*
Top of Head:	*Bob's words emotions*

I asked her then, if she were to look at it now could she guess now how intense she would feel on that scale of 0 – 10 and she said she felt it would probably be about a 5, she felt much better, her breathing had visibly improved so we continued working with that. She said she had felt winded, like her breath had been taken away.

Repeat 3 times while tapping the Karate Chop:

Even though it took my breath away I deeply and completely love and accept myself

Eyebrow:	*Feeling winded*
Side of Eye:	*Losing my breath*
Under Eye:	*Taking my breath away*
Under Nose:	*Feeling breathless*
Chin:	*Feeling winded*
Collar Bone:	*Losing my breath*
Under Arm:	*Taking my breath away*
Top of Head:	*Feeling breathless*

Repeat 3 times while tapping the Karate Chop:

Even though I had this redundancy shock I deeply and completely love and accept myself

Eyebrow:	*Redundancy shock*
Side of Eye:	*I wasn't expecting it*

Under Eye:	Redundancy shock
Under Nose:	Taking my breath away
Chin:	That shocking news
Collar Bone:	I wasn't expecting it
Under Arm:	Redundancy shock
Top of Head:	My redundancy shock

We worked our way through a lot of different aspects until she was able to look at the entire movie without any emotional response and also to tell me the story.

I don't know whether this shock contributed in any way to Sarah's diagnosis, and even if it did, it is unlikely to be the sole factor. However, the resounding theme of loss of life as she knew it was clearly still impacting on Sarah in the present day, and having worked through this episode she was able to re-access a feeling of being in charge of her own life, which in turn was hugely helpful in the way she managed her cancer diagnosis.

The ability to release the ongoing impact of trauma for ourselves with tapping is revolutionising the field of psychotherapy. For the most part, it is a relatively easy process. However, you may prefer to work with a trained practitioner at this point. The test is to start working through your Personal Peace Procedure list, as in Chapter 3. If you find you are getting stuck, or are avoiding certain issues, then that is the moment to work with a practitioner, either in person or on the telephone, either way is equally effective.

In the following chapter we are going to look at lifestyle choices, in particular smoking, and find ways of creating changes in those choices to support you in your healing journey.

CHAPTER 19

LIFESTYLE

'The principles you live by create the world you live in; if you change the principles
you live by, you will change your world'
Blaine Lee

Stress weakens the immune system so it is important to locate any ongoing stressors aside from the treatment/disease itself.

Cancer is a disease that affects the whole family. Having cancer may create anxiety, guilt, anger, frustration and upset, which in turn will affect your relationships with your family, friends and colleagues. Often there is a loss of identity and self which accompany the label of cancer, and people feel they are seen as their disease, not the person they used to be.

Finances may be affected with loss of income, and sometimes a loss of career too. This can lead to both family and personal stress. Lifestyles may need to be adapted and belts tightened. It can mean a setback or even loss of a career if the ensuing treatment means that the cancer sufferer will be unable to resume work at their current level of intensity. This can bring considerable grief with the loss of dreams and expectations, and the adaptation process can be difficult for everyone affected.

There may be lifestyle issues which need changing, such as smoking, drinking or drug abuse, recreational or otherwise.

Many of the fears and anxieties will be shared, and tapping on these together serves to reduce this and diminish the power the cancer has over them. Involve children too, it is important they feel included in the process. Cancer can be very hard on partners and caregivers. They may feel powerless, unable to help and not want to share their concerns with you for fear of adding extra stress. Teaching them to tap can be hugely beneficial (see Chapter 23).

Lifestyle Changes

'Bad habits are easier to abandon today than tomorrow.'
Yiddish Proverb

A cancer diagnosis shines a spotlight instantly on your lifestyle, maybe you have habits you need to change, for example smoking or drinking, or perhaps you need to make some dietary changes. Everything gets thrown into sharp focus at this point. Whilst under normal circumstances changing a habit or addressing an addiction is a personal choice, at the time of a cancer diagnosis that choice may be taken away from you and you could be put under pressure by the medical profession and others who care for you.

Smoking cessation

In this chapter I am going to look briefly at some possible necessary lifestyle changes and how the tapping can help and support you through them. The first I will look at is smoking cessation as this is often the most urgent. However, if this is not relevant to you, please change the words to address your issue, such as food, drink, drugs and so forth.

I am not able to write an entire smoking protocol here, that would be a book in its own right, but I am going to give you some ideas as to how to handle the craving for a cigarette and how to take back the controls around smoking. It may be that you need to see a qualified practitioner for an individual session to complete the work. But you may find that the protocols here are enough to help you take back the control over your smoking and become a non smoker easily.

> *'The best way to stop smoking is to just stop - no ifs, ands or butts.'*
> *Edith Zittler*

It is important to consult your physician before embarking on giving up smoking, especially at this point in your cancer journey.

The majority of people who smoke do it because they feel it gives them something positive and very often this can be a form of stress release. The reality is that the chemicals in tobacco/ nicotine actually speed your system up so your mind is playing a very good trick on you if you think you are feeling relaxed as a result of smoking. However, if you are one of the people who associates smoking with stress release then right now, having had a cancer diagnosis, the urge, the need to have a cigarette is likely to be extremely high.

If you are a long-term smoker you may consider yourself to be a "hardened smoker". If this resonates with you it may be too much of a shock for your system, for your emotional well being, to just stop in that moment. It may be more appropriate to take it gently, give yourself a little bit of time to adjust to your new situation and to get used to the prospect of losing your stress buster. You are under enough stress right now, it is not helpful to add to it. However, you can still begin to get a foot in the door.

> *'To cease smoking is the easiest thing I ever did.*
> *I ought to know because I've done it a thousand times.'*
> *Mark Twain, attributed*

Does this quote describe you? Consider the following questions and then do the tapping that follows.

- **Are you an expert at stopping smoking?**
- **How many times have you tried?**
- **What happened?**
- **How long did you last?**
- **Do you believe it is possible for you?**

Tapping Section: Tapping for inability to stop smoking

Repeat 3 times while tapping the Karate Chop:

Even though I can't stop smoking forever I deeply and completely love and accept myself

Eyebrow:	*I can't stop forever*
Side of Eye:	*It will never work for me*
Under Eye:	*I won't be able to do it*
Under Nose:	*I just can't stop forever*
Chin:	*I can't stop forever*
Collar Bone:	*It will never work for me*
Under Arm:	*I won't be able to do it*
Top of Head:	*I just can't stop forever*

Repeat 3 times while tapping the Karate Chop:

Even though this will never work for me I deeply and completely love and accept myself

Eyebrow:	*It will never work for me*
Side of Eye:	*Nothing works for me*
Under Eye:	*Tapping won't work for me*
Under Nose:	*Nothing works for me*
Chin:	*It will never work for me*
Collar Bone:	*Nothing works for me*
Under Arm:	*Tapping won't work for me*
Top of Head:	*Nothing works for me*

Repeat 3 times while tapping the Karate Chop:

Even though nothing ever works for me I deeply and completely love and accept myself

Eyebrow:	*It won't work for me*
Side of Eye:	*It will never work for me*
Under Eye:	*Nothing works for me*
Under Nose:	*This won't work for me*
Chin:	*It won't work for me*
Collar Bone:	*Why would it?*
Under Arm:	*Nothing works for me*

Top of Head: *Maybe*

Repeat 3 times while tapping the Karate Chop:

Even though I just can't do it I deeply and completely love and accept myself

> *Eyebrow:*   *I can't do it*
>
> *Side of Eye:*   *Maybe*
>
> *Under Eye:*   *What if I can?*
>
> *Under Nose:*   *I can't do it*
>
> *Chin:*   *It will never work for me*
>
> *Collar Bone:*   *Maybe*
>
> *Under Arm:*   *What if it did?*
>
> *Top of Head:*   *What if I could?*

Repeat 3 times while tapping the Karate Chop:

Even though I am still not sure I choose to surprise myself at how easy it can be

> *Eyebrow:*   *I choose to surprise myself*
>
> *Side of Eye:*   *I choose for this to be surprisingly easy*
>
> *Under Eye:*   *I am open to the possibility that I can do this*
>
> *Under Nose:*   *Maybe*
>
> *Chin:*   *I choose to surprise myself*
>
> *Collar Bone:*   *I choose for this to be surprisingly easy*
>
> *Under Arm:*   *I am open to the possibility that I can do this*
>
> *Top of Head:*   *Maybe*

At this stage I am not expecting you to be 100% solid in your belief of success, just being open to the possibility is enough for now.

> *'Do what you can, with what you have, where you are.'*
> *Theodore Roosevelt*

Tapping for Cravings

Begin by tapping on your cravings for a cigarette, without the need to have one or not have one, nothing matters apart from tapping on just the craving, and seeing what happens. Tap with the craving for a few rounds and then check in with it. If you still want to have that cigarette then, at this point, go ahead and light up, noticing how that cigarette tastes, feels etc. What changes do you notice?

Assess your current craving on the SUDS intensity scale of 0 – 10.

Tapping Section: Tapping for cigarette cravings

Repeat 3 times while tapping the Karate Chop:

Even though I have this craving I deeply and completely love and accept myself

Eyebrow:	*This craving*
Side of Eye:	*Cigarette craving*
Under Eye:	*This craving*
Under Nose:	*Cigarette craving*
Chin:	*This craving*
Collar Bone:	*Cigarette craving*
Under Arm:	*This craving*
Top of Head:	*Cigarette craving*

Repeat 3 times while tapping the Karate Chop:

Even though I still have some of this craving I deeply and completely love and accept myself

Eyebrow:	*Remaining craving*
Side of Eye:	*Remaining craving*
Under Eye:	*Remaining craving*
Under Nose:	*Remaining craving*
Chin:	*Remaining craving*
Collar Bone:	*Remaining craving*
Under Arm:	*Remaining craving*
Top of Head:	*Remaining craving*

Repeat 3 times while tapping the Karate Chop:

Even though I really have to have that cigarette now I deeply and completely love and accept myself

Eyebrow:	*I have to have it*
Side of Eye:	*It's mine*
Under Eye:	*I have to have it*

299

Under Nose:	*It's mine and I'm keeping it*
Chin:	*I have to have it*
Collar Bone:	*It's mine*
Under Arm:	*I have to have it*
Top of Head:	*It's mine and I'm keeping it*

Repeat 3 times while tapping the Karate Chop:

Even though I want a cigarette right now I deeply and completely love and accept myself

Eyebrow:	*I want it*
Side of Eye:	*I want a cigarette now*
Under Eye:	*This wanting*
Under Nose:	*This wanting*
Chin:	*I want it*
Collar Bone:	*I need it*
Under Arm:	*I want it*
Top of Head:	*I need it*

When you have done a few rounds, using whichever of those protocols feels right for you, check in again. Notice what has happened, it may be that the craving has completely reduced, maybe that it has partially gone or it maybe that it has increased, occasionally that will happen. Notice what feelings, what emotional response you are having to the following words:

How much would you like that cigarette RIGHT now?

If you do this every time you crave a cigarette, giving yourself permission to have one after you have finished the tapping if you still want one, you will gradually be reducing some of the underlying emotional contributors to the addiction without needing to explore them further. It takes commitment to tap first, smoke second, but it is an easy door into beginning to let the addiction go.

The Ritual/Habit

> *'A habit is something you can do without thinking - which is why most of us have so many of them.'*
> *Frank A. Clark*

Most smokers have a ritual when they like to smoke – is it with a coffee, is it on the telephone, in the car, after a meal, with alcohol – you will recognize your own ritual.

Write out a typical day, mapping out your day through cigarettes.

When do you light up? What feeling tells you it is time for a smoke?

So maybe you have your first one with your morning coffee so: Cigarette 1 – morning coffee. Notice whether you have a cigarette when you are on the phone, notice whether it is before or after a meal. Write down the times when normally, habitually you tend to smoke so that you begin to get a pattern of your smoking.

Then choose one cigarette that it may be possible to lose in that pattern, maybe the first cigarette of the day, maybe the last. Choose one of those cigarettes that you would possibly be comfortable with the thought of losing, as a way of beginning to cut down on your cigarette intake.

Time of cigarette	**Feeling before lighting up**
1	
2	
3	
Etc.	

As you chart your cigarettes throughout the day, consider the following questions and write the answers in your chart:

- **How does having that cigarette make you feel?**
- **How does the thought of not having that one cigarette, make you feel?**

Then take a look at the following tapping protocols and see whether any of them relate to you and if they do tap along with them.

Tapping Section: Tapping for smoking as a reward

Repeat 3 times while tapping the Karate Chop:

Even though it's my reward/treat I deeply and completely love and accept myself

Eyebrow:	*It's my reward*
Side of Eye:	*I deserve it*
Under Eye:	*It is my treat*
Under Nose:	*I deserve my reward*
Chin:	*I deserve my cigarette*
Collar Bone:	*My reward*
Under Arm:	*Needing a treat*
Top of Head:	*Needing a reward*

Repeat 3 times while tapping the Karate Chop:

Even though I will feel deprived without it I deeply and completely love and accept myself

301

Eyebrow:	*Feeling deprived*
Side of Eye:	*Fear of deprivation*
Under Eye:	*Feeling deprived*
Under Nose:	*Fear of deprivation*
Chin:	*Feeling deprived*
Collar Bone:	*Fear of deprivation*
Under Arm:	*Feeling deprived*
Top of Head:	*Fear of deprivation*

Repeat 3 times while tapping the Karate Chop:

Even though I need cigarettes to relax I deeply and completely love and accept myself

Eyebrow:	*Needing cigarettes*
Side of Eye:	*Cigarettes mean relaxation for me*
Under Eye:	*I need to smoke*
Under Nose:	*Smoking means relaxation to me*
Chin:	*Needing cigarettes*
Collar Bone:	*Cigarettes mean relaxation for me*
Under Arm:	*I need to smoke*
Top of Head:	*Smoking means relaxation to me*

Check in again and notice how you are doing. If after about 5 minutes of tapping you still desperately want that cigarette then allow yourself to have it but as you do that:

- **Notice how you feel**
- **How it tastes**
- **Is it as satisfying as you expect it to be?**
- **Does it make you relax?**
- **Does it speed up your heart rate?**
- **What happens for you?**

Make a note of how you feel about that particular cigarette in the space provided on the chart.

The next step is how you connect to a cigarette emotionally. How do you identify yourself, are YOU a smoker? I often hear:

'But I am a smoker. I have always been a smoker.'

302

Tapping Section: Tapping for identifying as a smoker

Repeat 3 times while tapping the Karate Chop:

Even though I am a smoker I deeply and completely love and accept myself

Eyebrow:	*I'm a smoker*
Side of Eye:	*It is what I do*
Under Eye:	*Who I am*
Under Nose:	*I am a smoker*
Chin:	*I'm a smoker*
Collar Bone:	*It is what I do*
Under Arm:	*Who I am*
Top of Head:	*I am a smoker*

Were you born smoking? Of course not. At some point you made the decision to smoke. Very often that happens when we are teenagers and we do it for very good reasons, usually to belong, to become part of a group, to fit in, to be cool, peer pressure. And it is usually the best thing that you could have done at that point to get you what you wanted, to get you acceptance and acknowledgement in a group. These things are incredibly important to a teenager. The problem comes decades later when you are still applying the same technology to a different problem. In a way it is as if you need to do a computer update, you need to download a new programme.

Back then, smoking did get you accepted by the group, so it worked. But if you look at it in the world that we live in today as an adult – does it get you group acceptability now? In many countries now you can't smoke in restaurants, you can't smoke in bars, you can't smoke on public transport. In fact you are shut out of many places were you might go to socialise in a group. So in fact that behaviour that was getting you something positive as a teenager, now is doing the exact opposite isn't it?

Take yourself back to the memory of your first cigarette. Chances are it didn't feel that great! What did it get for you that was positive? Here are some possibilities, but please adapt them to meet your own experience.

Repeat 3 times while tapping the Karate Chop:

Even though smoking got me friends I deeply and completely love and accept myself

Eyebrow:	*I got accepted*
Side of Eye:	*I was really cool*
Under Eye:	*Smoking got me friends*
Under Nose:	*Needing to belong*
Chin:	*Needing to belong*
Collar Bone:	*Being cool*

303

| *Under Arm:* | *Needing to belong* |
| *Top of Head:* | *Maybe* |

'Cigarettes are my best friend'

Clients often say that, and the thought can be accompanied by an enormous amount of grief. Grief at the thought of the impending loss, the thought of losing something that is reliable, that's dependable, that's always there for you. If that is the case for you, tap around on this

'When there is no enemy within, the enemies outside cannot hurt you.'
African Proverb

Tapping Section: Tapping for cigarettes as best friend

Repeat 3 times while tapping the Karate Chop:

Even though I'm going to lose my best friend I deeply and completely love and accept myself

Eyebrow:	*Fear of losing my best friend*
Side of Eye:	*Fear of feeling alone*
Under Eye:	*Fear of loss*
Under Nose:	*Fear of losing my best friend*
Chin:	*Fear of losing my best friend*
Collar Bone:	*Fear of feeling alone*
Under Arm:	*Fear of loss*
Top of Head:	*Fear of losing my best friend*

Continue:

Eyebrow:	*Fear of losing my prop*
Side of Eye:	*I don't know how to be without my cigarettes*
Under Eye:	*Fear of losing my prop*
Under Nose:	*Fear of loss*
Chin:	*Fear of losing my prop*
Collar Bone:	*I don't know how to be without my cigarettes*
Under Arm:	*Fear of losing my prop*
Top of Head:	*Fear of loss*

Continue:

Eyebrow:	*Losing my best friend*
Side of Eye:	*This loss*
Under Eye:	*Losing my best friend*
Under Nose:	*Losing my support*
Chin:	*Losing my best friend*
Collar Bone:	*This loss*
Under Arm:	*Losing my best friend*
Top of Head:	*Losing my support*

Kate's story

Kate came with a lung cancer diagnosis, very early stage, probably as a result of smoking although not proven. She had been advised to stop smoking immediately and she really wanted to do it. She could appreciate that she had to do it, but every time she tried, for whatever reason, somehow she would find herself reaching out for the cigarettes again. She could do about 3 or 4 days, and was feeling really pleased with herself, but she couldn't go as long as a week without a cigarette.

I asked her a number of questions about that, to find out what was really going on for her and she said she felt lonely without her cigarettes, she felt as though she was losing a part of her, almost like losing her right hand. She didn't know what to do or how to be without her cigarettes. It felt like being bereft of her best friend. We tapped a few rounds using the protocols above and she suddenly said to me:

'You know, I don't think it is my best friend, cigarettes can't be my best friend, if they were my best friend they wouldn't be killing me.'

This moment turned the whole thing around and Kate saw her relationship with cigarettes in a new light. Rather than being her best friend, and something that was relaxing her and giving her pleasure and enjoyment, she was actually able to see the reality that it was unhealthy and that potentially could have the ability to kill her. Having come to that realization, she then became incredibly angry at herself.

- *How could she not have seen that?*
- *How could she have bought into this myth that she had created when she was younger?*
- *Why was she so weak that she hadn't been able to do something about it before?*
- *Why was she so unintelligent that she hadn't seen it this way?*

A string of self judgments and self-attack exploded. We gently tapped through all the layers of it until Kate was able to see that when she started smoking she was just being a teenager, she was rebelling against her parents, against society, she was doing exactly what a teenager's instructions are, she was creating her own identity, claiming her individuality.

However, she had attached herself so strongly to that teenage identity that it was no longer useful to her. When she really got insight, the self-blame and the self-attack evaporated. She was able to thank that teenage her, who started smoking, and have a conversation with her whilst imagining tapping on her, telling the teenager that she recognized why she did it and that it was great idea at the time, but now she felt that she needed to move from her teenage years up into adulthood.

From that session onwards Kate has never felt the need for a cigarette, she hasn't had to use willpower or brave her way through bad moments, it just simply hasn't been part of her life. It is almost as if she has never smoked, and her husband and friends can't believe how easy it seems to have been. This was a couple of years ago now, and Kate is still a non smoker. The cancer is in remission and she got a completely new positive outlook on life.

> *'Success will never be a big step in the future, success is a small step taken just now.'*
> *Jonatan Mårtensson*

Refusing to quit smoking!
So, if you are not feeling strong enough to fully become a non-smoker now, begin by considering dropping one of your ritual cigarettes and at the same time tapping on the craving for every other one.

After a relatively short period of time, days rather than weeks, you will notice that your need for that cigarette will become less and less and it will become a choice rather than being fuelled by unconscious emotional drivers. At this point, it is time to drop that one completely and focus on the next.

Set yourself a timetable for becoming a non smoker permanently. If you have a problem with timetables, (some people don't like to be button-holed into a frame like that), just have a sense of a timeframe. Perhaps by the spring or the summer, or whichever season you happen to be in; or maybe before you start treatment. Be gentle on yourself. Recognise that this is something that you do need to do. You CAN do it!

However, this is about stopping in a nurturing way, in a way that is safe for you, that is safe for your body. If you have been a long-term smoker, it may not be safe for you to stop suddenly. Your body may have grown so accustomed to the chemical input, that you may have an adverse reaction. I would suggest that you cut down gradually and speed up that gradualness only when it feels appropriate.

Smoking has been controlling you for years, now it is your turn to take control over it. See it as the first step in your healing process, you CAN do it and you will do it but the first trick is WANTING to do it. If you find that you are really, really against doing it say it as it is and tap as follows, really giving emphasis to the words, maybe even shouting them.

Tapping Section: Tapping for refusing to quit

Repeat 3 times while tapping the Karate Chop:

Even though I REFUSE to give up smoking I deeply and completely love and accept myself

    Eyebrow: *I refuse to give up smoking*

Side of Eye:	*I refuse to stop*
Under Eye:	*I won't do it*
Under Nose:	*I refuse to do it*
Chin:	*I refuse to give up smoking*
Collar Bone:	*I refuse to stop*
Under Arm:	*I won't do it*
Top of Head:	*I refuse to do it*

Repeat 3 times while tapping the Karate Chop:

Even though they say I should do it and I'm NOT going to and I deeply and completely love and accept myself

Eyebrow:	*I won't do it*
Side of Eye:	*They want me to*
Under Eye:	*But I won't do it*
Under Nose:	*Why should I?*
Chin:	*I won't do it*
Collar Bone:	*Not for them*
Under Arm:	*Not for me*
Top of Head:	*I won't do it*

Repeat 3 times while tapping the Karate Chop:

Even though it is who I am and I'm NOT going to change, I refuse to change I deeply and completely love and accept myself

Eyebrow:	*It's who I am*
Side of Eye:	*I refuse to change*
Under Eye:	*I won't do it*
Under Nose:	*I refuse*
Chin:	*It's who I am*
Collar Bone:	*I refuse to change*
Under Arm:	*I won't do it*
Top of Head:	*I refuse*

Repeat 3 times while tapping the Karate Chop:

Even though it's mine and I'm keeping it I deeply and completely love and accept myself

Eyebrow:	*It's mine*
Side of Eye:	*And I'm keeping it*
Under Eye:	*You can't make me stop*
Under Nose:	*It's mine*
Chin:	*It's mine*
Collar Bone:	*And I'm keeping it*
Under Arm:	*You can't make me stop*
Top of Head:	*It's mine*

A conflict of parts

> *'The part can never be well unless the whole is well.'*
> *Plato*

I have yet to meet a smoker who wants 100% to become a non-smoker. I guess those that do never make it to my door. Most smokers have a part of them which really does not want to stop, that is completely normal. For most people there is a positive gain from smoking which is enormously important and which, in an ideal world, they would want to keep. The mistake is to think that smoking is the only way of getting this positive gain. It isn't, and as you tap through the emotions which are currently hidden under the layer of smoke, that positive feeling will become available to you again, only this time it will be an internally driven state and therefore much more powerful. It is only the mind that gives your power to the cigarette, the cigarette itself, and even the chemicals in it, do not have the ability to make you calm, happy etc. You are doing that and if you can do it in that way you can also find new, healthier ways of creating that same feeling for yourself, letting go of the need to smoke.

So, make a note of the things that are going through your mind about smoking. Tap on whatever you are saying to yourself, tap on the conflict between the part of you that wants to stop smoking and the part that wants to remain a smoker:

Tapping Section: Tapping for self-talk about smoking

Repeat 3 times while tapping the Karate Chop:

Even though I should stop smoking, I don't want to do it and I deeply and completely love and accept myself

Eyebrow:	*I should stop*
Side of Eye:	*I don't want to*
Under Eye:	*I want to stop*

Under Nose:	I don't want to
Chin:	I should stop
Collar Bone:	I don't want to
Under Arm:	I want to stop
Top of Head:	I don't want to

Repeat 3 times while tapping the Karate Chop:

Even though part of me wants to become a non-smoker, part of me wants to keep smoking and I deeply and completely love and accept myself

Eyebrow:	Wanting to smoke
Side of Eye:	Wanting to be a non-smoker
Under Eye:	Smoker
Under Nose:	Non-smoker
Chin:	Wanting to smoke
Collar Bone:	Wanting to be a non-smoker
Under Arm:	Smoker
Top of Head:	Non-smoker

There are many ways of communicating with both those parts of you and it is very common to have this conflict. You can really want to be a non-smoker and yet really want to be a smoker at the same time. As I said before, for almost everybody who has become a non-smoker there is likely still to be a part that would still like to have a cigarette, were they proven to be healthy or whatever. For all people who want to become a non-smoker, the part that still wants to be a smoker will be in action, so just acknowledge it as follows:

Repeat 3 times while tapping the Karate Chop:

Even though I just want to be a smoker I deeply and completely love and accept myself

Eyebrow:	Wanting to be a smoker
Side of Eye:	I just want to smoke
Under Eye:	Wanting to be a smoker
Under Nose:	Wanting to smoke
Chin:	Wanting to be a smoker
Collar Bone:	I just want to smoke
Under Arm:	Wanting to be a smoker
Top of Head:	Wanting to smoke

Repeat 3 times while tapping the Karate Chop:

Even though part of me still wants to smoke I deeply and completely love and accept myself

Eyebrow:	*That smoking part of me*
Side of Eye:	*That part of me*
Under Eye:	*And everything contributing to it*
Under Nose:	*Wanting to smoke*
Chin:	*That smoking part of me*
Collar Bone:	*That part of me*
Under Arm:	*And everything contributing to it*
Top of Head:	*Wanting to smoke*

Now check in with that smoking part of you, how do you feel about it now? Is it as strong? How does that part feel to finally be acknowledged and treated with importance and respect? How does that change your response to it? Do you still need to fight it or are you able to consider reintegrating it into the you here today, holding on to the positive gains from it, whilst letting go of the old behaviour of actually smoking?

The Emotions of Smoking /Smokers

Look at your emotional response to the thought of stopping smoking. Are people putting pressure on you to stop? Who in particular? Is everybody giving you their opinions as to how you should do this? The tapping will support any way of giving up smoking, whether you use patches, whether you decide to use hypnotherapy, cognitive behavioural therapy or anything else, or whether you do it with tapping alone. The tapping is just an extra tool that you can use to support yourself.

Now let's look at the emotions commonly experienced; a lot of smokers feel guilt:

Tapping Section: Tapping for feelings about smoking

Repeat 3 times while tapping the Karate Chop:

Even though I feel guilty about being a smoker I deeply and completely love and accept myself

Eyebrow:	*Smoking guilt*
Side of Eye:	*I shouldn't do it*
Under Eye:	*Smoking guilt*
Under Nose:	*I shouldn't smoke*

Chin:	Smoking guilt
Collar Bone:	I shouldn't do it
Under Arm:	Smoking guilt
Top of Head:	I shouldn't smoke

Continue:

Eyebrow:	I should want to stop smoking
Side of Eye:	I should be able to stop
Under Eye:	This guilt
Under Nose:	These shoulds and oughts
Chin:	I should want to stop smoking
Collar Bone:	I should be able to stop
Under Arm:	This guilt
Top of Head:	These shoulds and oughts

Shame is another emotion that is often there with smokers. Shame in itself is a very uncomfortable and often very private emotion and may well create the urge to smoke in its own right, as an anaesthetic to the feeling of shame which can become overwhelming for some.

Repeat 3 times while tapping the Karate Chop:

Even though I feel ashamed of smoking I deeply and completely love and accept myself

Eyebrow:	This shame
Side of Eye:	Smoking shame
Under Eye:	Shame
Under Nose:	Shame
Chin:	This shame
Collar Bone:	Smoking shame
Under Arm:	Shame
Top of Head:	Shame

Repeat 3 times while tapping the Karate Chop:

Even though I feel dirty smoking I deeply and completely love and accept myself

| Eyebrow: | Feeling dirty |

Side of Eye:	*Smoking emotions*
Under Eye:	*Feeling grubby*
Under Nose:	*Smoking emotions*
Chin:	*Feeling dirty*
Collar Bone:	*Smoking emotions*
Under Arm:	*Feeling grubby*
Top of Head:	*Smoking emotions*

Repeat 3 times while tapping the Karate Chop:

Even though I feel weak that I can't be a non-smoker I deeply and completely love and accept myself

Eyebrow:	*Feeling weak*
Side of Eye:	*I can't do it*
Under Eye:	*I should do it*
Under Nose:	*Feeling weak*
Chin:	*Feeling weak*
Collar Bone:	*I can't do it*
Under Arm:	*I should do it*
Top of Head:	*Feeling weak*

Repeat 3 times while tapping the Karate Chop:

Even though I feel angry that everyone is making me do this I deeply and completely love and accept myself

Eyebrow:	*This anger*
Side of Eye:	*This anger*
Under Eye:	*I wish they would all shut up*
Under Nose:	*I wish they would go away*
Chin:	*This anger*
Collar Bone:	*This anger*
Under Arm:	*I wish they would all just go away*
Top of Head:	*This anger*

Creating a new reality

> *'Reality leaves a lot to the imagination.'*
> *John Lennon*

312

John Lennon was right, we constantly create our own reality. What happens when you begin to create a reality where you are a non-smoker? Imagine yourself in that new reality:

- **How do you look?**
- **What does that feel like?**
- **What do you notice about it?**

The chances are that you will be feeling a little richer too, although strangely that is very rarely a motivating factor for people.

Step into that you as a non-smoker and really experience what that is like:

- **What is your sense of smell like?**
- **What is your sense of taste like?**
- **How is your breathing?**
- **How healthy do you look?**
- **What does your skin look like?**

If you are having a problem getting that image tap round as follows

Tapping Section: Tapping for being a non-smoker

Repeat 3 times while tapping the Karate Chop:

Even though I can't see myself as a non-smoker yet, I deeply and completely love and accept myself

Eyebrow:	*I can't see myself yet*
Side of Eye:	*I can't see myself as a non-smoker*
Under Eye:	*Something blocking me seeing myself as a non-smoker*
Under Nose:	*I can't quite seem myself yet*
Chin:	*I can't see myself yet*
Collar Bone:	*I can't see myself as a non-smoker*
Under Arm:	*I can't see myself yet*
Top of Head:	*I can't quite seem myself yet*

Repeat 3 times while tapping the Karate Chop:

Even though something is blocking me seeing myself as a non-smoker I deeply and completely love and accept myself

Eyebrow:	*Something blocking me seeing myself as a non-smoker*

Side of Eye:	*This block*
Under Eye:	*I can't see myself as a non-smoker*
Under Nose:	*This block*
Chin:	*Something blocking me seeing myself as a non-smoker*
Collar Bone:	*This block*
Under Arm:	*I can't see myself as a non-smoker*
Top of Head:	*Yet*

Repeat 3 times while tapping the Karate Chop:

Even though I can't see myself as a non-smoker yet, I deeply and completely love and accept myself

Eyebrow:	*I can't see myself yet*
Side of Eye:	*I can't quite see myself yet*
Under Eye:	*Maybe I can*
Under Nose:	*No, I can't quite see myself yet*
Chin:	*What if I could?*
Collar Bone:	*No, I can't quite see myself yet*
Under Arm:	*But what if I could?*
Top of Head:	*Maybe I can*

Now check again. What happens to that image now? How clear is it? Continue tapping until the picture becomes very clear – this may take a good number of rounds.

Then imagine stepping into that you in the picture. Feel what that feels like. How does it feel to be that you in this new place? Feel the freshness, feel the clarity and the ease of your breathing, notice the texture of your skin. Notice how people are responding to you. What does it feel like to be a non-smoker out there in the world? Notice your physiology, standing there, tall and proud, and as you do that give yourself a pat on the back and hear someone important to you saying:

'*I'm really proud of you, well done, that's fantastic, you look amazing.* '

If that brings any emotional response up for you, then tap to clear that too:

Repeat 3 times while tapping the Karate Chop:

Even though I feel embarrassed I deeply and completely love and accept myself

Eyebrow:	*Feeling embarrassed*
Side of Eye:	*This embarrassment*

314

Under Eye:	Feeling embarrassed
Under Nose:	This embarrassment
Chin:	Feeling embarrassed
Collar Bone:	This embarrassment
Under Arm:	Feeling embarrassed
Top of Head:	This embarrassment

Repeat 3 times while tapping the Karate Chop:

Even though I am not great at taking compliments I deeply and completely love and accept myself and I choose to recognize this powerful step I have taken along my healing path

Eyebrow:	This powerful step
Side of Eye:	This powerful step
Under Eye:	I choose to heal easily now
Under Nose:	This powerful healing step
Chin:	I choose to continue to support my body's healing process
Collar Bone:	I choose to work with my body towards healing
Under Arm:	This powerful healing step
Top of Head:	I choose to heal easily now

Continue:

Eyebrow:	I love and honour my body
Side of Eye:	And its healing process
Under Eye:	I choose to heal easily now
Under Nose:	I choose to support my body's continued healing
Chin:	I love and honour my body
Collar Bone:	And its healing process
Under Arm:	I choose to heal easily now
Top of Head:	I choose to support my body's continued healing

Repeat 3 times while tapping the Karate Chop:

Even though I can't imagine myself without a cigarette in my hand I deeply and completely love and accept myself

Eyebrow:	*I just can't imagine it*
Side of Eye:	*I don't know how I will look*
Under Eye:	*I just can't imagine it*
Under Nose:	*I can't see it*
Chin:	*I just can't imagine it*
Collar Bone:	*I don't know how I will look*
Under Arm:	*I just can't imagine it*
Top of Head:	*I can't see it*

You may find that there are particularly stressful times when you lapse and revert to old habits. If that happens accept that it has happened and take yourself back to the relevant tapping protocols and keep going! You are under considerable stress with your diagnosis and/ or treatment, so be kind to yourself, accept any slip-ups and get back on course as quickly as you are able to. You will not be doing yourself any favours by putting yourself under additional pressure, or by beating yourself up over the occasional lapse. Take it one day at a time, every cigarette you don't have is one step further along your path to optimum health.

Diet

'Let food be thy medicine, thy medicine shall be thy food.'
Hippocrates

Other lifestyle changes may include: change of diet, giving up alcohol, change of financial situation, change of environment etc.

Much has been written about the importance of diet in the healing of cancer. I am not a nutritionist so am not qualified to explore this, apart from helping you to find ways to tap through any blocks you might have to changing your lifestyle and your diet, having taken appropriate experienced advice.

When I say the word *diet* it always makes me slightly cringe because it brings with it a feeling of deprivation, a feeling of restriction. If that is the case for you too, begin there.

Tapping Section: Tapping for feelings about dieting

Repeat 3 times while tapping the Karate Chop:

Even though there is something about the word diet that gets me I deeply and completely love and accept myself

Eyebrow:	*That word*
Side of Eye:	*Something about that word*
Under Eye:	*That word getting me*

316

Under Nose:	*The 'diet' word*
Chin:	*That word*
Collar Bone:	*Something about that word*
Under Arm:	*That word getting me*
Top of Head:	*The 'diet' word*

Repeat 3 times while tapping the Karate Chop:

Even though I HATE that word I deeply and completely love and accept myself

Eyebrow:	*I hate that word*
Side of Eye:	*Diet*
Under Eye:	*That word*
Under Nose:	*And everything it means to me*
Chin:	*I hate that word*
Collar Bone:	*Diet*
Under Arm:	*That word*
Top of Head:	*And everything it means to me*

Repeat 3 times while tapping the Karate Chop:

Even though I don't want to change my diet I deeply and completely love and accept myself

Eyebrow:	*I don't want to change my diet*
Side of Eye:	*I don't want to change how I eat*
Under Eye:	*I don't have the energy*
Under Nose:	*It is too hard*
Chin:	*I don't want to do it*
Collar Bone:	*I can't change how I eat now*
Under Arm:	*I don't have the energy*
Top of Head:	*I can't do it*

Continue:

Eyebrow:	*I can't do it*
Side of Eye:	*What if I can?*
Under Eye:	*No, I can't do it*
Under Nose:	*It is too much right now*

Chin:	But what if I can?
Collar Bone:	What if it is possible?
Under Arm:	No, I can't do it
Top of Head:	Yes I can

Continue:

Eyebrow:	I'm open to the possibility I can make this change easily
Side of Eye:	I choose to eat a more healthy diet
Under Eye:	I choose to surround myself with healing foods
Under Nose:	I am open to the possibility it can be easy
Chin:	I'm open to the possibility I can make this change easily
Collar Bone:	I choose to eat a more healthy diet
Under Arm:	I choose to surround myself with healing foods
Top of Head:	I am open to the possibility it can be easy

Now think of a word to replace 'diet' that feels more appropriate for you. I used diet because that is usually what is used in books, but maybe *healthy eating regime* or *healthy lifestyle* would work better for you. From this point on, you are developing a new relationship with food. Food is going to become a form of natural medicine for you. With every mouthful, you can begin to connect to the healing properties of nature.

Obviously, one of the first steps is to start eating organic food, if you are not already. In many parts of the world organic food is considerably more expensive than non-organic, so this maybe an issue for you. In which case tap allowing with the following protocols:

Repeat 3 times while tapping the Karate Chop:

Even though organic food is just too expensive I deeply and completely love and accept myself

Eyebrow:	It's too expensive
Side of Eye:	I can't afford it
Under Eye:	I don't have the money
Under Nose:	Why should I pay for it?
Chin:	It is just too expensive
Collar Bone:	I can't afford it
Under Arm:	I don't have the money
Top of Head:	I can't afford organic food

318

Say it as it is

'Don't go around saying the world owes you a living. The world owes you nothing. It was here first.'
Mark Twain

If you have cancer you already have a lot on your plate. Does the idea of making these changes tip you over the edge? Does it feel unfair? It is unfair, you are already dealing with so much, but the evidence regarding dietary impact on healing is too strong to be ignored and unfortunately, unless you have the luxury of a cook/housekeeper, the person who is going to have to instigate these changes is you.

Tap for a few rounds and notice what emotions surface. Often there is anger or resentment; why should you have to do something that other people seem to get away with? If you find yourself feeling this repeat the exercises earlier in the book as follows:

Tapping Section: Tapping for attitudes about dieting

Repeat 3 times while tapping the Karate Chop:

Even though I feel resentful about having to change my lifestyle I deeply and completely love and accept myself

Eyebrow:	*This resentment*
Side of Eye:	*This resentment*
Under Eye:	*This resentment*
Under Nose:	*This resentment*
Chin:	*This resentment*
Collar Bone:	*This resentment*
Under Arm:	*This resentment*
Top of Head:	*This resentment*

Repeat 3 times while tapping the Karate Chop:

Even though it's not fair, why me? I deeply and completely love and accept myself

Eyebrow:	*It's not fair*
Side of Eye:	*Why me?*
Under Eye:	*I don't deserve this*
Under Nose:	*It's not fair*
Chin:	*Why me?*
Collar Bone:	*I don't deserve it*

Under Arm:	*No one deserves it*
Top of Head:	*Why me?*

Repeat 3 times while tapping the Karate Chop:

Even though I resent having to do this I deeply and completely love and accept myself

Eyebrow:	*This resentment*
Side of Eye:	*It's not fair*
Under Eye:	*This resentment*
Under Nose:	*It is just not fair*
Chin:	*This resentment*
Collar Bone:	*Why should I have to do this?*
Under Arm:	*This resentment*
Top of Head:	*It is just not fair*

What other emotions come up for you when you consider creating these changes? You are going through so much already. Does this feel like one step too far for your already depleted energy?

- Maybe you feel too exhausted to take on a change in diet?
- Maybe you feel the need for support?
- Maybe you feel overwhelmed at this point?

Repeat 3 times while tapping the Karate Chop:

Even though I don't have the energy to think about this now I deeply and completely love and accept myself

Eyebrow:	*Feeling exhausted*
Side of Eye:	*Got no energy*
Under Eye:	*Can't think about this now*
Under Nose:	*Feeling so exhausted*
Chin:	*Feeling exhausted*
Collar Bone:	*Got no energy*
Under Arm:	*Can't think about this now*
Top of Head:	*Feeling so exhausted*

Repeat 3 times while tapping the Karate Chop:

Even though I need support I deeply and completely love and accept myself

Eyebrow:	*Needing support*
Side of Eye:	*Needing support*
Under Eye:	*Needing support*
Under Nose:	*Needing support*
Chin:	*I need support*
Collar Bone:	*Needing support*
Under Arm:	*I need support*
Top of Head:	*Needing support*

At some point, when you feel those emotions beginning to shift, when the statements don't feel quite so true to you, I would like you to introduce a Choice. You could select the following or create one for yourself using the words that mean the most to you.

Eyebrow:	*I choose to embrace organic food easily now*
Side of Eye:	*I choose to embrace organic food easily now*
Under Eye:	*I choose to embrace organic food easily now*
Under Nose:	*I choose to embrace organic food easily now*
Chin:	*I choose to embrace organic food easily now*
Collar Bone:	*I choose to embrace organic food easily now*
Under Arm:	*I choose to embrace organic food easily now*
Top of Head:	*I choose to embrace organic food easily now*

Continue:

Eyebrow:	*I choose to enjoy the health benefits of organic food*
Side of Eye:	*I choose to enjoy the health benefits of organic food*
Under Eye:	*I choose to enjoy the health benefits of organic food*
Under Nose:	*I choose to enjoy the health benefits of organic food*
Chin:	*I choose to enjoy the health benefits of organic food*
Collar Bone:	*I choose to enjoy the health benefits of organic food*
Under Arm:	*I choose to enjoy the health benefits of organic food*
Top of Head:	*I choose to enjoy the health benefits of organic food*

Continue:

Eyebrow:	*I choose for my body to draw just the nutrients it needs from the foods that I eat*

Side of Eye:	*I choose for my body to draw just the nutrients it needs from the foods that I eat*
Under Eye:	*I choose for my body to draw just the nutrients it needs from the foods that I eat*
Under Nose:	*I choose for my body to draw just the nutrients it needs from the foods that I eat*
Chin:	*I choose for my body to draw just the nutrients it needs from the foods that I eat*
Collar Bone:	*I choose for my body to draw just the nutrients it needs from the foods that I eat*
Under Arm:	*I choose for my body to draw just the nutrients it needs from the foods that I eat*
Top of Head:	*I choose for my body to draw just the nutrients it needs from the foods that I eat*

Continue:

Eyebrow:	*I choose to trust in the healing qualities of nature to support my journey*
Side of Eye:	*I choose to trust in the healing qualities of nature to support my journey*
Under Eye:	*I choose to trust in the healing qualities of nature to support my journey*
Under Nose:	*I choose to trust in the healing qualities of nature to support my journey*
Chin:	*I choose to trust in the healing qualities of nature to support my journey*
Collar Bone:	*I choose to trust in the healing qualities of nature to support my journey*
Under Arm:	*I choose to trust in the healing qualities of nature to support my journey*
Top of Head:	*I choose to trust in the healing qualities of nature to support my journey*

There are many good books and diets for supporting cancer. As I said before, I am no expert and in no position to advise on this. However, I would suggest consulting a nutritionist (they often have them in hospitals) or go to your local cancer centre where they will have access to professional advice in this direction.

If you consult the internet, there are an endless number of resources which may be overwhelming, unless you are an information gatherer by nature! How do you select what is right for you? All your healing approaches, whether through nutrition, through medical intervention, or any other method you may be choosing to support yourself, need to be tailored individually to you. Thankfully, we are all different, and your choices must align with your belief system and values.

A Change of Financial Environment

'Ordinary riches can be stolen; real riches cannot. In your soul are infinitely precious
things that cannot be taken from you.'
Oscar Wilde

A cancer diagnosis may bring with it an immediate change in financial circumstances, especially if you are self-employed. The world as it was is no longer there, and you find yourself stepping into a new place with a view to creating a new future for yourself. This is not something you are doing through choice, but through necessity. Some people may have to take a considerable time off work, for those who have been in work for a long period of time this can be very disturbing, suddenly finding themselves out of the office community with all this *"free time"* on your hands.

You might find yourself sitting at home, lonely with time to think. Your life maybe becoming one of appointments, you may be being completely ruled by your diary as you move between consultants, specialists and/or complementary practitioners. There are often serious financial implications. While some people have good insurance plans in their working environment, many others are self-employed with no back up. You may be supporting your family. You may be the main breadwinner and suddenly not be in a position to bring in the same amount of money, or indeed any amount of money for a while. This can be an additional shock and worry.

If this resonates with you, think about how you are feeling and adapt the following protocols to suit your specific needs.

Tapping Section: Tapping for worry about finances

Repeat 3 times while tapping the Karate Chop:

Even though I am really worried about money I deeply and completely love and accept myself

Eyebrow:	*Worried about money*
Side of Eye:	*How am I going to cope?*
Under Eye:	*How will I support myself?*
Under Nose:	*Money worries*
Chin:	*Worried about money*
Collar Bone:	*How am I going to cope?*

| Under Arm: | How will I support myself? |
| Top of Head: | Money worries |

Repeat 3 times while tapping the Karate Chop:

Even though I won't be able to earn as much for a while I deeply and completely love and accept myself

Eyebrow:	Earning anxiety
Side of Eye:	Earning anxiety
Under Eye:	Unable to earn as much
Under Nose:	Unable to make as much money
Chin:	Earning anxiety
Collar Bone:	Earning anxiety
Under Arm:	Unable to earn as much
Top of Head:	Unable to make as much money

Repeat 3 times while tapping the Karate Chop:

Even though I won't be able to support the family I deeply and completely love and accept myself

Eyebrow:	Fear of not supporting the family
Side of Eye:	Fear of not being able to support the family
Under Eye:	Fear of not supporting the family
Under Nose:	Fear of not being able to support the family
Chin:	Fear of not supporting the family
Collar Bone:	Fear of not being able to support the family
Under Arm:	Fear of not supporting the family
Top of Head:	Fear of not being able to support the family

In conclusion, it is important to discuss any changes of diet and lifestyle with your doctor before putting them into action. There is an enormous amount of seemingly contradictory information out there and it is easy to become overwhelmed and confused. Take small steps towards your goal, get used to one change at a time or you will feel overloaded and be more likely to give up on supporting your healing plan. Tell your family and friends, you will need their support and it will help them feel involved in your healing.

We are now going to look at other ways in which you can consciously set about creating a future that you want.

CHAPTER 20

THE FUTURE

'Life loves to be taken by the lapel and told: "I am with you kid. Let's go."'
Maya Angelou

What happens when you think of the future? For many people with cancer, just the thought of looking further ahead than the next appointment, the next round of treatment creates anxiety and fear. They hardly dare imagine what it will be like to be healthy again. Sometimes people say they don't want to tempt fate. If this resonates with you then begin by working with the fear of the future.

Fear of the Future

How do you see the future? Some people will be unable to see one at all... Tap to clear the fears around this until you are able to visualise.

Tapping Section: Tapping for fear of the future

Repeat 3 times while tapping the Karate Chop:

Even though I can't see my future I deeply and completely love and accept myself

Eyebrow:	*Can't see my future*
Side of Eye:	*Can't see my future*
Under Eye:	*Can't see my future*
Under Nose:	*Can't see my future*
Chin:	*Can't see my future*
Collar Bone:	*Can't see my future*
Under Arm:	*Can't see my future*
Top of Head:	*Can't see my future*

Repeat 3 times while tapping the Karate Chop:

Even though I am afraid to look at the future I deeply and completely love and accept myself

Eyebrow:	*Fear of looking at the future*
Side of Eye:	*Fear of what I may see*
Under Eye:	*Fear of going there*

Under Nose:	*Fear of looking at the future*
Chin:	*Fear of looking at the future*
Collar Bone:	*Fear of what I may see*
Under Arm:	*Fear of going there*
Top of Head:	*Fear of looking at the future*

Create positive affirmations about the future…. This is not about creating false hope. However, we are still learning here and we do not know what is possible, so go for gold, no matter how impossible it may seem. State your positive affirmations aloud and then create a Choice around them. For example:

Repeat 3 times while tapping the Karate Chop:

Even though I am scared of the future I choose to live a long and healthy life

Eyebrow:	*Fear of the future*
Side of Eye:	*Fear of the future*
Under Eye:	*Really scared of the future*
Under Nose:	*Fear of the future*
Chin:	*Fear of the future*
Collar Bone:	*Fear of the future*
Under Arm:	*Really scared of the future*
Top of Head:	*Fear of the future*

Continue:

Eyebrow:	*I choose to live a long and healthy life*
Side of Eye:	*I choose a long and healthy life*
Under Eye:	*I choose to live a long and healthy life*
Under Nose:	*I choose a long and healthy life*
Chin:	*I choose to live a long and healthy life*
Collar Bone:	*I choose a long and healthy life*
Under Arm:	*I choose to live a long and healthy life*
Top of Head:	*I choose a long and healthy life*

Continue:

Eyebrow:	*Fear of the future*
Side of Eye:	*I choose a long and healthy life*

Under Eye:	*Fear of the future*
Under Nose:	*I choose to live a long and healthy life*
Chin:	*Fear of the future*
Collar Bone:	*I choose a long and healthy life*
Under Arm:	*Fear of the future*
Top of Head:	*I choose to live a long and healthy life*

Now visualise your future self at a time when you are already healed from your cancer, at a time when cancer is part of your history, and over in real time. Ask yourself the following questions and then tap on any blocks that come up such as being unable to get a clear picture yet (See below and also Chapter 15). What tells you that you are completely healed in your picture?

- **Is it a feeling?**
- **Where do you feel it in your body?**
- **What quality does it have?**
- **Is it hot/cold/warm?**
- **Does it move?**
- **What do you see?**
- **What do you look like?**
- **Are you hearing people talking to you?**
- **What are they saying that allows you to know you are healthy again?**
- **How do you know you are totally healthy?**

However you perceive yourself as healthy is appropriate, there is no right or wrong here, just do it. Even if it seems very hidden from you now, you do know what it is like to feel healthy. Otherwise it would be difficult to know when you are unhealthy.

Visualise yourself in one year's time, how do you look? If you can't get a clear picture yet it doesn't matter, all it means is that you have yet to actively start creating a future that draws you to it. Guess the answers to the following questions, what would you like to see, and then continue with the following tapping protocols to remove the blocks to visualising. Remember, that visualising does not necessarily mean a clear photographic image, although some people will experience this, it is more of a clear sense of how you will look.

For example, if I asked you to imagine the colour of your front door you would be able to tell me very quickly. Your unconscious mind will have had to access your visual system in order to provide that information but you will not necessarily have a clear picture of your house and front door in your mind. So:

- **What are you wearing?**
- **What does your hair look like?**
- **How energised are you?**

- **What are you doing?**
- **How healthy are you?**

Then repeat this for 2 years, 5 years 10 years and into the distant future.

If you experience any resistance to this, or are unable to visualise or get a sense of it at all, tap to clear these blocks:

Repeat 3 times while tapping the Karate Chop:

Even though I can't see myself in x years I deeply and completely love and accept myself

Eyebrow:	*This block*
Side of Eye:	*This resistance*
Under Eye:	*I can't see myself*
Under Nose:	*This block*
Chin:	*This resistance*
Collar Bone:	*I don't believe it*
Under Arm:	*I can't see myself*
Top of Head:	*This resistance*

Repeat 3 times while tapping the Karate Chop:

Even though it doesn't feel safe to see myself in x years time I deeply and completely love and accept myself anyway.

Eyebrow:	*It doesn't feel safe*
Side of Eye:	*Not feeling safe*
Under Eye:	*It is tempting fate*
Under Nose:	*Maybe, maybe not*
Chin:	*It doesn't feel safe*
Collar Bone:	*Not feeling safe*
Under Arm:	*It is tempting fate*
Top of Head:	*Maybe, maybe not*

Repeat 3 times while tapping the Karate Chop:

Even though I don't dare to hope and I can't see myself I deeply and completely love and accept myself

Eyebrow:	*I can't do it*

328

Side of Eye:	I don't dare hope
Under Eye:	What if I am disappointed?
Under Nose:	Fear of disappointment
Chin:	I can't do it
Collar Bone:	I don't dare hope
Under Arm:	What if I am disappointed?
Top of Head:	Fear of disappointment

Repeat 3 times while tapping the Karate Chop:

Even though something is blocking me seeing myself in perfect health I choose to be open to the possibility that I can enjoy a long and healthy life

Eyebrow:	This block
Side of Eye:	Block to that image
Under Eye:	This block
Under Nose:	Block to that image
Chin:	This block
Collar Bone:	Block to that image
Under Arm:	This block
Top of Head:	Block to that image

Continue:

Eyebrow:	I choose to see myself in perfect health
Side of Eye:	It is possible for me
Under Eye:	I can do it
Under Nose:	I choose to enjoy perfect health and longevity
Chin:	I choose to believe it is possible for me
Collar Bone:	I choose to release any remaining blocks now
Under Arm:	It is possible
Top of Head:	And I choose perfect health and longevity

Continue:

Eyebrow:	These remaining blocks
Side of Eye:	I choose health and longevity
Under Eye:	This remaining resistance

Under Nose:	*I am open to the possibility I can let it go*
Chin:	*I deserve to let it go*
Collar Bone:	*It is safe to let it go*
Under Arm:	*I choose health and longevity*
Top of Head:	*I choose for that to be possible for me*

Continue:

Eyebrow:	*I choose to see myself in perfect health*
Side of Eye:	*It is possible for me*
Under Eye:	*I can do it*
Under Nose:	*I choose to enjoy perfect health and longevity*
Chin:	*I choose to believe it is possible for me*
Collar Bone:	*I choose to release any remaining blocks now*
Under Arm:	*It is possible*
Top of Head:	*And I choose perfect health and longevity*

When you are holding a positive image in your head, imagine taking a still photograph of it, frame it and return to it in your mind as often as possible during the day. If you have difficulty holding onto it, then return to the tapping as above. Each time you do this, you will be opening your mind to the possibility of a healthy future.

Consciously creating your future

> *'The best way to predict the future is to create it!'*
> Jason Kaufmann

People sometimes feel that they might be jinxed if they so much as seem to presume that they can heal from cancer.

If that is you, have a look at what you gain by **NOT** being able to see a future in which you are healthy and having a life that you really love and which is free of cancer. Are there any positives to NOT being able to see that? I didn't think so. So your opportunity now is to begin to create that future.

Realistically, you don't know what you will be doing, where you will be, how you will be feeling physically. However, I would like you to make the assumption that, following this journey you are on right now, when you are free of the cancer, you are able to create or step into a life that really works for you, a life that is in integrity with who you are, that matches your values and gives you choices. You don't need to be totally specific about this, just holding it as a possibility and as a goal.

330

Actively imagine yourself in a place, a whole new place, where you want to be, where you have life in the real sense of that word, whatever that means to you. As you read this you may have already got that image in mind. You may know exactly what you want, who you want to be, what you want to be doing.

However, the chances are that most of you won't know the answers to all of these questions. Most of you will have been knocked sideways and are only able at the moment to focus on the cancer and the treatments and the fears.

But we do need to get a foot in the door here as early as possible, and introduce the possibility of a healthy positive future. The sooner you can begin to train your neurology to focus on what you want, rather than the negative, the more rapid the results. You need to be opening the door to the possibility of regaining total health from the start, all the time clearing the negative thoughts and beliefs which threaten to sabotage that intention by reintroducing negativity. Sadly, negativity is a pervasive human trait.

So, when you have cleared some of the initial anxiety around not being able to see into the future, not knowing where this is leading you, let's begin to introduce some choices as follows:

Tapping Section: Tapping for possibilities about the future

Repeat 3 times while tapping the Karate Chop:

Even though I can't see my future yet I choose to begin to consciously create a future that works for me in its entirety

Eyebrow:	*I can't see myself healed*
Side of Eye:	*I can't see the future*
Under Eye:	*I just can't imagine life after cancer*
Under Nose:	*I just can't see it*
Chin:	*I can't see myself healed*
Collar Bone:	*I can't see the future*
Under Arm:	*I just can't imagine life after cancer*
Top of Head:	*I just can't see it*

Continue:

Eyebrow:	*I choose to accept the possibility of total health*
Side of Eye:	*I choose to consciously create a future that works for me*
Under Eye:	*I choose to have fun consciously creating that future*
Under Nose:	*I choose to enjoy creating a healthy new future*

Chin:	I choose to accept the possibility of total health
Collar Bone:	I choose to consciously create a future that works for me
Under Arm:	I choose to have fun consciously creating that future
Top of Head:	I choose to enjoy creating a healthy new future

Continue:

Eyebrow:	I can't see myself healed
Side of Eye:	I choose to accept the possibility of total health
Under Eye:	I can't see the future
Under Nose:	I choose to consciously create a future that works for me
Chin:	I just can't imagine life after cancer
Collar Bone:	I choose to have fun consciously creating that future
Under Arm:	I just can't see it
Top of Head:	I choose to enjoy creating a healthy new future

'There are no rules of architecture for a castle in the clouds.'
G K Chesterton

Louis's story

Louis was in remission, but said he felt that the Sword of Damocles would be hanging over him for ever, that he would never be free of the grip of cancer, he would be forever frightened, worrying about his health. Cancer would be always at the forefront of his mind, like a dark cloud hovering. Whilst there is a degree of truth to this, he will never forget his cancer experience, and it is likely that he will have a better awareness around his health, Louis was unable to think of anything else.

Repeat 3 times while tapping the Karate Chop:

Even though I have the Sword of Damocles hanging over me I deeply and completely love and accept myself

Eyebrow:	The Sword of Damocles hanging over me
Side of Eye:	The Sword of Damocles hanging over me
Under Eye:	I will never be free of it
Under Nose:	The Sword of Damocles hanging over me

332

Chin:	*The Sword of Damocles hanging over me*
Collar Bone:	*The Sword of Damocles hanging over me*
Under Arm:	*I will never be free of it*
Top of Head:	*The Sword of Damocles hanging over me*

Repeat 3 times while tapping the Karate Chop:

Even though I will never escape the cancer shadow I deeply and completely love and accept myself

Eyebrow:	*I will never escape the cancer shadow*
Side of Eye:	*I will never get away from it*
Under Eye:	*It will always be there*
Under Nose:	*The terrifying cancer shadow*
Chin:	*I will never escape the cancer shadow*
Collar Bone:	*I will never get away from it*
Under Arm:	*It will always be there*
Top of Head:	*The terrifying cancer shadow*

After tapping about 4 – 5 rounds on each of the above, Louis said he felt that the word 'cancer' was less 'in his face. He could not yet imagine it not being a part of his everyday thinking, but the intensity around it had reduced. He continued to tap around his fear of being an invalid for ever, of there being no escape from his diagnosis. He did a little work on this at home every day and after a couple of weeks reported that whilst his health was still very much in his awareness (which was definitely important!), he had had a few long periods of time without feeling down about it or obsessing about it. This seems to me to be a healthy place to be in. He needs to keep an active eye on his health and lifestyle, without it dominating his every waking moment as it was doing previously.

If you feel like Louis, that cancer is this word hovering above you like a dark cloud, I would like you to actually do that, put the word **cancer** up there in a cloud over you

- **How does it look?**
- **How do you feel?**
- **Is it a very dark cloud?**
- **Is it light?**
- **May it is one of those beautiful fluffy clouds we sometimes see in a summer sky?**

Gary Craig referred to clouds as just a bunch of mist and that is a truth isn't it, clouds are just a bunch of mist.

Imagine your bunch of mist just to begin to dissolve, and notice how it reduces, how the colour changes, maybe it's turning into one of those beautiful fluffy clouds that get blown across the spring and summer skies.

Is the word **cancer** still there? Is it overhead or has it moved? I would like you to imagine taking the word **cancer** out of the cloud, putting it in front of you and shrinking it down, making it very, very tiny cancer. And as you do that, place it in the far left hand corner of your vision, so that it's there, you are aware of it, it is tiny and as you do that, note how you feel. If you have any blocks to this process then tap through them. For example:

Tapping Section: Tapping for the cancer cloud

Repeat 3 times while tapping the Karate Chop:

Even though the cloud won't move I deeply and completely love and accept myself

Eyebrow:	*It won't move*
Side of Eye:	*The cloud won't move*
Under Eye:	*I can't get it to move*
Under Nose:	*The cloud won't move*
Chin:	*It won't move*
Collar Bone:	*The cloud won't move*
Under Arm:	*I can't get it to move*
Top of Head:	*The cloud won't move*

Repeat 3 times while tapping the Karate Chop:

Even though something is blocking me shrinking it down I deeply and completely love and accept myself

Eyebrow:	*I can't shrink the word*
Side of Eye:	*I can't dissolve the clouds*
Under Eye:	*I just can't do it*
Under Nose:	*Something blocking me doing this*
Chin:	*I can't shrink the word*
Collar Bone:	*I can't dissolve the clouds*
Under Arm:	*I just can't do it*
Top of Head:	*Something blocking me doing this*

Once again notice how you feel in your body as you do this, notice where any fear is showing up and tap on that.

Repeat 3 times while tapping the Karate Chop:

334

Even though I have this fear in my chest I deeply and completely love and accept myself

Eyebrow:	*This fear in my chest*
Side of Eye:	*Fear in my chest*
Under Eye:	*This fear in my chest*
Under Nose:	*Fear in my chest*
Chin:	*This fear in my chest*
Collar Bone:	*Fear in my chest*
Under Arm:	*This fear in my chest*
Top of Head:	*Fear in my chest*

Repeat 3 times while tapping the Karate Chop:

Even though I this fear of the future in my stomach I deeply and completely love and accept myself

Eyebrow:	*Fear of the future*
Side of Eye:	*In my stomach*
Under Eye:	*This fear of the future*
Under Nose:	*In my stomach*
Chin:	*Fear of the future*
Collar Bone:	*In my stomach*
Under Arm:	*This fear of the future*
Top of Head:	*In my stomach*

Repeat 3 times while tapping the Karate Chop:

Even though I am really anxious about the future and it's showing up in my lower back I deeply and completely love and accept myself

Eyebrow:	*This anxiety in my lower back*
Side of Eye:	*Future anxiety just there in my lower back*
Under Eye:	*This anxiety in my lower back*
Under Nose:	*Future anxiety just there in my lower back*
Chin:	*This anxiety in my lower back*
Collar Bone:	*Future anxiety just there in my lower back*
Under Arm:	*This anxiety in my lower back*
Top of Head:	*Future anxiety just there in my lower back*

As you know from tapping with physical symptoms, the symptoms are likely to move and change. Continue to chase the pain until it clears and you can think about the future without getting any physical response or any negative emotions. You may not be able to imagine a perfect future or a healthy future yet, but by tapping away the fears I hope that you will be able to open yourself up to the possibility of creating that future and healing in a way that is appropriate and healthy for you.

Enjoy your creation!

In the next chapter we will expand on the concept of focussing on what you want, rather than what you are lacking or don't want. We will look at the power of positive thinking on the healing process, and at ways to enhance it.

CHAPTER 21

POSITIVE THINKING, AFFIRMATIONS & HUMOUR

'Whether or not you think you can or you can't, you are right'
Henry Ford

There is much talk of the power of positive thinking in cancer recovery. Doctors are increasingly recognising the importance of the mind in the treatment of serious disease.

We are repeatedly told to 'think positive' by New Age thinkers and 'pop psychology'. The Law of Attraction would dictate that our consistent thoughts do indeed become our reality, (A Course in Miracles). We are bombarded with advice such as 'You are what you eat', ' You get what you ask for', 'You can attract the life of your dreams', wise words from caring people, but how do we begin to action them. It is a good idea, but how do we actually do it? Positive thinking and a cancer diagnosis are not natural bedfellows. This in itself can seem overwhelming and bring with it added guilt and anxiety.

As we know, the body and mind are merely flip sides of the same coin and need to be in harmony to achieve total health and wellbeing. Positivity of mind brings happiness and inner peace, both of which are vital to the healthy functioning of the immune system.

In early 1900s Emile Coue, a French psychotherapist, discovered that repeating positive affirmations helped people improve their health over time. He asked his patients to repeat the following affirmation several times during every day and the results would indicate that this actually made a difference to their overall health:

'Every day in every way I am getting better and better'
Emile Coue

As always, start where you are at and for the sake of tapping, let's assume you're feeling overwhelmed and not feeling positive about positive affirmations.

Tapping Section: Tapping for overwhelm about affirmations

Repeat 3 times while tapping the Karate Chop:

Even though I am overwhelmed I deeply and completely love and accept myself

Eyebrow:	*Feeling overwhelmed*
Side of Eye:	*I don't know where to begin*
Under Eye:	*It's all too much*
Under Nose:	*I don't know where to start or what to do*
Chin:	*Feeling overwhelmed*

Collar Bone:	*Feeling overwhelmed*
Under Arm:	*Feeling anxious and overwhelmed*
Top of Head:	*Feeling anxious and overwhelmed*

Repeat 3 times while tapping the Karate Chop:

Even though positive affirmations don't work for me I deeply and completely love and accept myself

Eyebrow:	*Positive affirmations don't work for me*
Side of Eye:	*They are pointless*
Under Eye:	*They don't work for me*
Under Nose:	*Positive affirmations don't work*
Chin:	*They won't work for me*
Collar Bone:	*They never work for me*
Under Arm:	*Positive affirmations don't work for me*
Top of Head:	*Positive affirmations never work for me*

Repeat 3 times while tapping the Karate Chop:

Even though thinking positive is impossible for me right now I deeply and completely love and accept myself

Eyebrow:	*I can't do it*
Side of Eye:	*It feels impossible*
Under Eye:	*I've never been able to do it*
Under Nose:	*And I can't start now*
Chin:	*I don't feel positive*
Collar Bone:	*How can I feel positive with cancer?*
Under Arm:	*I can't do it*
Top of Head:	*It is impossible*

Continue:

Eyebrow:	*I should be able to do it*
Side of Eye:	*This guilt*
Under Eye:	*I should be able to think positive*
Under Nose:	*Other people can do it*

Chin:	But I can't
Collar Bone:	I should be able to do it
Under Arm:	I can't do it
Top of Head:	This guilt

Continue:

Eyebrow:	This anxiety
Side of Eye:	This guilt
Under Eye:	I can't do it
Under Nose:	I should be able to do it
Chin:	This anxiety
Collar Bone:	This guilt
Under Arm:	I can't think positively
Top of Head:	This anxiety and guilt

When you have reached a place where you are at least open to the possibility that things can be different for you, then you can begin to move forwards towards consciously creating that change.

'Our consistent thoughts become our reality'.
A Course in Miracles

At one level, we all know the above quote is true. If we think negative thoughts we feel negative, if we focus on pain, we tend to notice it more. That is one of the reasons we use the tapping to work with the negative, to rebalance ourselves to the energetic component of the negative issue and clear it, changing our focus to more positive areas.

The 'yes-buts'
Equally, when we focus on the positive, making sure there are no 'yes buts' attached to it, we are likely to achieve it. 'The yes buts' are the blocks to realising our positive intentions. However, with the tapping we have the perfect tool to work through our 'yes buts' (in EFT terms these are known as tail enders), so that our focus returns to the positive.

We are bombarded with messages constantly through the media, books and DVDs about thinking positively. We are encouraged to make positive affirmations and return to them regularly, repeat them to ourselves frequently. And sometimes they work, but most times they do not. Why is that? It is because there are too many negative beliefs/ thoughts/ judgments hanging under the positive affirmation, and the human mind gives the power to the negative. Therefore, the negative becomes the real affirmation.

So how do we turn this around and create successful powerful positive affirmations that really work. It is simple, we create the affirmation and then ask ourselves whether there are any 'yes buts' hanging off it – I like to think of them as hanging on coat hangers which we can easily remove.

Those who use positive affirmations like to state their affirmation in the present, as though they already have the desired state. I think this is a step too far initially for many people suffering from a serious disease such as cancer. This is why I prefer to use Choices, it is an interim stage and the words 'I choose' seem to bypass our conscious defences to a point.

Repeat the following two sentences and notice which one you are more in harmony with:

- **I am completely healthy**
- **I choose to be completely healthy**

My guess is the latter feels more congruent right now. **'I am completely healthy'** is likely to have thrown up a load of tail-enders, or yes buts, such as:

- **Yes but I'm not**
- **Yes but I have cancer**
- **Yes but that isn't true**

And so forth.

There is a point in your journey, when you first go into remission, that it is useful to change the affirmation to 'I am completely healthy', but even then, check inside and see whether that feels really true for you or whether you have a few doubts (yes buts) lurking.

Lets take 'I choose to be completely healthy' or 'I choose total health'. That in itself may still bring up a few yes buts, such as:

- **Yes but I can't get over this**
- **Yes but I will never be truly free of cancer**
- **Yes but I can never have that**
- **Yes but I have cancer and that means X**

Notice what you are saying to yourself and then create a tapping protocol around it, tapping for several rounds if necessary, until the words no longer sound true to you. For example:

Tapping Section: Tapping for the negatives

Repeat 3 times while tapping the Karate Chop:

Even though I can't get over this I deeply and completely love and accept myself

Eyebrow:	*I can't get over this*
Side of Eye:	*I'll never get over this*

Under Eye:	I can't get over this
Under Nose:	I'll never get over this
Chin:	I can't get over this
Collar Bone:	I'll never get over this
Under Arm:	I can't get over this
Top of Head:	I'll never get over this

Repeat 3 times while tapping the Karate Chop:

Even though I will never be truly free of cancer I deeply and completely love and accept myself

Eyebrow:	I will never be truly free of cancer
Side of Eye:	I will never completely heal
Under Eye:	I will always have some cancer
Under Nose:	I will never be truly free
Chin:	I will never be truly free of cancer
Collar Bone:	I will never completely heal
Under Arm:	I will always have some cancer
Top of Head:	I will never be truly free

Tom's story

Tom was in remission from lung cancer. He was very happy with the concept of positive affirmations, and considered himself to be a cup half full type of man. He also felt extremely lucky to have had excellent care and treatment for his cancer, which had led to his being in remission. However, when working on an affirmation for total health he kept coming up against a major block, the essence of which was that he felt he would always be in the shadow of cancer. We tapped with this:

Tapping Section: Tapping for the shadow of cancer

Repeat 3 times while tapping the Karate Chop:

Even though I will always be in the shadow of cancer I deeply and completely love and accept myself

Eyebrow:	Always in the shadow of cancer
Side of Eye:	It will always be with me
Under Eye:	Always in the shadow of cancer
Under Nose:	I will never be totally free
Chin:	Always in the shadow of cancer

Collar Bone:	*It will always be with me*
Under Arm:	*Always in the shadow of cancer*
Top of Head:	*I will never be totally free*

This thought created an enormous fear, which showed up in Tom's chest to the point that he could hardly breathe. We continued to tap, focussing on this physical symptom:

Repeat 3 times while tapping the Karate Chop:

Even though I have this cancer shadow fear in my chest I deeply and completely love and accept myself.

Eyebrow:	*Cancer shadow fear*
Side of Eye:	*Cancer shadow fear*
Under Eye:	*Taking my breath away*
Under Nose:	*Stopping me breathing*
Chin:	*Cancer shadow fear*
Collar Bone:	*Getting in the way of my fullest breath*
Under Arm:	*Cancer shadow fear*
Top of Head:	*Stopping me breathing*

Repeat 3 times while tapping the Karate Chop:

Even though this fear is blocking my fullest breath I deeply and completely love and accept myself

Eyebrow:	*Fear blocking my fullest breath*
Side of Eye:	*This block to my fullest breath*
Under Eye:	*This fear*
Under Nose:	*Blocking my fullest breath*
Chin:	*Fear blocking my fullest breath*
Collar Bone:	*This block to my fullest breath*
Under Arm:	*This fear*
Top of Head:	*Blocking my fullest breath*

Repeat 3 times while tapping the Karate Chop:

Even though this frightening shadow of cancer is taking my breath away I deeply and completely love and accept myself

Eyebrow:	*Frightening cancer shadow*

Side of Eye:	*Following me, always with me*
Under Eye:	*Taking my breath away*
Under Nose:	*Shadow of cancer*
Chin:	*Frightening cancer shadow*
Collar Bone:	*Following me, always with me*
Under Arm:	*Taking my breath away*
Top of Head:	*Shadow of cancer*

We did a few rounds like this until Tom's breathing returned to normal. Suddenly he laughed. I asked him what was happening and he said he had a cartoon picture of himself with his shadow, and the thought that he could never catch his shadow and therefore perhaps his shadow could never catch him either. He could see himself playing with it, stretching it, running in and out of the sun, and he felt that he could have a positive relationship with the cancer shadow, it was just there to keep him 'on the straight and narrow'. It was literally on his case!

We then returned to the original affirmation of 'I am completely healthy' and Tom said he felt OK and in tune with that affirmation. We are now two year's since we completed that piece of work and I have just had a Christmas card from Tom, with the affirmation written in it, updating me on his news and confirming that he continues to be completely healthy and his check ups have all been clear.

Health is our natural tendency
The human body is designed to be healthy, and to develop a disease as serious as cancer there have to be many contributors, as previously stated. A tendency towards negative self-destructive thinking is an important component, but do only negative people get cancer? I don't think so!

However, positive affirmations **DO** work, but only when they have no negative affirmations hanging off them. In tapping terms, we call these tail-enders. They are the negative beliefs or self-talk that may be attached to the positive affirmation. Unfortunately, the human mind inclines towards the negative if allowed to, and if tail enders are present they will become the affirmation. Listen to your self-talk, allow it to have a voice and then tap to clear the negatives.

Begin by making a positive affirmation of what you really want in your life. For example, **I want to be healthy**.

Say it aloud and notice what comes up immediately afterwards. It may be something like:

- **But it's not possible for me**
- **But the doctors say X**
- **But I can't do it**
- **Other people can but not me**
- **People like me can't do X**

Then tap to clear the negative thoughts that you have.

343

Tapping Section: Tapping for thoughts about being healthy

Repeat 3 times while tapping the Karate Chop:

Even though it's not possible for me to be healthy I deeply and completely love and accept myself

Eyebrow:	*It's not possible for me to be healthy*
Side of Eye:	*I can't do it*
Under Eye:	*I'll never do it*
Under Nose:	*I don't believe it is possible for me to be healthy*
Chin:	*They say it isn't possible*
Collar Bone:	*I can't do it*
Under Arm:	*It isn't possible to do it*
Top of Head:	*It is just not possible for me*

If you get little or no movement with the belief you will need to investigate a little deeper. Ask yourself:

- **According to who?**
- **Why?**
- **When did I learn this?**
- **Who taught me?**
- **What did they say?**
- **How does it feel when I think that thought? (tap on any physical feelings that accompany it)**
- **What would it mean if I didn't think that thought?**
- **What might I have to do that I am not doing now?**

Be totally honest. Our natural tendency is to squash these negative thoughts down, push them away. But they don't go, they fester and re emerge later on. With the tapping, we address the negatives head on and work to clear them. There may be good 'evidence' supporting the tail ender. We can usually justify our negativity to ourselves as truths, and we buy our own story as well as other people's. What if that story were a positive one, what would that mean to our healing process?

Tess's story
Tess, a consummate tapper, recently went for a scan to assess the progression of her 4th grade lung cancer post chemotherapy. Not only had the tumours reduced, and some totally disappeared, which exceeded the expectations of the medical team who were regarding the treatment as purely palliative, but the consultant, when told how she was supporting herself, said **'Cancer, it is all to do with the mind'.**

344

This is not to say that the chemotherapy and other medical approaches are a waste of time, absolutely not, they have a vital role in the healing process. But the key to this is the attitude of mind during treatment, and whether the treatment itself fits with the individual's belief system. If the belief system and the treatment are in alignment it seems the outcome is more positive.

With the tapping, we can work to clear negative beliefs to allow any treatment, medical, complementary or both, to be received and accepted by the body easily. We can change the backchat to our positive affirmations in such a way that they become truly positive and unpolluted by our former negative thoughts and feelings.

Again, I want to stress the importance of being completely honest and upfront with yourself as you answer these questions. Sometimes our negative thoughts are so shocking that we fear even admitting them, let alone saying them aloud as tapping statements. However, it is vital to get all of them out on the table to be examined and tapped to clear. The subtlest of our negative thinking can sneak up on us and surprise us. We may even argue with it when we hear it, but whether it resonates or not, the fact that you have had that thought makes it worth applying the tapping to it.

Mary's story

Mary was struggling badly with her healing process. She seemed to manage to scrape through all her treatments, she had felt sick during her chemotherapy and her blood count would drop each time, but somehow would always pick up just enough for the next round. Her treatment had ended now and she was functioning but seemed unable to fully focus on more than a day at a time, and could not recover from the after effects of the chemotherapy, despite it now being six months on. We had tapped around all the obvious negative thoughts and beliefs but it was clear that something more deeply unconscious was driving Mary.

We decided to move our focus away from dredging through yet more negative memories and feelings and begin creating some positive affirmations in the hope that that might provide a different avenue of thought for her mind to follow.

We began with the Coue affirmation above, as Mary already knew it so it would be no effort to remember it. However, no sooner had we started tapping with it when Mary said, out of the blue, 'I can't afford to get better!'. This statement actually shocked Mary far more than it did me. I had a sense that something like that was going on, and in tapping terms we refer to it as being psychologically reversed to total health.

So I asked Mary 'What might you have to do that you are not doing now if you heal?'

Occasionally, I will come across people who are really stuck with their illness, they are actually dependent on their illness in order to survive and one of these was Mary. Obviously, this belief is usually deeply unconscious, but seems to reveal itself during tapping.

Mary had been made redundant from her job about six months before the cancer diagnosis, she hadn't been able to find another one, it was the beginning of the recession and she was in her late fifties, and in her words "not hugely employable in an ageist society".

That was a belief to start with and we did look at that, but the bottom line was that she was receiving an invalidity benefit, housing benefit and other financial benefits from the government. All of her benefits depended on her being incapable of working, and depended on her remaining ill.

If she healed, if she was completely free of cancer she wouldn't be able to survive, she would lose a lot of money and she would have to find a job, which, in her belief system was impossible. It is important to note that it wasn't that Mary wanted to be on benefits, that is not the point. The point is that she was completely dependent on these benefits and couldn't see a way of bridging from being ill to being financially stable and secure and healthy.

It seemed an impossible leap to make. She actually said to me "What I really need to do is just keep a little bit of this cancer, not enough to kill me but just enough to keep me on the benefits because I won't be able to survive otherwise". I will always respect my client's views, and had Mary been happy with her realisation I would have left it at that. However, she was shocked as her conscious thinking had always been of healing, finding a new job and beginning life afresh, she had just been totally unable to motivate herself in this direction, hardly surprising given the unconscious self-talk.

So we tapped as follows. Please tap along:

Repeat 3 times while tapping the Karate Chop:

Even though I can't survive without cancer I deeply and completely love and accept myself

Eyebrow:	*Can't survive without cancer*
Side of Eye:	*That thought*
Under Eye:	*Can't survive without cancer*
Under Nose:	*That shocking thought*
Chin:	*Can't survive without cancer*
Collar Bone:	*That thought*
Under Arm:	*Can't survive without cancer*
Top of Head:	*That shocking thought*

Repeat 3 times while tapping the Karate Chop:

Even though I need cancer to survive I deeply and completely love and accept myself

Eyebrow:	*I need my cancer to survive*
Side of Eye:	*That thought*
Under Eye:	*Needing cancer to survive*
Under Nose:	*That shocking thought*
Chin:	*I need my cancer to survive*

346

Collar Bone:	*That thought*
Under Arm:	*Needing cancer to survive*
Top of Head:	*That shocking thought*

Repeat 3 times while tapping the Karate Chop:

Even though I have to be ill to live I deeply and completely love and accept myself

Eyebrow:	*Having to be ill to live*
Side of Eye:	*I have to be ill to live*
Under Eye:	*No I don't*
Under Nose:	*I have to be ill to live*
Chin:	*Having to be ill to live*
Collar Bone:	*I have to be ill to live*
Under Arm:	*No I don't*
Top of Head:	*No I don't*

When Mary was unable to connect to these statements any longer we worked on a positive affirmation, or Choice. Mary wanted to use the Coue affirmation so we tapped on each point while repeating **'Every day in every way I am getting better and better'.**

Eventually Mary began to realise that there might be other possibilities and she applied to go and retrain on a government retraining scheme where she learnt some new IT skill sets and as a result she managed to find herself temporary work easily and get a reasonable income.

*When she realised that actually there was work out there for her, that it was possible and that she did have skills that were transferable, that were wanted, she was able to put her total faith into her healing process and to becoming healthy. In fact she became really excited about the idea of getting out into a new workplace. I am happy to report that, six months later, Mary is doing very well and she is in a job that she loves with new people and she has a new lease of life, she is going out, she looks younger **and** she is being paid!*

The Law of Attraction

The Law of Attraction is a very popular metaphysical principle, brought into public awareness by the films 'The Secret' and 'What the Bleep do We Know.' I cannot write this book without mentioning it.

The Law of Attraction comes from the Teachings of Abraham, which have been channelled through Esther Hicks and subsequently transcribed in a series of books and cds, http://www.abraham-hicks.com/. Abraham is best described by Esther as "infinite intelligence", which for me translates again to universal unconsciousness as purported by Carl Jung's theory of the same name, zero point, the universal energy field.

For many of you, this concept may seem too 'out there' and as yet it has no scientific recognition. However, for some people intuitively it makes sense, and along with the tapping, offers exciting, real, possibilities for positive change. These ideas are very much at the centre of the newly emerging field of Quantum Physics, and if you are drawn to exploring them further some suggested reading is listed in the reference section of this book. As this topic is a massive one, I will only touch on the Law of Attraction here. My main concern is with the potential damage misinterpretation may lead to. It is important to recognise that the Law of Attraction is **not** saying that you consciously created/ attracted your cancer. The ideas are based on a far more complex metaphysical construct.

The Law of Attraction, in a nutshell, says that 'Like attracts like' or 'That which is likened unto itself is drawn'. In essence this means that we get what we focus on, whether it is positive or negative.

So when you hear people speaking about the Law of Attraction what are you saying to yourself, what is your inner critic telling you?

Tapping Section: Tapping for having attracted cancer

Repeat 3 times while tapping the Karate Chop:

Even though I think I attracted this I deeply and completely love and accept myself

Eyebrow:	*I attracted this*
Side of Eye:	*I attracted the cancer*
Under Eye:	*I attracted this*
Under Nose:	*I attracted my cancer*
Chin:	*I attracted this*
Collar Bone:	*I attracted the cancer*
Under Arm:	*I attracted this*
Top of Head:	*I attracted my cancer*

Repeat 3 times while tapping the Karate Chop:

Even though part of me believes this I am open to the possibility that it is not that simple

Eyebrow:	*I attracted my cancer*
Side of Eye:	*Part of me believes this*
Under Eye:	*That is what The Law of Attraction says*
Under Nose:	*Maybe*
Chin:	*Maybe not*
Collar Bone:	*I attracted my cancer*

| Under Arm: | *Maybe* |
| Top of Head: | *Maybe not* |

Continue:

Eyebrow:	*I am open to the possibility that it is not that simple*
Side of Eye:	*I am open to the possibility that that is not what the Law of Attraction means*
Under Eye:	*I am open to that possibility*
Under Nose:	*What if it is not that simple?*
Chin:	*I am open to the possibility that it is not that simple*
Collar Bone:	*I am open to the possibility that that is not what the Law of Attraction means*
Under Arm:	*I am open to that possibility*
Top of Head:	*What if it is not that simple?*

Cora's story

Cora was very concerned about the Law of Attraction. In her words, she **knew** that she should be attracting positive health through positive thinking; this was what she had read; everything had to be focussed on what she wanted. She felt she was pushing down a load of stuff and she just couldn't keep positive. She felt she should be focussed on the positive every minute of every day. But the familiar negative thoughts kept popping back, such as:

- *I can't stay positive so I'll die of this*
- *I have brought this cancer on myself.*
- *It's all my fault*
- *I won't get better unless I am 100% positive*

- everything that she had translated the Law of Attraction to mean.

What was happening was that this was creating huge amounts of guilt:

- *I should*
- *I ought*
- *I shouldn't have*
- *I ought not to have done*

She was tying herself up in metaphorical and physical knots and becoming increasingly anxious. She had unremitting pain in her stomach and described it as a twisting fist of tension. We started there, and did a number of rounds until the tension relaxed and the fist went away.

Repeat 3 times while tapping the Karate Chop:

Even though I have this twisting fist of tension in my stomach I deeply and completely love and accept myself

Eyebrow:	Twisting fist of tension in my stomach
Side of Eye:	Twisting fist of tension in my stomach
Under Eye:	Twisting fist of tension in my stomach
Under Nose:	Twisting fist of tension in my stomach
Chin:	Twisting fist of tension in my stomach
Collar Bone:	Twisting fist of tension in my stomach
Under Arm:	Twisting fist of tension in my stomach
Top of Head:	Twisting fist of tension in my stomach

Then we continued by tapping through the various beliefs that were showing up.

Repeat 3 times while tapping the Karate Chop:

Even though I'm attracting bad things onto myself I deeply and completely love and accept myself

Eyebrow:	Attracting bad things to myself
Side of Eye:	Attracting bad things to myself
Under Eye:	Attracting bad things to myself
Under Nose:	Attracting bad things to myself
Chin:	Attracting bad things to myself
Collar Bone:	Attracting bad things to myself
Under Arm:	Attracting bad things to myself
Top of Head:	Attracting bad things to myself

Repeat 3 times while tapping the Karate Chop:

Even though it's all my fault I am ill I deeply and completely love and accept myself

Eyebrow:	It's all my fault
Side of Eye:	That's what the Law of Attraction says
Under Eye:	Maybe
Under Nose:	Maybe not
Chin:	I am open to the possibility that I have made a mistake
Collar Bone:	What if I didn't deliberately attract my illness?
Under Arm:	I am open to that possibility
Top of Head:	What if it is not my fault?

Repeat 3 times while tapping the Karate Chop:

Even though I should be feeling positive ALL the time I deeply and completely love and accept myself

Eyebrow:	*I should feel positive all the time*
Side of Eye:	*It won't work unless I am positive all the time*
Under Eye:	*Fear of not feeling positive all the time*
Under Nose:	*I should feel positive all the time*
Chin:	*I should feel positive all the time*
Collar Bone:	*It won't work unless I am positive all the time*
Under Arm:	*Maybe not*
Top of Head:	*Maybe it will*

Repeat 3 times while tapping the Karate Chop:

Even though I should be thinking positively ALL the time I deeply and completely love and accept myself

Eyebrow:	*I should constantly have positive thoughts*
Side of Eye:	*I am not allowed to think anything negative*
Under Eye:	*That's what they say*
Under Nose:	*Maybe*
Chin:	*I am open to the possibility that all I can ask myself*
Collar Bone:	*Is to increase my awareness of negative thoughts*
Under Arm:	*I am open to that possibility*
Top of Head:	*I choose to do the best I can*

Repeat 3 times while tapping the Karate Chop:

Even though I can't do it I deeply and completely love and accept myself

Eyebrow:	*I can't do it*
Side of Eye:	*It's not possible*
Under Eye:	*I can't do it*
Under Nose:	*Yes I can*
Chin:	*I choose to develop a healthy awareness of my thinking*
Collar Bone:	*And I choose to harness the positive power of my thoughts*

351

Under Arm:	*I choose awareness*
Top of Head:	*I am doing the best I can*

Repeat 3 times while tapping the Karate Chop:

Even though I have created this problem I deeply and completely love and accept myself

Eyebrow:	*I've created this problem*
Side of Eye:	*It is all my fault*
Under Eye:	*I created this*
Under Nose:	*Maybe*
Chin:	*Maybe not*
Collar Bone:	*I am open to the possibility that I did not consciously create this problem*
Under Arm:	*I am open to the possibility that it is not my fault*
Top of Head:	*And I choose to remember I am doing my very best right now*

The list was endless, and we needed to be very persistent, and keep returning to each belief and checking the intensity until Cora could not connect to the thoughts any more, until they seemed meaningless to her.

When we had tapped through all these yes-buts, and these shouldn'ts and ought's, Cora was able to see that she hadn't deliberately set about creating a lifestyle to bring on cancer, in fact she couldn't have predicted it at all. There was nothing in her genes that would indicate that she would be a cancer sufferer, there was no obvious root and it certainly had not been in her thoughts at all, in fact up until this point she had led a very healthy life.

Then we addressed the fact that she was having negative thoughts around the cancer itself, which was only natural. In fact, to return to the concept of denial, if she hadn't been thinking these thoughts at all, and had been focussing purely on the future and the positives without acknowledging her reality, then that would, possibly, have been a case of being in denial. So once again we got these thoughts up on the table, addressed them and tapped through them one at a time.

Repeat 3 times while tapping the Karate Chop:

Even though I have these thoughts sometimes I deeply and completely love and accept myself

Eyebrow:	*These thoughts*
Side of Eye:	*These negative thoughts*

Under Eye:	*These thoughts*
Under Nose:	*These negative thoughts*
Chin:	*These thoughts*
Collar Bone:	*These negative thoughts*
Under Arm:	*These thoughts*
Top of Head:	*These negative thoughts*

Repeat 3 times while tapping the Karate Chop:

Even though I feel sabotaged by these negative thoughts I deeply and completely love and accept myself

Eyebrow:	*Feeling sabotaged*
Side of Eye:	*Sabotaged by my thinking*
Under Eye:	*Feeling sabotaged*
Under Nose:	*Sabotaged by my thinking*
Chin:	*Feeling sabotaged*
Collar Bone:	*Sabotaged by my thinking*
Under Arm:	*Feeling sabotaged*
Top of Head:	*Sabotaged by my thinking*

After a few rounds, I asked Cora how she felt when she thought 'I ought to be feeling positive all the time'. She said she felt OK and calm. So I tested our work by asking her 'Is it true you should be feeling positively all the time?' Her reply was: 'I'm only human, what is true is that when I have negative thoughts, I need to address them, acknowledge them and work to clear them'.

At this point it felt to me like she was stepping back into her own healing power, rather than setting herself up to achieve the seeming impossible. She was able to focus on using the Law of Attraction in a way that worked for her. She knew what she wanted, total health, and she was also able to see a route to getting it, instead of being sabotaged every time she had a negative thought. She was able to see those thoughts as opportunities for healing rather than threats to her future. Three years later she still does!

The power of the post it note!

'Memory is a way of holding on to the things you love, the things you are, the things you never want to lose.'
Paul Arnold

When you have created some positive affirmations that truly resonate for you, that state exactly what you want, and that have no tail enders hanging off them, then write them down on Post-it notes. Stick the notes anywhere and everywhere around your home, your office, anywhere else you visit frequently.

Put them on your fridge door, your bathroom mirror, your bedside table, in your wallet, by the loo. You want to saturate your conscious and unconscious minds with the affirmations, with what you want that is positive. You don't need to tap every time you read the affirmations (although of course I would love you to!!), but flood yourself with positivity at every available opportunity.

I would also suggest that you enhance this by surrounding yourself with positivity. Allow your friends, relations and colleagues to know that this is important to you and that you need them to be positive around you too. Don't watch negative programmes on the television, don't read the newspapers. If you really need to keep up on current events, then tap along whilst you watch the news or read the papers. Watch out for anything that you may be surreptitiously experiencing that has a negative impact on you, particularly through the media. Just remember to tap!

Humour

'What soap is to the body, laughter is to the soul.'
Yiddish Proverb

Some people like to watch comedy programmes repeatedly, to allow that laughter into their lives. Humour is enormously healing, and the more you can access that state the better you are likely to feel. I suggest you rent comedy DVDs, and download funny podcasts and audio books, allowing laughter into your life. Only see friends who make you laugh, if at all possible. Avoid those friends who collude in your negativity – you will know who those are. They may be fantastic friends, but in the current situation they are not useful to your healing.

Music

'What we play is life.'
Louis Armstrong

Music is very emotive and can provoke intense emotional responses. Listen to upbeat inspiring music, sing along! Conversely, if there are particular pieces that trigger poignant or negative memories, tap whilst you listen to the music to release any intense emotions. Music can be a very useful way of enhancing your Personal Peace Procedure as certain songs or tunes may remind you of people or places and offer tapping material.

Photographs

'A photograph is memory in the raw.'
Carrie Latet

Photographs can be used in a similar way. Surround yourself with photos of happy times, positive memories. Alternatively, tapping your way through your photo albums can be another useful way to enhance your Personal Peace Procedure. Just stop and tap on any negative emotions that arise as you scan through your life in pictures.

In the following chapter we are going to look at the power of meditation and how you can begin to meditate, using a very simple technique.

354

CHAPTER 22

MEDITATION

'Health is a state of complete physical, mental and social well-being, and not merely the absence of disease or infirmity.'
World Health Organization, 1948

Meditation is a mind/body practice aimed at increasing calmness and relaxation, which in turn helps us cope with dis-ease, both physical and emotional. For me, meditation is all about stilling the mind, taking time out from the overwhelm of life, with or without a cancer diagnosis. I believe that this place of stillness is where the body has its optimum healing opportunity, when we are able to quieten the backdrop of chatter that plagues so many of us in every day life. The chatter of our self talk, our beliefs, our judgments. Suspending these, even for a minute, and focussing our attention on something other, however forced that may feel initially, allows us a moment of peace in this chaotic world.

Studies have found that regular meditation can dramatically benefit your health. It has been found to decrease anxiety and stress levels, which in turn reduces high blood pressure, pain levels, depression and more. Meditation can enable the body to change the fight or flight response, which is so often the ongoing result of trauma, and refocus on healing from the dis-ease state.

But how do you get to this place of inner quietness when your mind and body are only present to the turmoil that a cancer diagnosis brings? Is trying to meditate not just an added stress and pressure? At this stage, I would suggest you just put out some exploratory feelers around meditation, opening your mind to the possibility of beginning to practise yourself. No more, no less, just put the thought out there.

If you have read this far and have been tapping along with the exercises in this book, you can take heart, you are already well on your way to finding this healing space. In a very practical way, by tapping through the exercises in this book, you are systematically working through your negative beliefs, thoughts and emotions. Every time you experience a release through your tapping you are one step nearer on this path. I hope you are noticing a change in your stress levels by now.

A controlled study published in 2000 looked at 90 cancer patients who did mindfulness based stress reduction meditation for 7 weeks (A Randomized, Wait-List Controlled Clinical Trial: The Effect of a Mindfulness Meditation-Based Stress Reduction Program on Mood and Symptoms of Stress in Cancer Outpatients Michael Speca, PsyD, Linda E. Carlson, PhD, Eileen Goodey, MSW and Maureen Angen, PhD). They found that people who meditated had 31% lower stress symptoms and 65% less mood disturbance than people who did not meditate.

However, the reality may be that with a cancer diagnosis you may still be thinking thoughts such as:

- **How can I possibly clear my mind of thoughts?**

- **There is so much to think about I can't possibly do it?**
- **It's not possible for me**
- **I'll never do it**

Start tapping there:

Tapping Section: Tapping for inability to meditate

Repeat 3 times while tapping the Karate Chop:

Even though I can't do it I deeply and completely love and accept myself

Eyebrow:	*I can't do it*
Side of Eye:	*It's impossible*
Under Eye:	*I'll never do it*
Under Nose:	*I just can't*
Chin:	*I can't do it*
Collar Bone:	*It's impossible*
Under Arm:	*I'll never do it*
Top of Head:	*I just can't*

Repeat 3 times while tapping the Karate Chop:

Even though I will never be able to clear my mind I deeply and completely love and accept myself

Eyebrow:	*I'll never be able to clear my mind*
Side of Eye:	*I'll never do it*
Under Eye:	*No way*
Under Nose:	*I'll never be able to do it*
Chin:	*I'll never be able to clear my mind*
Collar Bone:	*I'll never do it*
Under Arm:	*No way*
Top of Head:	*I'll never be able to do it*

Repeat 3 times while tapping the Karate Chop:

Even though this is asking the impossible I deeply and completely love and accept myself

Eyebrow:	*It's impossible*

356

Side of Eye:	*Asking too much*
Under Eye:	*It feels impossible*
Under Nose:	*It is too big an ask*
Chin:	*It's impossible*
Collar Bone:	*Asking too much*
Under Arm:	*It feels impossible*
Top of Head:	*It is too big an ask*

Do a few rounds like this to take the edge off the thoughts and then continue:

Repeat 3 times while tapping the Karate Chop:

Even though I will never do it, maybe, I deeply and completely love and accept myself

Eyebrow:	*I'll never do it*
Side of Eye:	*It feels impossible*
Under Eye:	*I can't do it*
Under Nose:	*Yet*
Chin:	*I can't do it*
Collar Bone:	*Maybe*
Under Arm:	*Maybe I can*
Top of Head:	*What if I can*

Repeat 3 times while tapping the Karate Chop:

Even though I can't do it yet I deeply and completely love and accept myself

Eyebrow:	*I can't do it*
Side of Eye:	*Yet*
Under Eye:	*I can't do it*
Under Nose:	*Not yet*
Chin:	*This frustration*
Collar Bone:	*I can't do it yet*
Under Arm:	*Maybe*
Top of Head:	*Maybe I can*

Repeat 3 times while tapping the Karate Chop:

Even though it feels impossible I am open to the possibility and I deeply and completely love and accept myself

Eyebrow:	*I am open to the possibility that I can learn a new skill*
Side of Eye:	*I am open to the possibility that I can do it*
Under Eye:	*No, I can't*
Under Nose:	*Yes I can*
Chin:	*It still feels impossible*
Collar Bone:	*Maybe, maybe not*
Under Arm:	*I am open to the possibility that I can do it*
Top of Head:	*I am open to that possibility*

Now tune in with your thoughts around meditating and notice what has changed. You may need to do a few rounds. Remember, I am not asking you to be an instantly expert meditator, just open to the possibility that you can allow yourself a little time out to have a go.

There are many different types of meditation and I am not an expert. My aim is to offer you a starting point which, if you enjoy the experience, you can take further for yourself, maybe by joining a class, or by reading up on the different forms of meditative artistry. My intention is to open the door to meditation for you, to set you on an exploratory path, and to inspire you. However, meditation does not suit everyone, and if it is not for you then that is OK too.

For me, the following method is the easiest.

'From within or from behind, a light shines through us upon things, and makes us aware that we are nothing, but the light is all.'
Ralph Waldo Emerson

- Make yourself comfortable, preferably sitting on the floor supported by cushions. Make sure you are warm enough, sitting still can quickly lower your body temperature.

- Invest in a beautiful candle, possibly scented, and place it in the space in front of you.

- Light the candle and turn your focus towards the flame.

- Watch it move, flicker, change.

- Whenever you notice your thoughts wandering away from the flame observe them and bring your attention back to the flame itself.

- Allow yourself to be drawn into the energy of the light, feel yourself bathed in its purity.

- Continue focussing on the light itself for as long as feels comfortable for you – initially this may only be a few minutes and that is fine.

358

- When you feel ready to end your meditation, thank the flame for its healing qualities and return to the room.

How do you feel? What was that like? Did you notice any particular thoughts or feelings? Initially, that place of stillness and being fully present to yourself may bring up some emotional discomfort. If it does, tap as follows:

Tapping Section: Tapping for discomfort about meditating

Repeat 3 times while tapping the Karate Chop:

Even though I feel X I deeply and completely love and accept myself

Eyebrow:	*Feeling X*
Side of Eye:	*Feeling X*
Under Eye:	*Feeling X*
Under Nose:	*Feeling X*
Chin:	*Feeling X*
Collar Bone:	*Feeling X*
Under Arm:	*Feeling X*
Top of Head:	*Feeling X*

The more you practice this meditation, the calmer and more peaceful you will become, even when dealing with the maelstrom of cancer treatment.

Meditation and pain management
A new study examining the perception of pain and the effects of various mental training techniques has found that relatively short and simple mindfulness meditation training can have a significant positive effect on pain management. The research is by UNC Charlotte psychologists Fadel Zeidan, Nakia S. Gordon, Junaid Merchant and Paula Goolkasian.

> *'Turning off the "thought factory" is the ultimate ideal of meditation'.*
> *George Jelinek*

When you are completely focused concentrating on a task, then thinking is usually absent. You are in a trance or meditative state. Remember being completely absorbed in your favourite book, or piece of music. Someone can come into the room and talk to you and you may not even notice, you are so focused on your inner experience of that book or music.

The purpose is one of observation, watching yourself, your mind, your emotions, your body, your environment, without reacting to what you observe. This is likely to be quite challenging for people who have cancer, particularly at the beginning of your journey, but it is still worth having a go. When you can sit with your emotions you will notice that they pass through you, that whilst they are there in the moment, they are transient.

This experience allows you to take back your power around your emotional state. Emotions are not your enemy, even if they sometimes feel like it, they are there to let you know something is going on for you, and they will move through you. They are on your side, being there to look after you and protect you, however unlikely that may seem right now.

Excuses not to meditate, not to sit, not to have time, not to be comfortable, all these will arise at first – these are all good tapping material!

Tapping Section: Tapping for beliefs about meditating

Repeat 3 times while tapping the Karate Chop:

Even though I don't have the time to meditate I deeply and completely love and accept myself

Eyebrow:	*I don't have the time*
Side of Eye:	*I'm too busy*
Under Eye:	*I have too much on already*
Under Nose:	*I just don't have the time*
Chin:	*I don't have the time*
Collar Bone:	*I'm too busy*
Under Arm:	*I have too much on already*
Top of Head:	*I just don't have the time*

Is that true? In essence what you are saying here is you don't have time for you. What does that feel like?

Continue:

Repeat 3 times while tapping the Karate Chop:

Even though I don't have time to meditate, maybe, I deeply and completely love and accept myself

Eyebrow:	*I don't have the time*
Side of Eye:	*There is never enough time*
Under Eye:	*Not enough time*
Under Nose:	*Maybe*
Chin:	*Maybe I do*
Collar Bone:	*I choose to find the time to meditate easily*
Under Arm:	*I am open to that possibility*
Top of Head:	*I choose to find time easily now*

Repeat 3 times while tapping the Karate Chop:

Even though I don't have time for me I deeply and completely love and accept myself

Eyebrow:	*I don't have the time for me*
Side of Eye:	*No time for me*
Under Eye:	*I don't have any time for me*
Under Nose:	*Just no time for me*
Chin:	*I don't have the time for me*
Collar Bone:	*No time for me*
Under Arm:	*I don't have any time for me*
Top of Head:	*Just no time for me*

Repeat 3 times while tapping the Karate Chop:

Even though there is never enough time I deeply and completely love and accept myself

Eyebrow:	*Never enough time*
Side of Eye:	*Not enough time*
Under Eye:	*Never enough time*
Under Nose:	*Not enough time*
Chin:	*No time*
Collar Bone:	*Not enough time*
Under Arm:	*Never enough time for me*
Top of Head:	*Maybe*

Jo's story

I met Jo in my practice at Breast Cancer Haven. She came to see me for help with stress management as she was dealing with returning to a full time job very quickly after surgery, and whilst undergoing chemotherapy. Her office mates were very supportive of her, but she was putting herself under enormous pressure to prove that she was still capable of doing all her work – and more. Reducing her workload and taking time out didn't seem like an option for her so I taught her how to tap on the physiological effects of the pressure she was putting herself under (she reported feeling on edge, her blood pressure was high, she was unable to settle). In fact, she was the least likely candidate to meditate!

I had two sessions with Jo, and she used the tapping effectively to lower her physical stress responses. However, she was still operating at a high rate of anxiety and pressure.

At Breast Cancer Haven, Caroline Hoffman runs regular group Mindfulness sessions and it was suggested that Jo attend these. She made the commitment (with a lot of tapping on guilt and responsibility) to do one of Caroline's eight

361

week courses. I bumped into Jo at reception recently and she looked totally different, she seemed lighter and happier despite the fact that she was still having chemotherapy and she had lost her hair. When I asked her how she had been getting on she said that she was 'in love' with mindfulness. She made space to practice for a short time every day, and she had noticed dramatic reduction in her stress levels. In fact, everyone had commented on the changes in her.

It helps to meditate at a regular, pre-selected time and place. But any time is better than no time, and anywhere is better that nowhere! Just give it a go – you might enjoy it! You may find it good to meditate with your friends or family, in a small group with the sole purpose of just being.

We will look into other ways of supporting those who are supporting you on your journey in the next chapter.

CHAPTER 23

SUPPORTING FAMILY AND FRIENDS

'Families are like fudge - mostly sweet with a few nuts.'
Author Unknown

Inevitably a cancer diagnosis is going to be traumatic for those close to you, in particular your family and your friends and any children involved. Often they will feel useless, unable to help. All they can do is watch, and possibly take you to hospital appointments. They can't take an active part in your healing process. At least that may be their belief. It can be much harder to see someone you love suffering than to suffer yourself.

I find that very often, by teaching the tapping to your family and friends, regardless of age or relationship, you introduce them to a way to ease their own feelings. As they address these issues for themselves, it paves the way for everybody to work together to support themselves, you, and each other – all coming from the same healing place.

There are likely to be a number of different issues showing up for those close to you, some of which they may be afraid to share with you. There may be some of the similar fears that you have been going through:

- **Fear of the diagnosis**
- **Fear of the cancer**
- **Fear of how the future will be**
- **Fear of losing you**
- **Not understanding**
- **Not having the medical knowledge**
- **Feeling inadequate**
- **and that is just for starters.**

First of all, working with the adults around you, work through each of those issues with them, or give them the pages of this book and suggest they work through each of the areas that are relevant to them. Explain to them exactly how to do this, maybe even get them to photocopy the exercise pages of this book. If you initiate doing this work with them, or suggest that this book might help them as well, you are acknowledging their feelings and challenges, giving them permission to feel the way they're feeling, and being with them as they express them. Obviously, this may also be very emotional for you, so please remember to tap along on any emotions as they come up. This is such a bonding process for any relationship, tapping together.

Either sit with them and tap along with them or let them tap on their own. Either way, quickly you will notice a change, a strengthening of your relationship with that person, and also a change in the way they are around you and how they cope with your diagnosis and your treatment.

Candy's story in her words

I found that my cancer had become the elephant in the room. We were all carefully stepping around it, occasionally playing lip service to it when it demanded we bumped into it via a hospital visit, but otherwise we had our heads very firmly in the sand. It wasn't that we didn't want to talk about it, it was that we simply didn't know how. My husband and friends were anxious about upsetting me and didn't want to add their stress to my already, in their minds, overloaded system. I could see how stressed they were and felt totally disempowered by their continual attempts to reassure me that they were 'fine'. For all of us, the pressure of the unspoken gained momentum until I finally exploded at them. Having subsequently discovered the tapping, I can see how easily we might have avoided reaching to this point had we been able to work through our fears of communicating how we felt to each other.

I am through my treatment now, and although I only discovered your work towards the end of my chemotherapy I just want to say how grateful I am for the tapping tools and how I intend for them to become part of my life, with or without dis-ease. I tell all my friends about them and teach anyone who will let me! I may have to tap on my fears of becoming evangelical!
Thank you, thank you!
Candy

So if you too feel like you have an elephant in the room and don't know what to do about it tap as follows:

Tapping Section: Tapping for the elephant in the room

Repeat 3 times while tapping the Karate Chop:

Even though there is this elephant in the room I deeply and completely love and accept myself

Eyebrow:	*The elephant in the room*
Side of Eye:	*Elephant in the room emotions*
Under Eye:	*The elephant in the room*
Under Nose:	*Elephant in the room emotions*
Chin:	*The elephant in the room*
Collar Bone:	*Elephant in the room emotions*
Under Arm:	*The elephant in the room*
Top of Head:	*Elephant in the room emotions*

Repeat 3 times while tapping the Karate Chop:

Even though I am too scared to start a conversation I deeply and completely love and accept myself

Eyebrow:	*Fear of talking about it*

364

Side of Eye:	*Fear of starting a conversation*
Under Eye:	*Fear of talking about it*
Under Nose:	*Fear of starting a conversation*
Chin:	*Fear of talking about it*
Collar Bone:	*Fear of starting a conversation*
Under Arm:	*Fear of talking about it*
Top of Head:	*Fear of starting a conversation*

Repeat 3 times while tapping the Karate Chop:

Even though I don't know how to begin I deeply and completely love and accept myself

Eyebrow:	*I don't know how to begin*
Side of Eye:	*Not knowing how to start*
Under Eye:	*I just don't know how to*
Under Nose:	*I don't know how to begin*
Chin:	*I don't know how to begin*
Collar Bone:	*Not knowing how to start*
Under Arm:	*I just don't know how to*
Top of Head:	*I don't know how to begin*

Repeat 3 times while tapping the Karate Chop:

Even though I am scared of upsetting him/her I deeply and completely love and accept myself

Eyebrow:	*Fear of upsetting him/her*
Side of Eye:	*What if I upset him/her*
Under Eye:	*He/she is dealing with so much already*
Under Nose:	*What if I make it worse?*
Chin:	*Fear of upsetting him/her*
Collar Bone:	*What if I upset him/her?*
Under Arm:	*He/she is dealing with so much already*
Top of Head:	*What if I make it worse?*

Continue:

Eyebrow:	*I am open to the possibility that talking might help*
Side of Eye:	*I am open to that possibility*
Under Eye:	*What if I upset him/her?*
Under Nose:	*What if I don't?*
Chin:	*I am open to the possibility that talking might help*
Collar Bone:	*I am open to that possibility*
Under Arm:	*What if I upset him/her?*
Top of Head:	*What if I don't?*

Check in and see how you feel about the possibility of addressing that elephant now. If there is still a high intensity, continue tapping, noticing where you feel it in your body and what the specific emotion is:

Tapping Section: Tapping for fear of discussing cancer

Repeat 3 times while tapping the Karate Chop:

Even though I have this talking fear in my throat I deeply and completely love and accept myself

Eyebrow:	*Fear in my throat*
Side of Eye:	*Talking fear in my throat*
Under Eye:	*Fear in my throat*
Under Nose:	*Talking fear in my throat*
Chin:	*I can't do it*
Collar Bone:	*I can do it*
Under Arm:	*Remaining fear in my throat*
Top of Head:	*Remaining talking fear in my throat*

When you feel OK about the idea of talking to your family or friends, run a few conversations through your head, imagine the response you are getting, and notice whether anything triggers any more intensity for you. If it does, continue to tap and release it.

Tapping with Children

'If children have the ability to ignore all odds and percentages, then maybe we can all learn from them. When you think about it, what other choice is there but to hope? We have two options, medically and emotionally: give up, or fight like hell.'
Lance Armstrong

Do you have children? How old are they? Maybe they are too young to know exactly what is going on or what a cancer diagnosis is. They may not have the fear of cancer that an adult has, simply because they do not have the information and the knowledge, but they **will** know that you are not feeling great, that you may be losing your hair, maybe you have had surgery, maybe you have got burn marks from radiotherapy. They will notice that everything isn't as normal.

Do not underestimate the intuition of a child, however small he or she is. They pick up on the most subtle nuances and whilst your desire will be to protect them, the best way to do that is to give them some carefully selected truths so that they feel included and comforted. Children are far more resilient than we often give them credit for, and when communicated with honestly you will find that, whilst they may be upset, they will deal with the situation far more easily that if they had been left to guess at what is going on at home.

Children love constancy, they thrive on consistency and routine. So it is more than likely that, even if you don't think they are being affected by your illness, they will have picked up on something not being right. If you haven't spoken to them it is important to find a way to do so, and to teach them to tap on anything that worries them. Keep it very simple and straightforward.

Tap before you talk in order to clear your own emotions around the conversation. Trust in your child's ability to deal with this, knowing he/she has your support and openness. Encourage questions, and share your feelings and thoughts with them too. Not only will this be bonding, but it will also help both of you deal with a difficult time ahead during your treatment and recovery.

Sarah's story
Sarah brought 4 year old Evie to meet me because she wanted to meet 'the tapping lady'! Sarah had introduced Evie to tapping as a way of including her in her breast cancer journey. Sarah was already familiar with the tapping techniques as we had started working together early on in her diagnosis. At my suggestion she had taught them to Evie, partly to help her with the household changes that the cancer brought, and partly because she had just started primary school and Sarah felt that any tool would be useful.

However, she really hadn't expected Evie to become so enthralled with the technique! Evie turned out to be a fabulous tapper! She tapped on her mum, her toys, and also her school friends. She had taught her class to tap and at 4 years old had already given a demonstration of the tapping in the school assembly! No fear of public speaking there!! And she is even cool with 'I deeply and completely love and accept myself' although she insisted on adding and Mummy and Daddy and X and X – a long list of other people she thought needed help! She was such a cutie! We need more Evie's in this world.

To me, this was a wonderful example of how children are uncluttered by negative judgments. To Evie, this was something that made her feel better and she wanted everyone else to feel better too, including her mum.

Teach your children, however little, letting go of any investment in whether they use it or not. It is a beautiful gift to offer them, and I wonder how different the world would be were all primary school children to be taught to tap as part of the curriculum.

'We worry about what a child will become tomorrow, yet we forget that he is someone today.'
Stacia Tauscher

367

When you're too tired
The chances are that the most obvious impact on your child will be your feeling too tired or ill to do everything you did before you had cancer. You may have lower energy levels at the moment. Don't pretend this isn't happening, don't treat him/her as though they don't exist. Explain this to them and let them know that you hope it won't last for too long. Either tap on them, or with them. Get them to tell you about their day, tapping at the same time. Turn this into quality time together.

Adapt your Set Up Statement to language better suited to your child's age. I have offered a few ideas in the following tapping rounds, but change them to meet your child's needs.

Tapping Section: Tapping for children's feelings

Repeat 3 times while tapping the Karate Chop:

Even though Mummy is too tired to help me do this at the moment she loves me anyway

Eyebrow:	*Mummy is too tired*
Side of Eye:	*She can't help me*
Under Eye:	*I want her to help me*
Under Nose:	*I need her to help me*
Chin:	*Sad because Mummy is too tired*
Collar Bone:	*Feeling sad*
Under Arm:	*She can't help me*
Top of Head:	*I want her to help me*

Repeat 3 times while tapping the Karate Chop:

Even though I am worried I am a good kid

Eyebrow:	*Feeling worried*
Side of Eye:	*Feeling worried*
Under Eye:	*Feeling worried*
Under Nose:	*Feeling worried*
Chin:	*Feeling worried*
Collar Bone:	*Feeling worried*
Under Arm:	*Feeling worried*
Top of Head:	*Feeling worried*

Repeat 3 times while tapping the Karate Chop:

Even though I feel sad I am a great kid

Eyebrow:	*Feeling sad*
Side of Eye:	*Feeling sad*
Under Eye:	*Feeling sad*
Under Nose:	*Feeling sad*
Chin:	*Feeling sad*
Collar Bone:	*Feeling sad*
Under Arm:	*Feeling sad*
Top of Head:	*Feeling sad*

Repeat 3 times while tapping the Karate Chop:

Even though Mum is ill and I am scared I am OK

Eyebrow:	*Feeling scared*
Side of Eye:	*Feeling scared*
Under Eye:	*Feeling scared*
Under Nose:	*Feeling scared*
Chin:	*Feeling scared*
Collar Bone:	*Feeling scared*
Under Arm:	*Feeling scared*
Top of Head:	*Feeling scared*

Repeat 3 times while tapping the Karate Chop:

Even though Dad hasn't got the energy for a long game of football I am cool

Eyebrow:	*Dad's tired*
Side of Eye:	*He hasn't got enough energy*
Under Eye:	*Dad's tired*
Under Nose:	*I want him to play with me*
Chin:	*Sad because he can't*
Collar Bone:	*Cross because he can't*
Under Arm:	*Dad being tired feelings*
Top of Head:	*Dad being tired feelings*

There is an excellent book for children called "The Rainbow Feelings of Cancer" by Carrie Martin and Chia Martin, which can be a very useful bridge to explaining cancer to young children.

Tapping with teenagers

'Don't laugh at a youth for his affectations; he is only trying on one face after another to find a face of his own.'
Logan Pearsall Smith, "Age and Death," Afterthoughts, 1931

Teenagers can react unpredictably to life generally, and often can be very angry when they first hear the news: angry at the world, angry at the parent who is ill, angry at the parent who is healthy, somehow trying to find a way of explaining it to themselves, making it make sense and dealing with their fears and worries.

Others will take on the mantle of carer and try and take responsibility for nursing you. They may become clingy. However they react is OK, you need to encourage them to either tap with you or on their own. If they are really not open to the idea all you can do is offer the tapping to them as a tool to support themselves with. You may need to tap on yourself to deal with any adverse reactions.

The following are a few suggestions of possible tapping protocols for your teenager. As always, adapt them to suit the mood and personality of the individual. Obviously, the rounds above will also be suitable for everybody.

Tapping Section: Tapping for teenagers' feelings

Repeat 3 times while tapping the Karate Chop:

Even though I am really pissed off with this I am cool

Eyebrow:	*Feeling really pissed off*
Side of Eye:	*I am really pissed off about this*
Under Eye:	*Feeling really pissed off*
Under Nose:	*I am really pissed off about this*
Chin:	*Feeling really pissed off*
Collar Bone:	*I am really pissed off about this*
Under Arm:	*Feeling really pissed off*
Top of Head:	*I am really pissed off about this*

Repeat 3 times while tapping the Karate Chop:

Even though it's getting in the way of my life I am OK

Eyebrow:	*This irritation*
Side of Eye:	*Interrupting my life*

370

Under Eye:	It isn't fair
Under Nose:	I don't want him/her to be ill
Chin:	This irritation
Collar Bone:	Interrupting my life
Under Arm:	It isn't fair
Top of Head:	I don't want him/her to be ill

Just let him/her say it as it is, whatever you might feel about it. Talk to your children and teach them to tap at the same time, so they can tap and say whatever it is that they need to say, no matter how negative it is.

Once those around you accept the tapping as a way of managing their emotional state and also supporting your healing process, the dynamics in the household will change, everything will seem more peaceful and easier and you may find that your relationship with your family improves substantially. Likewise your friends will respond to your diagnosis in different ways. Whilst they will all be concerned for you, some may not want to step in too close, others won't know how to deal with it at all. If at all possible, teach them to tap with you. You can introduce them to it by something like, "*I know this must be difficult for you but have a go at the tapping, I find it really useful to help me calm down*". Even just having them tap with you whilst you talk will be therapeutic to both of you.

Cass's story

Cass had a teenage daughter who had become increasingly difficult and distant during her cancer diagnosis and treatment. Whichever way she approached it Cass was having problems communicating with her. Nothing seemed to be getting through and her daughter was just incredibly hostile all the time for no obvious reason. So Cass started off by doing a bit of tapping on her own about how she felt about this:

Tapping Section: Tapping for teenagers' communication

Repeat 3 times while tapping the Karate Chop:

Even though she won't communicate I deeply and completely love and accept myself

Eyebrow:	She won't communicate
Side of Eye:	She just won't communicate
Under Eye:	Why won't she communicate?
Under Nose:	She just won't communicate
Chin:	She won't communicate
Collar Bone:	She just won't communicate
Under Arm:	Why won't she communicate?
Top of Head:	She just won't communicate

Repeat 3 times while tapping the Karate Chop:

Even though I'm losing her I deeply and completely love and accept myself

Eyebrow:	*I'm losing her*
Side of Eye:	*I'm really losing her*
Under Eye:	*I'm losing her*
Under Nose:	*I'm really losing her*
Chin:	*I'm losing her*
Collar Bone:	*I'm really losing her*
Under Arm:	*I'm losing her*
Top of Head:	*I'm really losing her*

Repeat 3 times while tapping the Karate Chop:

Even though I feel really sad I deeply and completely love and accept myself

Eyebrow:	*I feel really sad*
Side of Eye:	*This sadness*
Under Eye:	*Feeling, really sad*
Under Nose:	*This sadness*
Chin:	*I feel really sad*
Collar Bone:	*This sadness*
Under Arm:	*Feeling really sad*
Top of Head:	*This sadness*

Repeat 3 times while tapping the Karate Chop:

Even though I feel so hurt I deeply and completely   love and accept myself

Eyebrow:	*This hurt*
Side of Eye:	*This deep hurt*
Under Eye:	*This hurt*
Under Nose:	*This deep hurt*
Chin:	*This hurt*
Collar Bone:	*This deep hurt*
Under Arm:	*This hurt*
Top of Head:	*This deep hurt*

Having cleared her own feelings, and being a little bit more relaxed, Cass also changed her energy around her daughter. She decided to, very tentatively, speak to her again and approach the fact that maybe they could speak and tap together. Her daughter was aware of the tapping although she thought it was very 'un cool'.

So Cass sat down one evening after supper and started a conversation, along the lines of 'I know you must be finding this really tough, I know that you are cross with me for having cancer'. As she was speaking, she was tapping on herself. Whilst her daughter didn't actually tap, she began to release some of her emotions around the cancer and to acknowledge them: 'Yes I am very angry, I'm not meant to be, I'm not allowed to be, everybody says I have to be so supportive and it's all about you. But what about me? I don't know how to handle it and feel out of my depth'.

As they continued to talk, and Cass continued to tap on herself, her daughter visibly relaxed and was able to voice all sorts of concerns and fears that up until now she had been bottling up inside.

Notice that Cass' daughter never actually tapped for herself and maybe she doesn't need to. Maybe Cass tapping and allowing her to open the conversation in an unthreatening manner and in a straightforward sense, opened enough doors for her daughter to be able to deal with the situation in a different way. Certainly, since then their communication has increased enormously and they have a much closer and more open relationship. Her daughter has even gone with Cass to a couple of her chemotherapy treatments.

Tapping protocols for loved ones
The following are a number of tapping protocols which may be suitable for spouses, children, parents and friends. Please adapt them to match your own needs, they are just examples.

Tapping Section: Tapping suggestions for loved ones

Repeat 3 times while tapping the Karate Chop:

Even though I feel helpless I deeply and completely love and accept myself

Eyebrow:	*Feeling helpless*
Side of Eye:	*Feeling helpless*
Under Eye:	*Helpless*
Under Nose:	*Feeling helpless*
Chin:	*Feeling helpless*
Collar Bone:	*Feeling helpless*
Under Arm:	*Helpless*
Top of Head:	*Feeling helpless*

Repeat 3 times while tapping the Karate Chop:

Even though I can't bear to see him/her so ill I deeply and completely love and accept myself

Eyebrow:	*I can't bear to see X so ill*
Side of Eye:	*I can't handle it*
Under Eye:	*I don't know what to do*
Under Nose:	*How to help*
Chin:	*I can't bear to see X so ill*
Collar Bone:	*I can't handle it*
Under Arm:	*I don't know what to do*
Top of Head:	*How to help*

Repeat 3 times while tapping the Karate Chop:

Even though I feel so frightened I deeply and completely love and accept myself

Eyebrow:	*This fear*
Side of Eye:	*This fear*
Under Eye:	*Fear of X*
Under Nose:	*Fear of X*
Chin:	*This fear*
Collar Bone:	*This fear*
Under Arm:	*Fear of X*
Top of Head:	*Fear of X*

Repeat 3 times while tapping the Karate Chop:

Even though I don't understand why X is so ill I deeply and completely love and accept myself

Eyebrow:	*I don't understand what is happening*
Side of Eye:	*I don't understand*
Under Eye:	*I don't know what is happening*
Under Nose:	*I don't understand*
Chin:	*I don't understand what is happening*
Collar Bone:	*I don't understand*
Under Arm:	*I don't know what is happening*
Top of Head:	*I don't understand*

374

Repeat 3 times while tapping the Karate Chop:

Even though I feel sad I deeply and completely love and accept myself

Eyebrow:	*Feeling sad*
Side of Eye:	*Feeling sad*
Under Eye:	*Feeling sad*
Under Nose:	*Feeling sad*
Chin:	*Feeling sad*
Collar Bone:	*Feeling sad*
Under Arm:	*Feeling sad*
Top of Head:	*Feeling sad*

Repeat 3 times while tapping the Karate Chop:

Even though I feel useless, I can't do anything to help I deeply and completely love and accept myself

Eyebrow:	*Feeling useless*
Side of Eye:	*Feeling useless*
Under Eye:	*Can't help X*
Under Nose:	*Can't help X*
Chin:	*Feeling useless*
Collar Bone:	*Can't help X*
Under Arm:	*Feeling useless*
Top of Head:	*Can't help X*

Repeat 3 times while tapping the Karate Chop:

Even though I feel desperate I deeply and completely love and accept myself

Eyebrow:	*Feeling desperate*
Side of Eye:	*This desperation*
Under Eye:	*Feeling desperate*
Under Nose:	*This desperation*
Chin:	*Feeling desperate*
Collar Bone:	*This desperation*
Under Arm:	*Feeling desperate*
Top of Head:	*This desperation*

375

As human beings we are naturally sociable and the support of the group, be it family, friends or colleagues, is of great importance and healing value. Those around you will benefit from the tapping as much as you, and what a fabulous gift to share with them!

The penultimate chapter next looks at when, for whatever reason, living is no longer an option. Regardless of whether you are in this final stage or not, it is an important chapter to tap through as it will help alleviate those hidden fears we all have: fear of dying, fear of the unknown and so on. It is also written for those who are caring for their loved ones at the end of their life, to help them release their fears and experience a peaceful end to this period of their lives.

CHAPTER 24

WHEN LIFE IS NO LONGER AN OPTION

'For what is it to die,
But to stand in the sun and melt into the wind?'
Kahlil Gibran, from 'The Prophet'

Before we even begin to explore the subject of death, and the possibility of dying from cancer or of witnessing a loved one dying, let's do some tapping. The very word 'death' will bring up a spectrum of different emotions for people, depending on their particular beliefs and spiritual path.

Tapping Section: Tapping for feelings about death

Repeat 3 times while tapping the Karate Chop:

Even though that word makes me feel X I deeply and completely love and accept myself

Eyebrow:	*That word*
Side of Eye:	*Feeling X*
Under Eye:	*That word*
Under Nose:	*Death*
Chin:	*That word*
Collar Bone:	*How it makes me feel*
Under Arm:	*That word*
Top of Head:	*Death*

Repeat 3 times while tapping the Karate Chop:

Even though there is something about that word that makes me X I deeply and completely love and accept myself

Eyebrow:	*This X*
Side of Eye:	*This X*
Under Eye:	*Feeling X*
Under Nose:	*Feeling X*
Chin:	*This X*
Collar Bone:	*This X*

Under Arm:	*Feeling X*
Top of Head:	*Feeling X*

Repeat 3 times while tapping the Karate Chop:

Even though I have these death emotions I deeply and completely love and accept myself

Eyebrow:	*Death emotions*
Side of Eye:	*Death emotions*
Under Eye:	*Death emotions*
Under Nose:	*Death emotions*
Chin:	*Death emotions*
Collar Bone:	*Death emotions*
Under Arm:	*Death emotions*
Top of Head:	*Death emotions*

Say the word aloud – 'Death' – what happens in your body?

Repeat 3 times while tapping the Karate Chop:

Even though I have this death fear in my stomach I deeply and completely love and accept myself

Eyebrow:	*Death fear in my stomach*
Side of Eye:	*Death fear in my stomach*
Under Eye:	*Death fear in my stomach*
Under Nose:	*Death fear in my stomach*
Chin:	*Death fear in my stomach*
Collar Bone:	*Death fear in my stomach*
Under Arm:	*Death fear in my stomach*
Top of Head:	*Death fear in my stomach*

Continue to tap until you can think about death and dying without a strong emotional or physical response. For some people, this may take a number of rounds, sometimes over a period of days. If you have a very strong response to the concept of death and dying, do a little tapping at a time, easing your way into working through this safely and gently. Take care of yourself!

From the heart of a witness
As I begin to write this chapter, I am wary of the arrogance of intruding on this most intimate and personal time, the end of life. I cannot pretend to know how it feels, or what it is like, to be facing one's death. However, I have had the

privilege of accompanying a few people on this last stage of their human journey and it is from that place that I offer this chapter, from the place of a witness.

Healing from cancer is not always about living. This is a very difficult topic to face for some. In my experience in the therapeutic world, working in this area, I have learned that we need to respect the patient's individual journey, putting our own need for a particular outcome to one side. Whilst I used to want a happy ending, according to my terms, for my clients I have realised that this only served to get in the way of the work we were doing and that my 'agenda' was not relevant.

With the tapping, it is possible for you to guide your own process, not as an onlooker but as an active participant, be that preparing for death, releasing resentments, angers, fears in that particular area, enhancing your own spiritual beliefs or looking to a positive future.

A positive future may well be a positive future in a different life, a different world, depending on your beliefs and culture. It is not for me, or anyone else to intrude here. The important thing about this is that you strengthen your own beliefs in a way that works for you.

If your cancer is leading towards death, you have the opportunity to allow that transition to be as peaceful and as beautiful as it is possible for it to be, not only for you but for those around you as well. You can support yourself by clearing your fears, your anxieties, your angers, any blocking thoughts towards this in order to reach a peaceful conclusion to this life, if that is what is appropriate for you at this point.

Death is the one thing that is going to happen to everyone. It is life's only certainty. All of us are going to experience dying at some stage, whether it is now, in ten years, in fifty years. So this work is very important, wherever you are at, whether you have cancer or not, whether you are completely healthy with no shadow of death on the horizon, or otherwise. It doesn't matter, this is a very healthy way of preparing yourself for the inevitable path that we are all on in this life.

We have already worked directly with the fear of death in earlier chapters. This chapter is mainly written for those who are with their loved ones at this final stage of life, to help them support them and care for them in a very beautiful, but also practical way.

Trite though it may sound, tapping seems to be a very valuable tool during this important transition from life to death. Start by working with any immediate fears of death, the unknown etc. Here we are working towards acceptance and a state of inner peace, which is beautiful to observe. Your role is merely to accompany the person on their soul's journey, preparing them as they place their trust in a Higher Self, whatever form that might take, and helping them let go of their physical being as they face the inevitability of death.

In my opinion, and in my experience, this can be where the tapping is at its most pure, gently removing any remaining unspoken obstacles and allowing the patient to 'be', accepting their spiritual self.

Your role here is one of facilitator, merely to be there, gently tapping on their finger points. The power of the soft physical touch at this point is reassuring and is all that is needed, words no longer play a part. Allow yourself to be a bridge between this world and the next, whatever and wherever that is.

There are no tapping protocols specifically applicable here, although clearly any fears should be tapped with, but at this point it is simply a case of gentle contact and finger tapping as much as feels comforting. Hopefully, pain relief will be being expertly managed, but tapping to reduce pain and discomfort can also help.

However, in essence, just being there and tapping is enough now. If anyone needs to talk, tapping at the same time is very calming and reassuring.

Some thoughts about death

'I am convinced that we do more harm by avoiding the issue (terminal illness) than by using the time and timing to sit, listen, and share.'
Elisabeth Kubler Ross

Elisabeth Kübler Ross is renowned worldwide for her psychological model of the five stages of grief. She offers an easy-to-understand framework for the stages of grief experienced during the dying process (as well as being applicable to other traumatic events). It is an extremely valuable insight into the mindset and emotions surrounding death and bereavement and I offer it here as a means of recognising 'normal' emotions and behaviours during this time.

Elisabeth Kübler Ross died in 2004. Her gravestone reads 'Graduated to Dance in the Galaxies'. Her spirit lives on in the EKR Foundation, www.ekrfoundation.org

Stage 1   Denial
Stage 2   Anger
Stage 3   Bargaining
Stage 4   Depression
Stage 5   Acceptance

The final stage of acceptance, and self-acceptance, is the intended destination of all therapeutic work, in one sense or another. It is very much a concept in evidence with the tapping right from the beginning, with its inclusion in the default affirmation repeated throughout this book, I deeply and completely love and accept myself.

By working through our fears, angers, and resentments, we are able to reach the space where we can love and accept ourselves, even in death. When we have true self acceptance, it brings with it a sense of peace and understanding of ourselves and our role in the bigger scheme of life.

'I do not want the peace which passeth understanding, I want the understanding which bringeth peace'
Helen Keller

Anna's story
At this point I want to introduce you to Dr Anna Donald, who I had the privilege to get to know through our work together. Anna's journey with cancer has been well documented, including a fantastic log for the British Medical Journal.

It is with kind permission of her husband Michael that I talk about Anna here because her journey to dying from metastatic breast cancer was inspirational to us all. I honestly think I can say that I have never met anyone quite like Anna, she was more than beautiful, she was brilliant, she was intelligent and yet she had this childlike joy and excitement around her. She achieved some amazing things in her life and yet was completely natural and unaffected by all the glory that surrounded her. In August 2008, Anna had an article published in the Australian Good Weekend magazine and I would just like to quote from that article a couple of things that she says:

> *"On Tuesday February 27th 2007, today I learn that I am riddled with cancer, it's everywhere, lungs, bones, liver maybe brain, there is more cancer than me, how could this have happened so fast and how did I not know about it*
>
> *Evening*
>
> *'I cried with my husband behind the curtain now wrapped around my hospital bed, just then my brother and business partner walked in, two tall men pink cheeked and cheery from having walked the winter streets, we told them the news, my brother sank to his knees on the linoleum by my bed, no hope, no cure no possibility at all, he couldn't take it in, he put his head in his hands.*
>
> *My business partner, a doctor, still in his coat bundled me into his arms and wept. I felt so loved and so grief stricken at that moment with three men in the world who mean so much to me, the registrar slipped away, after a day of cacophony all the noises in the room stopped except for the sound of us sobbing. But after that initial burst of intense grief, something entirely unexpected happened the next morning. It was the weirdest experience, Anna recalls, we cried a lot, I had gone to sleep and the next morning I woke up and it was a beautiful Spring morning, looking over Hampstead Heath as clear as anything and all I could feel was 'I'm going to die and I'm totally loved and looked after and this is completely fine". Not only was I fine but I knew that absolutely everyone else was too.'*

I ask you to hear Anna's words and her remarkable acceptance of what was to follow. She actually lived for another two years after that and during that time made a massive impact upon everyone she came across, as she had throughout her life. She made her cancer an adventure. She wrote a letter to her old friend Dr Richard Smith saying:

"It's so interesting, this is the most interesting part of my life by miles so far".

She reframed her cancer as the most intensely absorbing research project of her life and that attitude held right up until the day that she died.

Anna's question *'How did I not know about I, how could I have been this ill and not know?'* is a question many people ask. Sadly, this seems to be one of the mysteries of cancer, that it can become life threatening before we are even aware of its existence. If you find that this is a question that you have asked yourself following a diagnosis, be aware that we don't always know, can't always know, such is the nature of the disease so if you are feeling any of those feelings, blaming yourself, you should have found it earlier or whatever you are feeling, tap as follows

381

Tapping Section: Tapping for not having known about illness

Repeat 3 times while tapping the Karate Chop:

Even though I didn't know, I deeply and completely love and accept myself

Eyebrow:	*I didn't know*
Side of Eye:	*I didn't know*
Under Eye:	*I should have known*
Under Nose:	*I should have known*
Chin:	*How could I not have known*
Collar Bone:	*How could I not have known*
Under Arm:	*Even though I should have known but didn't*
Top of Head:	*I deeply and completely love and accept myself*

Repeat 3 times while tapping the Karate Chop:

Even though I should have known, I deeply and completely love and accept myself

Eyebrow:	*I should have known*
Side of Eye:	*I really should have known*
Under Eye:	*How could I not have known*
Under Nose:	*I should have known*
Chin:	*I didn't know*
Collar Bone:	*I didn't know*
Under Arm:	*Even though I should have known*
Top of Head:	*I deeply and completely love and accept myself.*

Repeat 3 times while tapping the Karate Chop:

Even though I don't know how I couldn't have known, I deeply and completely love and accept myself

Eyebrow:	*How could I not have known?*
Side of Eye:	*I don't know how I couldn't have known*
Under Eye:	*I didn't know*
Under Nose:	*I just didn't know*
Chin:	*I should have known*
Collar Bone:	*How could I have known?*
Under Arm:	*Even though I don't know how I could have known*

Top of Head: *I deeply and completely love and accept myself*

In conclusion, not everyone will have the luxury of time to prepare for dying and death, and that is the way of things. But if you, or your loved one, do have some time to be together on this final piece of your journey in this lifetime, then tapping can be a wonderfully powerful way of enhancing your connection with each other and with the greater system, as well as releasing fears and pain management. It offers everyone involved the opportunity to come together and help the person dying to have a peaceful loving transition from this life.

'Don't cry when the sun is gone, because the tears won't let you see the stars.'
Violeta Parra

CHAPTER 25

THE POWER OF ACCEPTANCE, FORGIVENESS, GRATITUDE AND LOVE

As I think about ending this book, I am struck again by the fact that there is no order in which it needs to be read. This final chapter has a place at the beginning, the middle and the end. I write it here in the hope that you will do as I do when checking out whether a book is of interest to me, and look at both the beginning and the end before reaching a decision to buy it. I wonder whether that is why the final chapter might be called the conclusion. I hope you conclude that this book can help you.

Why have I left what I consider to be the most important chapter till last? I am aware that at the start you might have found these concepts challenging, I am confident that they will resonate with you more strongly now and that you will have already reached these places intuitively. You will already *know* that which I am going to try and put into writing now. You will have already accessed these core states of acceptance, forgiveness, gratitude and love.

One of my hopes in writing this book was to open new doors for you and your healing process by offering you an additional valuable tool and exercises to support yourself through your healing. One of the inevitable bonuses of working with the tapping in the ways described is a stronger understanding of Self, and a reconnection of the body, mind and spirit.

Acceptance

> *'Each day comes bearing its own gifts. Untie the ribbons.'*
> *Ruth Ann Schabacker*

Cancer may be a gift. It is just, as my friend Carol Look so eloquently puts it … in crap wrapping paper! One thing that seems next to impossible is to experience healing from cancer without re-evaluating your life and priorities. For many people, cancer ultimately offers an opportunity to fully embrace life, to change the things that were creating the dis-ease, both internally and externally, and create a fulfilling empowering life with new self values and beliefs, with integrity and love.

This outcome is sown from the beginning in our work with the tapping. The very wording of the Set-Up Statement is designed with this in mind. Say these words aloud:

Even though I have cancer I deeply and completely love and accept myself

What happens? How do you feel emotionally? How do you feel in your body? If you notice any negative response, tap to clear it. What you are saying here, and aiming for, is to love and accept yourself, even with the cancer.

'My cancer scare changed my life. I'm grateful for every new, healthy day I have. It has helped me prioritize my life.'
Olivia Newton-John

Somewhere along your journey, you may have experienced surprising insights and understandings. Many people reach a moment when they seem to understand their cancer, they can acknowledge its message for them, and in doing so, accept its existence in a positive sense. This does not mean they need to keep the cancer, it has merely served as a messenger for something more deep-rooted, and once this message has been understood, it is safe for the messenger to leave.

If, having worked your way through this book, you are still not at ease with the above concept, tap as follows:

Communicate with the cancer, tap on discovering what it wants:

Tapping Section: Tapping for communicating with cancer

Repeat 3 times while tapping the Karate Chop:

Even though I am struggling to understand why I have this cancer I deeply and completely accept myself anyway

Eyebrow:	*I don't understand*
Side of Eye:	*I don't get it*
Under Eye:	*I don't know what it wants for me*
Under Nose:	*I don't know what it is saying to me*
Chin:	*This frustration*
Collar Bone:	*I don't understand*
Under Arm:	*I can't hear it*
Top of Head:	*I don't see it*

Continue:

Eyebrow:	*What if I knew?*
Side of Eye:	*What if it could talk?*
Under Eye:	*What if I understood?*
Under Nose:	*What if I really knew?*
Chin:	*What if I did understand?*
Collar Bone:	*What if I could see it?*
Under Arm:	*What if I did get it?*
Top of Head:	*What if I really understood its message now?*

Eyebrow:	*This remaining frustration*
Side of Eye:	*This remaining not understanding*
Under Eye:	*This remaining frustration*
Under Nose:	*I want to understand*
Chin:	*I want to know*
Collar Bone:	*This remaining frustration*
Under Arm:	*This remaining frustration*
Top of Head:	*I choose to let it go*

Continue:

Eyebrow:	*What if I knew?*
Side of Eye:	*What if it could talk?*
Under Eye:	*What if I understood?*
Under Nose:	*What if I really knew?*
Chin:	*What if I did understand?*
Collar Bone:	*What if I could see it?*
Under Arm:	*What if I did get it?*
Top of Head:	*What if I really understood its message now?*

In the last round, just **guess**... Guessing comes from an inner knowing and is likely to be accurate at some level. One of my students offered me the thought that intuition is actually 'inner tuition', or tuition from within. I believe that to be very true, and the importance of listening to one's intuition in this work must not be underestimated. We do know.... Somewhere. So **GUESS**!

Then tap around on your '**guess**'.

Notice whether any emotions arise as a result of your guess and if so tap around on those as well, assessing them on the 0 to 10 scale and continuing to tap into the intensity is reduced to zero.

Forgiveness

'Forgiving does not erase the bitter past. A healed memory is not a deleted memory. Instead, forgiving what we cannot forget creates a new way to remember. We change the memory of our past into a hope for our future.'
Lewis B. Smedes

The concept of forgiveness is a tricky one, steeped as it is in religious dogma and cultural expectation. Here, I am referring to forgiveness in the role of 'letting go', forgiving self and others for anything you or they may have done which contributed to your dis-ease. This is not forgiveness from a hierarchical perspective, where you are being magnanimous in allowing someone 'off the hook'.

Tapping Section: Tapping for forgiving self

More, I am speaking of forgiveness and letting go from a place of knowing that you are more than that event or person. By holding onto resentments and bitterness, the person who is still hurting is you. And this includes self judgments. Here, I would like to focus on you again. Tap around on all the points as follows:

Eyebrow:	*I love and forgive myself*
Side of Eye:	*And anyone who may have contributed to this*
Under Eye:	*Anyone I may be blaming including myself*
Under Nose:	*And I choose to let this go*
Chin:	*It is safe to release this now and I deserve to release this now*
Collar Bone:	*I love and forgive myself*
Under Arm:	*And anyone who may have contributed to this*
Top of Head:	*Anyone I may be blaming including myself*

Continue:

Eyebrow:	*I love and accept myself*
Side of Eye:	*I love and forgive myself*
Under Eye:	*I am OK*
Under Nose:	*And I choose to heal now*
Chin:	*I love and accept myself*
Collar Bone:	*I love and forgive myself*
Under Arm:	*I am OK*
Top of Head:	*And I choose to heal now*

Gratitude Lists

'Gratitude is the heart's memory.'
French Proverb

In Chapter Two, I talked about beginning to collect positive states in your heart centre. Now I would like to introduce the concept of the gratitude list. A gratitude list is an easy way to focus on the positive in every day, and is an addition to collecting positive experiences in your heart centre.

Buy yourself a beautiful notebook, something that gives you pleasure the moment you set eyes on it.

Commit to doing this exercise every day, before you go to bed.

Before bed, write a list of ten things that you have to be grateful for today. These can be absolutely anything, it may be someone smiling at you, someone's love, a sunny day, a little extra energy…. It doesn't matter, all that is important is that you write them down and acknowledge them. If you want to further enhance this, you can tap around on the word gratitude as you tune into each of the things on your list.

Eyebrow:	*Gratitude*
Side of Eye:	*Gratitude*
Under Eye:	*Gratitude*
Under Nose:	*Gratitude*
Chin:	*Gratitude*
Collar Bone:	*Gratitude*
Under Arm:	*Gratitude*
Top of Head:	*Gratitude*

Love

'As you continue to send out love, the energy returns to you in a regenerating spiral… As love accumulates, it keeps your system in balance and harmony. Love is the tool, and more love is the end product.'
Sara Paddison, Hidden Power of the Heart

There is a certain irony to leaving love until the end, inasmuch as love is what has brought this book into reality. This work is a product of love and admiration for the many people I have worked with in this field over the years. Without them, and everything they have taught me, I could not have begun this writing.

I am not referring to love in the romantic sense of the word. I am talking about a quality that is at all of our core; love and compassion for others, and ultimately for our Selves. I believe we are born fully connected to Love, Source or whatever word you choose for yourself. Then life happens, and we become disconnected, separated from that sense of oneness. We learn to fear, judge, feel angry, resentful etc. Our purpose in this life is to work through these external manifestations of ego and ultimately to reconnect with the love that is our birthright.

The more I learn about the healing process, the more love seems to be the crux of it. I believe that, given the space and loving intention, anything is possible. Certainly, in the therapeutic environment, love is the essence of healing. No therapist can heal their client, that is an arrogance of ego. However, what a skilled therapist can do is create and hold a healing space for their client to access their own healing resources. I believe that this is often a place where words become superfluous and the unconscious connection between the therapist and client allows the healing to take place.

So, in conclusion, take with you the words of Buddha:

'You, yourself, as much as anybody in the entire universe,
deserve your love and affection.'

I hope that as you work through this book, you will have found hidden depths of love and compassion for yourself and others, which in turn will lead to true healing, and letting go of dis-ease, in whatever way is appropriate for you, it is not my place to suppose what that is.

'Love one another and help others to rise to the higher levels, simply by pouring out love. Love is infectious and the greatest healing energy.'
Sai Baba

Resources

www.theeftcentre.com
www.eftmasters.co.uk
www.eftmastersworldwide.com
www.attractingabundance.com
www.Energy-Therapist.net
www.aamet.org
www.thetappingsolution.com
www.mtt.com
www.attractingabundance.com
www.eftdownunder.com
www.drkatejames.com (Integrative Medical Practice)
Institute_of_Sexuality@compuserve.com (Relationship & Psychosexual Therapy)
www.innersource.net

Cancer Websites:

Breast Cancer Haven: www.breastcancerhaven.org.uk
Cancer Research UK: www.cancerResearchUK.org
Marie Curie Cancer Care: www.mariecurie.org.uk
Macmillan Cancer Support: www.macmillan.org.uk
CLIC Sargent: www.clicsargent.org.uk
The American Cancer Society: www.cancer.org
National Cancer Institute: www.cancer.gov
The Breast Cancer Charities of America: www.thebreastcancercharities.org
Maggie's Centre: www.maggiescentres.org
Cancer Active: www.canceractive.com

Recommended Reading:

The Healing Power of EFT & Energy Psychology: David Feinstein, Donna Eden and Gary Craig, Piatkus 2006
How Your Mind Can Heal Your Body: Dr David Hamilton, Hay House 2008
It's The Thought that Counts: Dr David Hamilton, Hay House 2006
Cancer, The Complete Recovery Guide: Jonathan Chamberlain, Long Island Press 2008
Anything Can Be Healed: Martin Brofman, Findhorn Press 2006
The Field: Lynn Mc Taggart, Libri 2003
Genie in Your Genes: Dawson Church, Energy Psychology Press 2007
Seven Experiments That Could Change The World: Dr Rupert Sheldrake, Inner Traditions International 2002
The Biology of Belief: Dr Bruce Lipton, Hay House 2005
The Body Bears the Burden: Trauma, Dissociation, and Disease: Robert C. Scaer, Haworth Press 2001
Loving What Is: Byron Katie, Random House 2003
The EFT Manual: Gary Craig, Energy Psychology Press 2008
The Rainbow Feelings of Cancer A Book for Children Who Have a Loved One with Cancer: Carrie Martin and Chia Martin, Hohm Press 2001
Healing the Addicted Heart: Sue Beer 2010 release
EFT & Beyond: ed. Pamela Bruner & John Bullough, Energy Publications Ltd 2009
Energy Medicine: Donna Eden, Piatkus 1998